easy yoga

any age · any place · any time

Jude Reignier

Consultant Osteopath
Sean Durkan

Illustrated by
Juliet Percival

eddison
BOOKS LIMITED

First published in Great Britain in 2007
This edition published in 2018 by
Eddison Books Limited
St Chad's House, 148 King's Cross Road
London WC1X 9DH
www.eddisonbooks.com

ISBN 978-1-85906-444-3

1 3 5 7 9 10 8 6 4 2

Printed in China

Contents

Introduction

Over the years I have taught a diverse range of clients, including children, expectant mothers and those with special needs, both in classes and on a one-to-one basis. I have found that most of my clients have little time to practise yoga, so they require their routines to be short and simple but effective. This book is written with those people in mind, and for anyone who doesn't have 1½ to 2 hours a day to practise but is keen to experience the benefits that a good yoga routine can offer.

Yoga can be practised in almost any calm environment where you won't be disturbed. Make sure any televisions, phones or computers are switched off and the lighting is soft. If the floor is uncarpeted, use a large towel or, if possible, a yoga mat, which you should be able to purchase from any good sports shop. Wear loose, comfortable clothing and keep your feet bare – this will make it much easier to grip the floor.

How to use this book

The book consists of one 45-minute session, followed by two sessions of 20 minutes and then two of 10 minutes. The postures in the full 45-minute sequence work the whole body system, massaging and stimulating the internal organs while gently stretching, firming and toning the muscles and ligaments. The shorter sessions will energize or relax you, depending on which one you choose. Each one is made up of twelve or six of the postures shown in the 45-minute sequence.

If possible, practise the 45-minute session twice a week. You will start to see benefits after just a few weeks. If you wish, however, you could incorporate this session into your daily routine, but do take one day off every week to give your body a rest. The 20- and 10-minute sessions can be practised every day, or even twice a day. You will see results quicker the more you practise. After completing any of the shorter routines, always relax for at least 5 minutes (20-minute session) or 2 minutes (10-minute session) by lying or sitting quietly with your eyes closed.

Never push your body beyond its natural limit. Take each posture only as far as your body allows. Once you have memorized the sequences, the postures will flow together without any thought. And, as you gain confidence, you will be able to let your body and mind go, and this way you will achieve maximum benefit.

Deep breathing

Normal, or passive, breathing involves movement of the diaphragm. When we breathe in, the diaphragm moves down, increasing the ribcage capacity and allowing the lungs to expand to take in more oxygen. As we breathe out, the diaphragm moves up, forcing out carbon dioxide.

An efficient breathing cycle results in a balance between the oxygen and carbon dioxide levels in the blood, which enhances the functions of the body. Shallow breathing often manifests itself as hyperventilation. This is usually a result of prolonged stress or poor posture, and means that we're breathing out too much carbon dioxide, altering the normal body chemistry and disturbing the body's acid–alkaline balance. It also affects the bloodflow to the heart and brain, producing symptoms such as pins and needles, dizziness, headaches, muscle spasms, depression, asthma and insomnia.

Yoga helps us to concentrate on our breathing and encourages us to breathe more deeply, thereby improving the efficiency of our vital functions.

Massaging the organs

As the diaphragm moves up and down, it compresses and stretches the internal organs. This enhances the circulation of the blood and lymphatic drainage, which is essential for good health. The instructions for each posture in this book include a diagram illustrating the internal organs that are being massaged (*see below*). This allows you to see at a glance whether the posture mainly benefits the organs above or below the diaphragm, and is a good reminder that yoga does much more than toning and stretching the muscles.

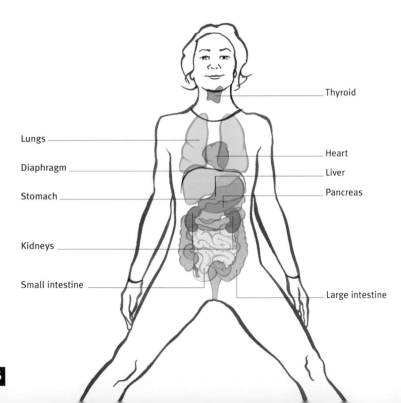

Thyroid

Lungs

Heart

Diaphragm

Liver

Pancreas

Stomach

Kidneys

Small intestine

Large intestine

Stretching the muscles

At the stage of each posture where the muscles become stretched, the illustrations show a dotted line to demonstrate which muscles are being worked (*see below*). This will not only tell you which parts of your body you are exercising, but will also act as a guide to whether you are performing the posture correctly as you should feel the muscles indicated become taut. If this isn't the case, relax, check that you're following the instructions correctly and assume the posture again. If you feel pain at any time, do not continue the posture.

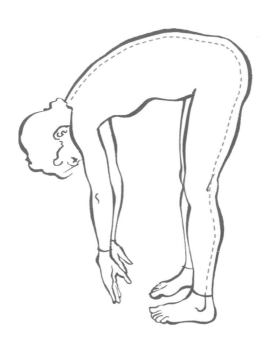

full-length sequence

45-MINUTE SESSION

❶ Focus your breath

Improves circulation to all organs • Relaxes muscles and ligaments • Relieves stress

Lie down and gently close your eyes. Slowly inhale through the nose and focus on your breath as it travels down the throat and into the bottom of the lungs and ribcage. Be aware of your lungs and ribcage expanding and your spine lengthening. You will feel the abdomen rise.

Exhale through your nose. Feel the abdomen fall. The out-breath should be longer than the in-breath.

Surrender the weight of your body into the ground. Let go of your thoughts. Focus your breathing.

- **The exhalation holds the key to relaxation. The more stale air you exhale, the more fresh air you can inhale, the deeper your breathing, the quieter the mind.**

  Focus your breath ... relax ... relax.

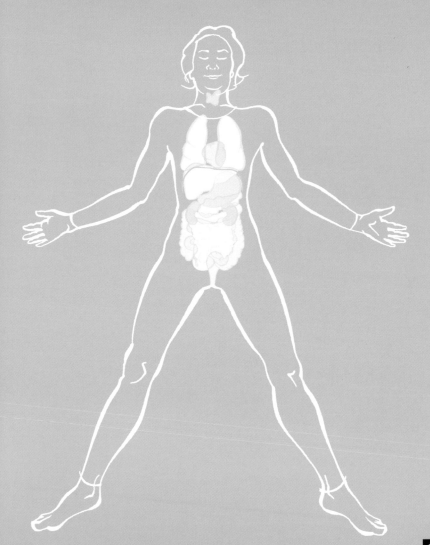

❷ The mountain

Improves circulation to all organs • Tones the arms • Firms the abdomen • Improves posture

1 Stand with your feet hip-width apart, heels turned out slightly. Stretch your arms out in front of you and link your fingers.

2 Inhale to prepare.

3 As you exhale, stretch your arms up above your head and root your feet firmly into the ground. Become aware of the opposite stretch creating space around your waist.

▶ Focus your breath as you stretch gently in the posture. Hold the stretch for 1 minute. Then release your arms and place them by your sides.

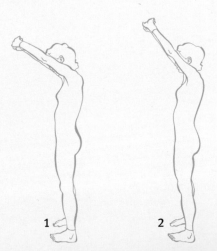

1   2   3

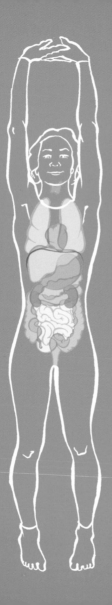

❸ Letting go

Stimulates the liver, kidneys and intestines • Helps to relieve stress, fatigue and indigestion • Stretches the calf muscles and hamstrings

Caution: Do not attempt this posture if you suffer from high blood pressure.

1 Standing with your feet hip-width apart and your heels turned out slightly, relax your body forwards, your arms hanging down.

2 Inhale as your body relaxes down.

3 As you exhale, drop your chin to your chest and slowly continue to release your spine, one vertebra at a time. Do not bounce. Root your feet firmly into the ground to keep your legs strong, and open the backs of the knees without locking them. Let go of the tension in the upper body.

▶ Exhale to release the spine, then the shoulders, arms, fingers, neck, face, jaw and eyes. Focus your breath as you hold the posture. Hold for 1 minute, then slowly come up to a standing position.

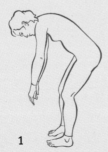
1

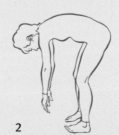
2

3

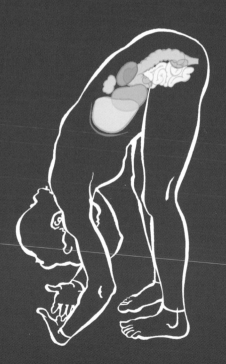

❹ The standing fish

Corrects rounded shoulders • Expands lungs • Tones the arms • Helps to relieve asthma, lethargy and anxiety

1 Standing with your feet hip-width apart, heels turned out slightly, link your fingers together behind your back.

2 Inhale to prepare.

3 As you exhale, slowly lift the centre of the chest and open the shoulders back, pulling the arms down. Root your feet firmly into the ground, keeping your legs strong and the backs of the knees open.

▶ As you focus your breath in the posture, your chest should be lifted and fully open and your arms pulled back. Hold for 1 minute. Then slowly release your arms and allow them to rest by your sides.

1   2   3

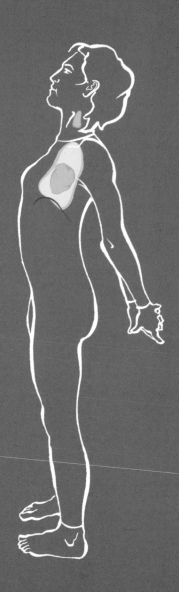

❺ The cobbler

Improves circulation to all organs • Stretches the inner thighs and groin • Opens the chest and shoulders • Helps to relieve asthma and menstrual discomfort

1   Lie on your back and bend your knees up towards the ceiling so that your feet are a few inches away from your buttocks, your feet and ankles together. Spread your arms to an angle of 45 degrees to your body. Keep your head centred and your chin tucked in. Inhale to prepare.

2   As you slowly exhale, begin to open your knees.

3   Continue to open your knees, keeping the lower back pressed into the ground.

▶   Focus your breath as you allow the hips to open fully. Hold for 1 minute. Then slowly bring the knees together.

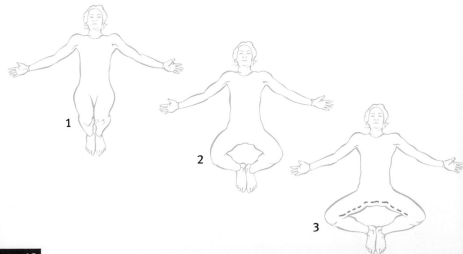

❻ The hip roll

Stimulates the liver, kidneys and intestines • Helps to relieve trapped nerves, indigestion and constipation • Stretches the thighs • Releases tension in the spine • Opens the shoulders and chest • Helps to relieve asthma

Caution: Do not attempt this posture if you are pregnant.

1 Lying on your back, feet together, bend your knees up to the ceiling. Bring your arms out, level with your shoulders, palms facing up. Your head should be centred and your chin tucked in. Inhale to prepare.

2 As you slowly exhale, drop your knees to the left as far as is comfortable. As you do so, turn your head to the right, twisting the spine.

3 Inhale. Then slowly exhale, bringing the knees and head back to centre.

▶ Repeat to the other side. Continue for 2 minutes, twisting to one side, then the other. To finish, bring the knees and head back to centre.

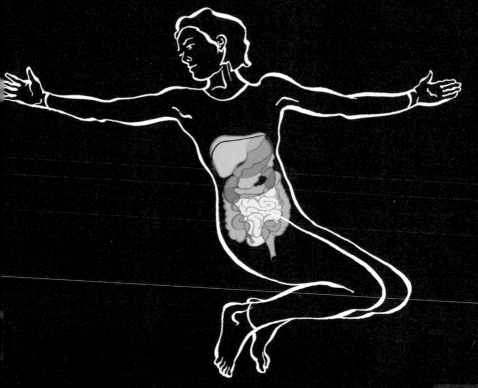

❼ The pelvic tilt

Stimulates the thyroid • Expands the lungs • Stretches the neck and thighs • Strengthens the lower back and abdominal muscles • Helps to relieve asthma, menstrual discomfort and back pain

Caution: Avoid this posture if you're pregnant or have a neck injury.

1 Lie on your back with your knees bent and your feet hip-width apart, heels turned out slightly. Place your arms by your sides, palms down. Keep your head centred and your chin tucked in. Inhale to prepare.

2 Slowly exhale, lifting your tail bone off the ground as you do so.

3 Lift each vertebra off the ground one by one until you reach the shoulder blades.

▶ Root your feet firmly into the ground. Become aware of your chest opening as you push the spine up as far as is comfortable. Inhale. Then exhale as you slowly lower the spine, one vertebra at a time – upper spine, central spine, lower spine, tail bone. Repeat the pelvic tilt for 1 minute.

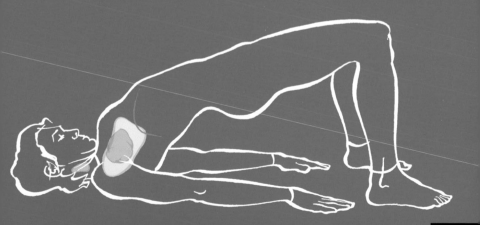

❽ The big toe

Improves circulation to all organs • Stretches the hamstrings and calf muscles • Tones the abdominal muscles • Improves flexibility in the hips • Helps to relieve back pain, indigestion and constipation

1 Lie on your back with your chin tucked into your neck, and your lower back pressed into the ground. Inhale to prepare.

2 Slowly exhale, raising your legs off the ground. Use your hands to support your upper legs.

3 Focusing your breath, raise the legs as far as you can manage, using your hands to guide them. Extend through the heels to open up the backs of the legs.

▶ Grab hold of your toes and gently pull your legs towards you as far as is comfortable, keeping the backs of the knees open. Hold the posture for 1 minute. Slowly lower your legs to the floor.

❾ The half dog

Stimulates the liver, kidneys and intestines • Helps to relieve lower back pain and indigestion • Tones the arms • Opens the chest, central spine and shoulders • Helps to relieve asthma

1 On all fours, position your hands in line with the shoulders, and your knees hip-width apart. Inhale to prepare.

2 As you exhale, widen the arms and move them forwards on the floor.

3 Slowly drop the chest and shoulders towards the ground, ensuring that the hips remain in line with the knees.

▶ Focus your breath, allowing the chest and shoulders to open and the spine to lengthen. Hold the posture for 1 minute, or less if it becomes uncomfortable. Then return to the starting position.

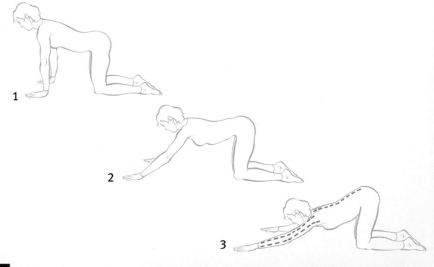

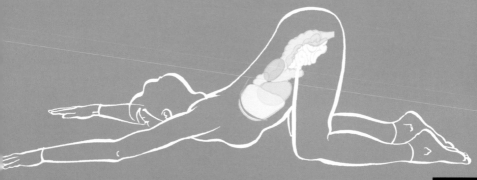

⑩ The cobra

*Improves circulation to all organs • Tones the arms and abdomen •
Expands the lungs • Helps to relieve asthma, menstrual discomfort,
constipation and indigestion*

Caution: Avoid this posture if you're pregnant or suffer from lower back pain.

1 Lie on your front with your forehead down, legs together and hands
   in line with the outside of your shoulders. Inhale to prepare.

2 As you exhale, slowly lift the forehead, chin and neck, pushing your
   hands into the ground.

3 Continue to push, lifting the chest and ribs. Draw the elbows down
   towards the waist, pull the shoulders back and down, and open the chest.

▶ Focus your breath. Hold the posture for 30 seconds. Then slowly lower
   the ribs, chest, neck, chin and finally the forehead, back to the floor.
   Then repeat.

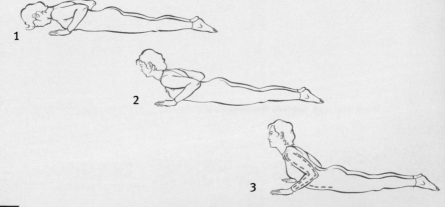

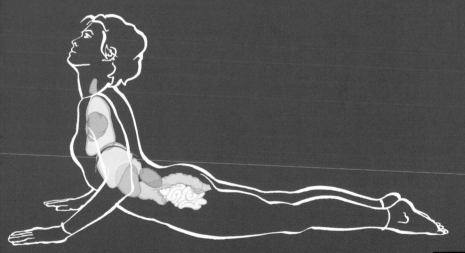

⓫ The locust

Stimulates the liver, kidneys and intestines • Helps to relieve indigestion • Stretches the thighs • Strengthens the lower back

Caution: Avoid this posture if you're pregnant or suffer from lower back pain.

1 Lie on your front with your throat lengthened along the floor. Place your arms by your sides, palms facing up, shoulders relaxed.

2 Inhale, slowly lifting your right leg off the ground. Ensure that your hips remain flat to the floor – do not allow them to twist. Exhale as you slowly lower your leg.

▶ Repeat with the left leg. Complete the locust 5 times with each leg.

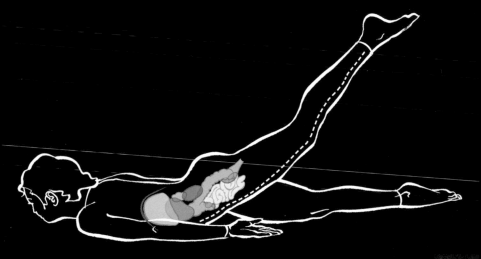

⑫ The dog

Improves circulation to all organs • Stretches the calf muscles, hamstrings, spine, arms and hands • Helps to relieve back pain, headache, fatigue and indigestion

Caution: Do not attempt this posture if you have high blood pressure.

1 On all fours, position your hands in line with the shoulders, knees hip-width apart. Inhale to prepare.

2 As you exhale, bring your weight onto the toes, and slowly lift the knees.

3 Push your tail bone up and out. With your heels turned outwards slightly, extend them to the floor to open out the backs of the knees.

▶ Lengthening the legs fully, relax the neck and face. Focus your breath. Hold the posture for 1 minute. Then slowly return to the starting position.

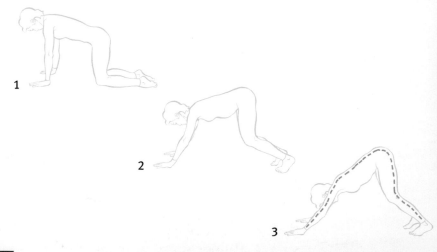

⓭ The wide-leg triangle

Stimulates the liver, kidneys and intestines • Helps to relieve indigestion • Improves balance and spinal flexibility • Tones the legs • Stretches the arms • Strengthens the lower back and abdominal muscles

1 Stand with your feet wide apart, toes pointing forwards. Raise your right arm so that it brushes against your ear, fingers pointing to the ceiling. Inhale to prepare.

2 With your face turned into the raised arm, slowly exhale. As you do so, stretch your arm and torso to the left, keeping the left arm straight, by your side.

3 As you stretch, root your right foot firmly into the ground. Ensure that your hips are pointing forwards – do not allow them to twist. If you experience any pain in your sides, stop.

▶ Focus your breath. Hold the posture for 30 seconds. Then slowly return to the standing position and release the arm. Repeat to the other side.

1   2   3

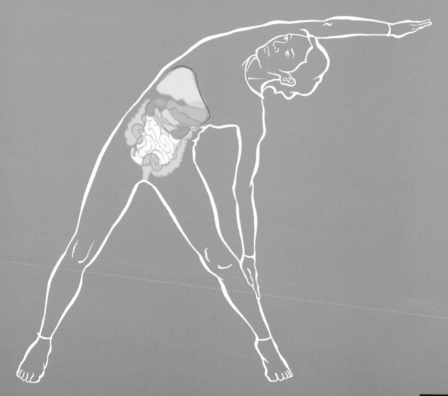

⑭ The triangle variation

Stimulates the kidneys, liver and intestines • Helps to relieve fatigue, stress, stiffness in the shoulders and indigestion • Stretches the calf muscles and hamstrings • Tones the arms

Caution: Do not attempt this posture if you suffer from high blood pressure or lower back pain.

1   Stand with your feet wide apart, toes pointing forwards. Root your feet firmly into the ground. Position your hands behind your back and link your fingers together. Inhale to prepare.

2   As you exhale, slowly bend forwards with the spine relaxed.

3   Continue to bend, taking your arms over your head.

▶ Focus your breath. Hold the posture for 1 minute. Then slowly return to the standing position and release the arms.

1

2

3

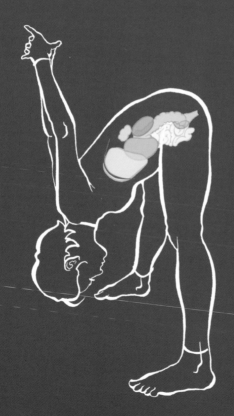

⑮ The warrior

Improves circulation to all organs • Stretches the groin and inner thighs • Strengthens the legs • Opens the chest • Helps to relieve asthma and stress • Improves stamina and balance

1 Stand with your feet as far apart as is comfortable. Slowly turn your left foot out 90 degrees, keeping your hips pointed forwards.

2 Raise both arms out to the sides level with your shoulders, keeping the shoulders relaxed. Your palms should be turned downwards. Inhale to prepare.

3 As you exhale, slowly bend the left knee, keeping your body centred.

▶ Continue to bend until your leg forms a right-angle. Turn your head to the left – you should be able to feel the lightness in your upper body and the strength in your legs. Focus your breath. Hold the posture for 30 seconds. Slowly return to the starting position, then repeat to the other side.

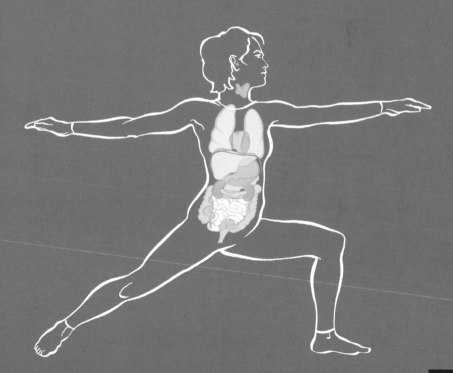

⑯ The stork

Improves circulation to all organs • Stretches the thighs and arms •
Expands the lungs • Opens the hips • Helps to relieve asthma and stress
• Improves concentration and balance

1 Stand with your feet hip-width apart, toes pointing forwards, arms by your sides.

2 Bend your right leg up behind you and take hold of the ankle with your right hand. Raise your left arm so that your fingers point towards the ceiling. Your arm should gently brush your ear. Inhale to prepare.

3 Root the left foot firmly into the ground and, as you exhale, slowly lean forwards and push your right foot up to the ceiling. Make sure your hips are straight throughout – do not allow them to twist. Keep the grounded leg strong and straight.

▶ Focus your breath. Hold the posture for 1 minute. Then slowly release the leg, and relax the arm. Repeat to the other side.

1

2

3

⓱ The shoulder stand

Improves circulation to all organs • Stretches the neck • Stimulates the thyroid • Invigorates the body • Tones the abdominal muscles • Helps to relieve asthma, indigestion and varicose veins

Caution: Avoid this posture if you're pregnant or suffering from high blood pressure, neck pain or injury, or pins and needles in the arms or hands.

1 Lie on your back with your legs together, arms by your sides, palms face down. Keep your head centred and your chin tucked in. Inhale to prepare.

2 As you exhale, slowly raise your legs until they're positioned over your torso. Then, pressing your hands into the floor, begin to lift your hips.

3 Support your back with both hands, fingers turned into the spine, thumbs around the hips. Continue to lift the legs and hips, gradually moving the hands up the back as the distance between your head and feet increases. Keep your elbows tucked in to distribute the weight evenly and avoid pressure on the neck and shoulders.

▶ Focus your breath. Hold the posture for 1–2 minutes, or less if it becomes uncomfortable. To release, slowly take your legs to an angle of 45 degrees over your head, and press your palms into the floor. Slowly lower the spine to the floor, one vertebra at a time, followed by the legs.

1   2   3

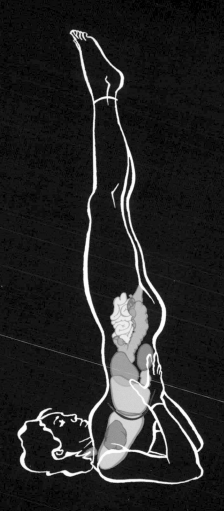

⑱ The plough

Improves circulation to all organs • Stretches the neck, spine, hamstrings and calf muscles • Stimulates the thyroid • Helps to relieve asthma, neck and back pain, indigestion and constipation

Caution: Avoid this posture if you're pregnant or suffering from high blood pressure, neck pain or injury, or pins and needles in the arms or hands.

1 Lie on your back with your legs together. Place your arms by your sides, palms down. Your head should be centred, chin tucked in. Inhale.

2 As you exhale, press your hands into the ground. Slowly raise your legs until they're positioned over your torso, then raise your hips.

3 Support your back with both hands, fingers turned into the spine and thumbs towards the hips. Tuck your elbows in. Slowly take your legs over your head. The aim is for your feet to touch the floor behind your head, but do not force them if it starts to feel uncomfortable.

▶ Tuck your toes in and straighten your legs. Keep the hips lifted and the chin tucked in to take the weight away from the neck and shoulders. Focus your breath. Hold the posture for 1 minute. To release, press your palms into the floor, then slowly lower the spine one vertebra at a time from the shoulders to the tail bone. Then gently lower the legs.

1   2   3

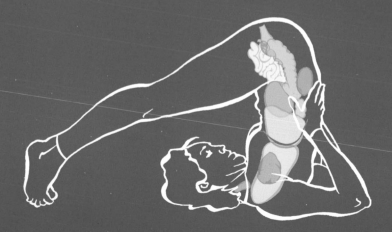

⑲ The fish

Expands the lungs • Stimulates the thyroid • Stretches the neck and spine •
Opens the shoulders • Tones the arms • Helps to relieve asthma and stress

**Caution: Avoid this posture if you have a neck injury or suffer from pins
and needles in the arms or hands.**

1   Lie on your back with your legs together. Place your arms by your
    sides, palms down. Keep your head centred, chin tucked in.

2   With your arms straight, position your hands underneath your buttocks
    so that your hands are side by side, pointing towards the thighs. Inhale
    to prepare.

3   Exhale, pressing your elbows into the floor. As you do so, arch your
    back and lift your chest.

▶   Slowly lower your head back until the top of the head touches the floor.
    Focus your breath. Hold the posture for 1 minute. To release, gently lift
    your head, then lower your body, returning your arms to your sides.

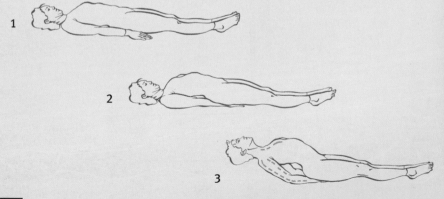

㉑ Tense and release

Improves circulation to all organs • Releases tension in the muscles

1 Lie on your back with your feet wide apart, arms at 45 degrees to the body. Your palms should be facing upwards, and your head centred. Tuck your chin in and gently close your eyes.

2 As you inhale, tense your hands and feet, making fists with your hands and curling your toes.

3 Lift your head, arms, hands, legs and feet 5–8 cm (2–3 in) off the floor. Feel the tension throughout your body. Hold for 10 seconds.

▶ As you exhale, let go completely. Release your head, arms, hands, legs and feet. Your whole body should feel totally relaxed. Focus your breath for 1 minute.

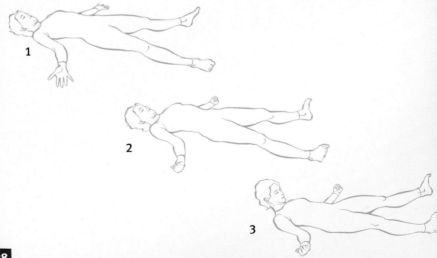

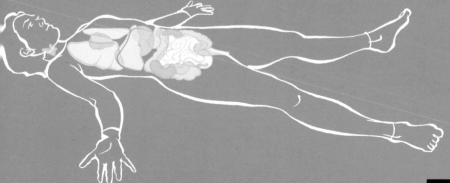

㉑ Auto-suggestion relaxation

Lowers the pulse rate • Reduces energy loss and stress build-up • Allows the whole body to rest • Relaxes the brain • Clears the mind

Lie on your back with your feet wide apart, arms at 45 degrees to your body, palms facing upwards. Keep your head centred and your chin tucked in. Focus your breath for a few minutes. As you do so, visualize your body with your mind's eye.

Taking your attention to the feet, silently say to yourself, 'I relax my feet … I relax my feet …. my feet are relaxed.'

Then take your attention to your legs and silently say to yourself, 'I relax my legs … I relax my legs … my legs are relaxed.'

One by one, repeat this process for the hips, spine, shoulders, arms, hands, fingers, neck, jaw, eyes, face, skull, liver, kidneys, stomach, intestines, pancreas, lungs, thyroid and heart.

When your heart is relaxed, let go … focus your breath. Your mind, body and spirit, your very being, should now feel totally relaxed.

Just lie still for 10 minutes. Focus on nothing but the calmness of your body and the quietness of your mind.

Inhale, and slowly bring your legs together and your arms above your head. Pressing the lower back into the floor, exhale, and stretch out the whole body as far as you can. Feel the stretch in your arms, legs, back and neck. Then slowly stand up.

■ By concentrating the mind on specific parts of the body, we're able to fully relax those areas. This is the perfect way to end the sequence.

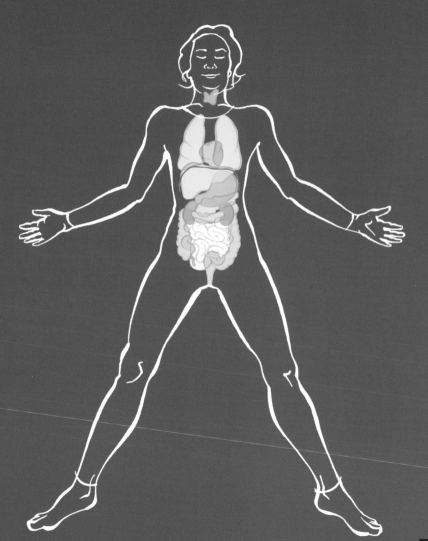

energize
and unwind

20-MINUTE SESSIONS

❶ The mountain

Improves circulation to all organs • Tones the arms • Firms the abdomen • Improves posture

1 Stand with your feet hip-width apart, heels turned out slightly. Stretch your arms out in front of you and link your fingers.

2 Inhale to prepare.

3 As you exhale, stretch your arms up above your head and root your feet firmly into the ground. Become aware of the opposite stretch creating space around your waist.

▶ Focus your breath as you stretch gently in the posture. Hold the stretch for 1 minute. Then release your arms and place them by your sides.

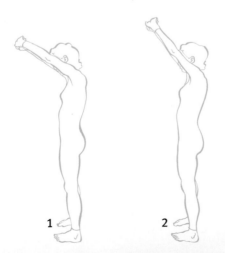

1   2   3

❷ Letting go

Stimulates the liver, kidneys and intestines • Helps to relieve stress, fatigue and indigestion • Stretches the calf muscles and hamstrings

Caution: Do not attempt this posture if you suffer from high blood pressure.

1 Standing with your feet hip-width apart and your heels turned out slightly, relax your body forwards, your arms hanging down.

2 Inhale as your body relaxes down.

3 As you exhale, drop your chin to your chest and slowly continue to release your spine, one vertebra at a time. Do not bounce. Root your feet firmly into the ground to keep your legs strong, and open the backs of the knees without locking them. Let go of the tension in the upper body.

▶ Exhale to release the spine, then the shoulders, arms, fingers, neck, face, jaw and eyes. Focus your breath as you hold the posture. Hold for 1 minute, then slowly come up to a standing position.

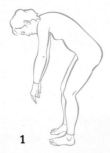
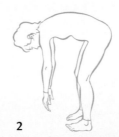

1   2   3

❸ The standing fish

Corrects rounded shoulders • Expands lungs • Tones the arms • Helps to relieve asthma, lethargy and anxiety

1 Standing with your feet hip-width apart, heels turned out slightly, link your fingers together behind your back.

2 Inhale to prepare.

3 As you exhale, slowly lift the centre of the chest and open the shoulders back, pulling the arms down. Root your feet firmly into the ground, keeping your legs strong and the backs of the knees open.

▶ As you focus your breath in the posture, your chest should be lifted and fully open and your arms pulled back. Hold for 1 minute. Then slowly release your arms and allow them to rest by your sides.

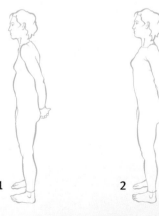

❹ The triangle variation

Stimulates the kidneys, liver and intestines • Helps to relieve fatigue, stress, stiffness in the shoulders and indigestion • Stretches the calf muscles and hamstrings • Tones the arms

Caution: Do not attempt this posture if you suffer from high blood pressure or lower back pain.

1 Stand with your feet wide apart, toes pointing forwards. Root your feet firmly into the ground. Position your hands behind your back and link your fingers together. Inhale to prepare.

2 As you exhale, slowly bend forwards with the spine relaxed.

3 Continue to bend, taking your arms over your head.

▶ Focus your breath. Hold the posture for 1 minute. Then slowly return to the standing position and release the arms.

1   2   3

⑤ The cobra

*Improves circulation to all organs • Tones the arms and abdomen •
Expands the lungs • Helps to relieve asthma, menstrual discomfort,
constipation and indigestion*

Caution: Avoid this posture if you're pregnant or suffer from lower back pain.

1 Lie on your front with your forehead down, legs together and hands
   in line with the outside of your shoulders. Inhale to prepare.

2 As you exhale, slowly lift the forehead, chin and neck, pushing your
   hands into the ground.

3 Continue to push, lifting the chest and ribs. Draw the elbows down
   towards the waist, pull the shoulders back and down, and open the chest.

▶ Focus your breath. Hold the posture for 30 seconds. Then slowly lower
   the ribs, chest, neck, chin and finally the forehead, back to the floor.
   Then repeat.

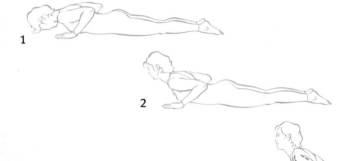

⑥ The locust

Stimulates the liver, kidneys and intestines • Helps to relieve indigestion • Stretches the thighs • Strengthens the lower back

Caution: Avoid this posture if you're pregnant or suffer from lower back pain.

1 Lie on your front with your throat lengthened along the floor. Place your arms by your sides, palms facing up, shoulders relaxed.

2 Inhale, slowly lifting your right leg off the ground. Ensure that your hips remain flat to the floor – do not allow them to twist. Exhale as you slowly lower your leg.

▶ Repeat with the left leg. Complete the locust 5 times with each leg.

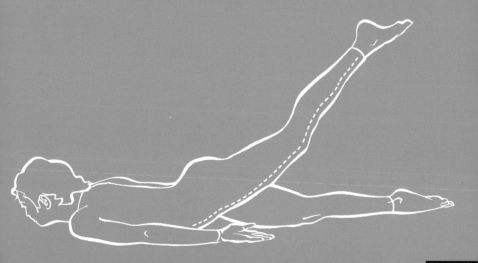

⑦ The dog

Improves circulation to all organs • Stretches the calf muscles, hamstrings, spine, arms and hands • Helps to relieve back pain, headache, fatigue and indigestion

Caution: Do not attempt this posture if you have high blood pressure.

1 On all fours, position your hands in line with the shoulders, knees hip-width apart. Inhale to prepare.

2 As you exhale, bring your weight onto the toes, and slowly lift the knees.

3 Push your tail bone up and out. With your heels turned outwards slightly, extend them to the floor to open out the backs of the knees.

▶ Lengthening the legs fully, relax the neck and face. Focus your breath. Hold the posture for 1 minute. Then slowly return to the starting position.

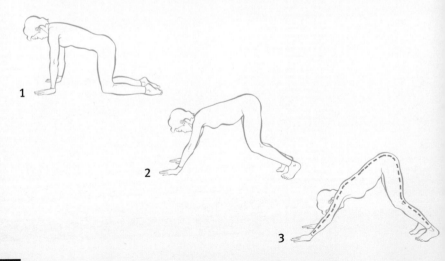

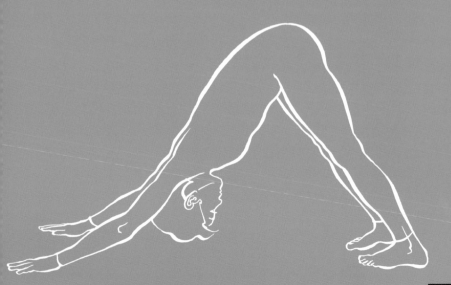

⑧ The wide-leg triangle

Stimulates the liver, kidneys and intestines • Helps to relieve indigestion
• Improves balance and spinal flexibility • Tones the legs • Stretches the
arms • Strengthens the lower back and abdominal muscles

1 Stand with your feet wide apart, toes pointing forwards. Raise your
   right arm so that it brushes against your ear, fingers pointing to the
   ceiling. Inhale to prepare.

2 With your face turned into the raised arm, slowly exhale. As you do so,
   stretch your arm and torso to the left, keeping the left arm straight, by
   your side.

3 As you stretch, root your right foot firmly into the ground. Ensure that
   your hips are pointing forwards – do not allow them to twist. If you
   experience any pain in your sides, stop.

▶ Focus your breath. Hold the posture for 30 seconds. Then slowly return
   to the standing position and release the arm. Repeat to the other side.

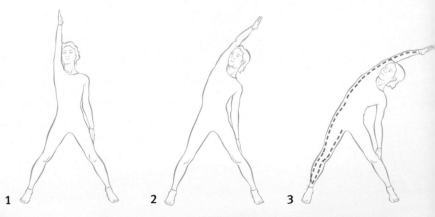

1   2   3

❾ The warrior

Improves circulation to all organs • Stretches the groin and inner thighs • Strengthens the legs • Opens the chest • Helps to relieve asthma and stress • Improves stamina and balance

1 Stand with your feet as far apart as is comfortable. Slowly turn your left foot out 90 degrees, keeping your hips pointed forwards.

2 Raise both arms out to the sides level with your shoulders, keeping the shoulders relaxed. Your palms should be turned downwards. Inhale to prepare.

3 As you exhale, slowly bend the left knee, keeping your body centred.

▶ Continue to bend until your leg forms a right-angle. Turn your head to the left – you should be able to feel the lightness in your upper body and the strength in your legs. Focus your breath. Hold the posture for 30 seconds. Slowly return to the starting position, then repeat to the other side.

1   2   3

⑩ The big toe

Improves circulation to all organs • Stretches the hamstrings and calf muscles • Tones the abdominal muscles • Improves flexibility in the hips • Helps to relieve back pain, indigestion and constipation

1 Lie on your back with your chin tucked into your neck, and your lower back pressed into the ground. Inhale to prepare.

2 Slowly exhale, raising your legs off the ground. Use your hands to support your upper legs.

3 Focusing your breath, raise the legs as far as you can manage, using your hands to guide them. Extend through the heels to open up the backs of the legs.

▶ Grab hold of your toes and gently pull your legs towards you as far as is comfortable, keeping the backs of the knees open. Hold the posture for 1 minute. Slowly lower your legs to the floor.

⑪ The shoulder stand

Improves circulation to all organs • Stretches the neck • Stimulates the thyroid • Invigorates the body • Tones the abdominal muscles • Helps to relieve asthma, indigestion and varicose veins

Caution: Avoid this posture if you're pregnant or suffering from high blood pressure, neck pain or injury, or pins and needles in the arms or hands.

1 Lie on your back with your legs together, arms by your sides, palms face down. Keep your head centred and your chin tucked in. Inhale to prepare.

2 As you exhale, slowly raise your legs until they're positioned over your torso. Then, pressing your hands into the floor, begin to lift your hips.

3 Support your back with both hands, fingers turned into the spine, thumbs around the hips. Continue to lift the legs and hips, gradually moving the hands up the back as the distance between your head and feet increases. Keep your elbows tucked in to distribute the weight evenly and avoid pressure on the neck and shoulders.

▶ Focus your breath. Hold the posture for 1–2 minutes, or less if it becomes uncomfortable. To release, slowly take your legs to an angle of 45 degrees over your head, and press your palms into the floor. Slowly lower the spine to the floor, one vertebra at a time, followed by the legs.

1   2   3

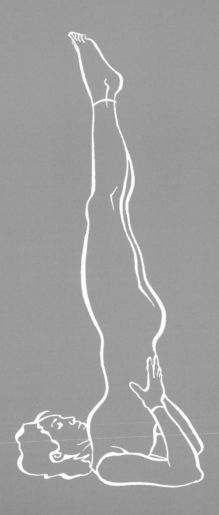

⑫ The fish

Expands the lungs • Stimulates the thyroid • Stretches the neck and spine •
Opens the shoulders • Tones the arms • Helps to relieve asthma and stress

Caution: Avoid this posture if you have a neck injury or suffer from pins and needles in the arms or hands.

1 Lie on your back with your legs together. Place your arms by your sides, palms down. Keep your head centred, chin tucked in.

2 With your arms straight, position your hands underneath your buttocks so that your hands are side by side, pointing towards the thighs. Inhale to prepare.

3 Exhale, pressing your elbows into the floor. As you do so, arch your back and lift your chest.

▶ Slowly lower your head back until the top of the head touches the floor. Focus your breath. Hold the posture for 1 minute. To release, gently lift your head, then lower your body, returning your arms to your sides.

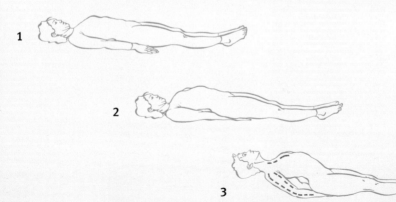

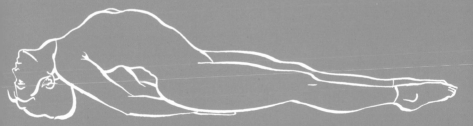

❶ Focus your breath

Improves circulation to all organs • Relaxes muscles and ligaments •
Relieves stress

Lie down and gently close your eyes. Slowly inhale through the nose and focus on your breath as it travels down the throat and into the bottom of the lungs and ribcage. Be aware of your lungs and ribcage expanding and your spine lengthening. You will feel the abdomen rise.

Exhale through your nose. Feel the abdomen fall. The out-breath should be longer than the in-breath.

Surrender the weight of your body into the ground. Let go of your thoughts. Focus your breathing.

■ **The exhalation holds the key to relaxation. The more stale air you exhale, the more fresh air you can inhale, the deeper your breathing, the quieter the mind.**

  Focus your breath ... relax ... relax.

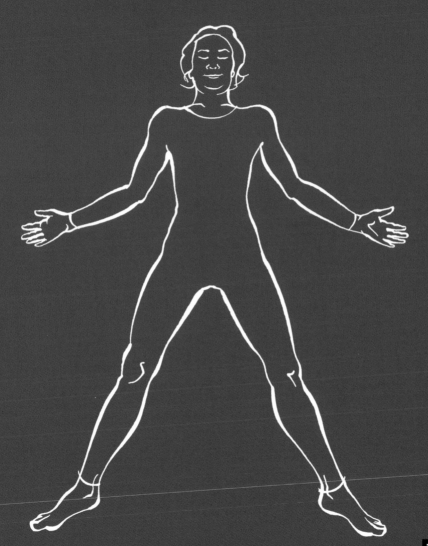

❷ The cobbler

Improves circulation to all organs • Stretches the inner thighs and groin • Opens the chest and shoulders • Helps to relieve asthma and menstrual discomfort

1 Lie on your back and bend your knees up towards the ceiling so that your feet are a few inches away from your buttocks, your feet and ankles together. Spread your arms to an angle of 45 degrees to your body. Keep your head centred and your chin tucked in. Inhale to prepare.

2 As you slowly exhale, begin to open your knees.

3 Continue to open your knees, keeping the lower back pressed into the ground.

▶ Focus your breath as you allow the hips to open fully. Hold for 1 minute. Then slowly bring the knees together.

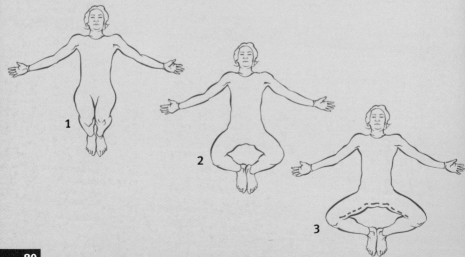

❸ The hip roll

Stimulates the liver, kidneys and intestines • Helps to relieve trapped nerves, indigestion and constipation • Stretches the thighs • Releases tension in the spine • Opens the shoulders and chest • Helps to relieve asthma

Caution: Do not attempt this posture if you are pregnant.

1 Lying on your back, feet together, bend your knees up to the ceiling. Bring your arms out, level with your shoulders, palms facing up. Your head should be centred and your chin tucked in. Inhale to prepare.

2 As you slowly exhale, drop your knees to the left as far as is comfortable. As you do so, turn your head to the right, twisting the spine.

3 Inhale. Then slowly exhale, bringing the knees and head back to centre.

▶ Repeat to the other side. Continue for 2 minutes, twisting to one side then the other. To finish, bring the knees and head back to centre.

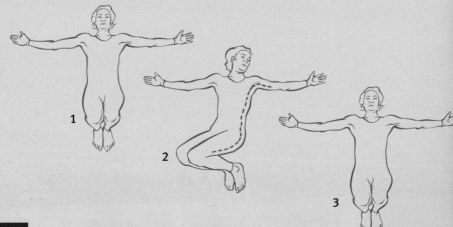

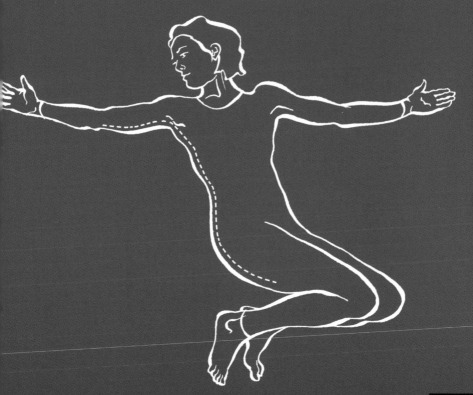

❹ The pelvic tilt

Stimulates the thyroid • Expands the lungs • Stretches the neck and thighs • Strengthens the lower back and abdominal muscles • Helps to relieve asthma, menstrual discomfort and back pain

Caution: Avoid this posture if you're pregnant or have a neck injury.

1 Lie on your back with your knees bent and your feet hip-width apart, heels turned out slightly. Place your arms by your sides, palms down. Keep your head centred and your chin tucked in. Inhale to prepare.

2 Slowly exhale, lifting your tail bone off the ground as you do so.

3 Lift each vertebra off the ground one by one until you reach the shoulder blades.

▶ Root your feet firmly into the ground. Become aware of your chest opening as you push the spine up as far as is comfortable. Inhale. Then exhale as you slowly lower the spine, one vertebra at a time – upper spine, central spine, lower spine, tail bone. Repeat the pelvic tilt for 1 minute.

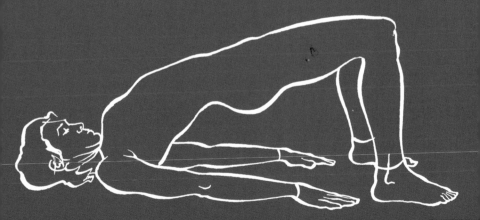

❺ The big toe

Improves circulation to all organs • Stretches the hamstrings and calf muscles • Tones the abdominal muscles • Improves flexibility in the hips • Helps to relieve back pain, indigestion and constipation

1 Lie on your back with your chin tucked into your neck, and your lower back pressed into the ground. Inhale to prepare.

2 Slowly exhale, raising your legs off the ground. Use your hands to support your upper legs.

3 Focusing your breath, raise the legs as far as you can manage, using your hands to guide them. Extend through the heels to open up the backs of the legs.

▶ Grab hold of your toes and gently pull your legs towards you as far as is comfortable, keeping the backs of the knees open. Hold the posture for 1 minute. Slowly lower your legs to the floor.

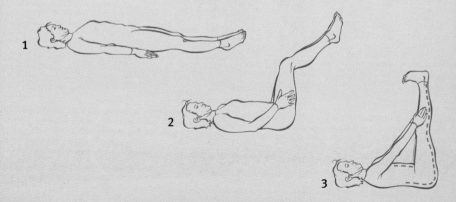

❻ The half dog

Stimulates the liver, kidneys and intestines • Helps to relieve lower back pain and indigestion • Tones the arms • Opens the chest, central spine and shoulders • Helps to relieve asthma

1 On all fours, position your hands in line with the shoulders, and your knees hip-width apart. Inhale to prepare.

2 As you exhale, widen the arms and move them forwards on the floor.

3 Slowly drop the chest and shoulders towards the ground, ensuring that the hips remain in line with the knees.

▶ Focus your breath, allowing the chest and shoulders to open and the spine to lengthen. Hold the posture for 1 minute, or less if it becomes uncomfortable. Then return to the starting position.

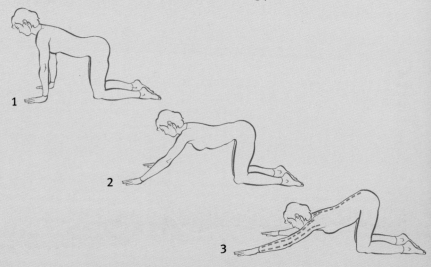

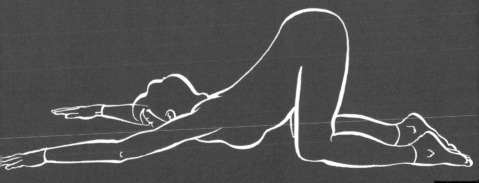

❼ The cobra

Improves circulation to all organs • Tones the arms and abdomen •
Expands the lungs • Helps to relieve asthma, menstrual discomfort,
constipation and indigestion

Caution: Avoid this posture if you're pregnant or suffer from lower back pain.

1 Lie on your front with your forehead down, legs together and hands
 in line with the outside of your shoulders. Inhale to prepare.

2 As you exhale, slowly lift the forehead, chin and neck, pushing your
 hands into the ground.

3 Continue to push, lifting the chest and ribs. Draw the elbows down
 towards the waist, pull the shoulders back and down, and open the chest.

▶ Focus your breath. Hold the posture for 30 seconds. Then slowly lower
 the ribs, chest, neck, chin and finally the forehead, back to the floor.
 Then repeat.

❽ The mountain

Improves circulation to all organs • Tones the arms • Firms the abdomen •
Improves posture

1   Stand with your feet hip-width apart, heels turned out slightly. Stretch
    your arms out in front of you and link your fingers.

2   Inhale to prepare.

3   As you exhale, stretch your arms up above your head and root your
    feet firmly into the ground. Become aware of the opposite stretch
    creating space around your waist.

▶   Focus your breath as you stretch gently in the posture. Hold the stretch
    for 1 minute. Then release your arms and place them by your sides.

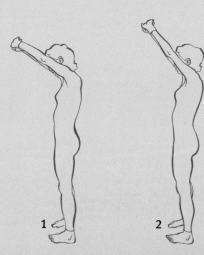

❾ The stork

Improves circulation to all organs • Stretches the thighs and arms •
Expands the lungs • Opens the hips • Helps to relieve asthma and stress
• Improves concentration and balance

1   Stand with your feet hip-width apart, toes pointing forwards, arms by
    your sides.

2   Bend your right leg up behind you and take hold of the ankle with your
    right hand. Raise your left arm so that your fingers point towards the
    ceiling. Your arm should gently brush your ear. Inhale to prepare.

3   Root the left foot firmly into the ground and, as you exhale, slowly lean
    forwards and push your right foot up to the ceiling. Make sure your
    hips are straight throughout – do not allow them to twist. Keep the
    grounded leg strong and straight.

▶   Focus your breath. Hold the posture for 1 minute. Then slowly release
    the leg, and relax the arm. Repeat to the other side.

1

2

3

⑩ The shoulder stand

Improves circulation to all organs • Stretches the neck • Stimulates the thyroid • Invigorates the body • Tones the abdominal muscles • Helps to relieve asthma, indigestion and varicose veins

Caution: Avoid this posture if you're pregnant or suffering from high blood pressure, neck pain or injury, or pins and needles in the arms or hands.

1 Lie on your back with your legs together, arms by your sides, palms face down. Keep your head centred and your chin tucked in. Inhale to prepare.

2 As you exhale, slowly raise your legs until they're positioned over your torso. Then, pressing your hands into the floor, begin to lift your hips.

3 Support your back with both hands, fingers turned into the spine, thumbs around the hips. Continue to lift the legs and hips, gradually moving the hands up the back as the distance between your head and feet increases. Keep your elbows tucked in to distribute the weight evenly and avoid pressure on the neck and shoulders.

▶ Focus your breath. Hold the posture for 1–2 minutes, or less if it becomes uncomfortable. To release, slowly take your legs to an angle of 45 degrees over your head, and press your palms into the floor. Slowly lower the spine to the floor, one vertebra at a time, followed by the legs.

1   2   3

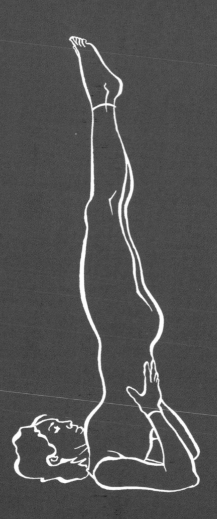

⑪ The plough

Improves circulation to all organs • Stretches the neck, spine, hamstrings and calf muscles • Stimulates the thyroid • Helps to relieve asthma, neck and back pain, indigestion and constipation

Caution: Avoid this posture if you're pregnant or suffering from high blood pressure, neck pain or injury, or pins and needles in the arms or hands.

1 Lie on your back with your legs together. Place your arms by your sides, palms down. Your head should be centred, chin tucked in. Inhale.

2 As you exhale, press your hands into the ground. Slowly raise your legs until they're positioned over your torso, then raise your hips.

3 Support your back with both hands, fingers turned into the spine and thumbs towards the hips. Tuck your elbows in. Slowly take your legs over your head. The aim is for your feet to touch the floor behind your head, but do not force them if it starts to feel uncomfortable.

▶ Tuck your toes in and straighten your legs. Keep the hips lifted and the chin tucked in to take the weight away from the neck and shoulders. Focus your breath. Hold the posture for 1 minute. To release, press your palms into the floor, then slowly lower the spine one vertebra at a time from the shoulders to the tail bone. Then gently lower the legs.

1   2   3

⑫ The fish

Expands the lungs • Stimulates the thyroid • Stretches the neck and spine •
Opens the shoulders • Tones the arms • Helps to relieve asthma and stress

**Caution: Avoid this posture if you have a neck injury or suffer from pins
and needles in the arms or hands.**

1 Lie on your back with your legs together. Place your arms by your
   sides, palms down. Keep your head centred, chin tucked in.

2 With your arms straight, position your hands underneath your buttocks
   so that your hands are side by side, pointing towards the thighs. Inhale
   to prepare.

3 Exhale, pressing your elbows into the floor. As you do so, arch your
   back and lift your chest.

▶ Slowly lower your head back until the top of the head touches the floor.
   Focus your breath. Hold the posture for 1 minute. To release, gently lift
   your head, then lower your body, returning your arms to your sides.

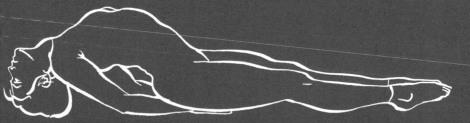

101

wake up
and let go
10-MINUTE SESSIONS

① The mountain

Improves circulation to all organs • Tones the arms • Firms the abdomen • Improves posture

1 Stand with your feet hip-width apart, heels turned out slightly. Stretch your arms out in front of you and link your fingers.

2 Inhale to prepare.

3 As you exhale, stretch your arms up above your head and root your feet firmly into the ground. Become aware of the opposite stretch creating space around your waist.

▶ Focus your breath as you stretch gently in the posture. Hold the stretch for 1 minute. Then release your arms and place them by your sides.

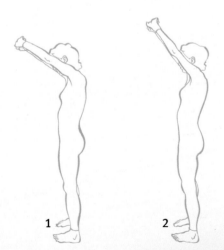

1   2   3

❷ Letting go

*Stimulates the liver, kidneys and intestines • Helps to relieve stress,
fatigue and indigestion • Stretches the calf muscles and hamstrings*

Caution: Do not attempt this posture if you suffer from high blood pressure.

1 Standing with your feet hip-width apart and your heels turned out
   slightly, relax your body forwards, your arms hanging down.

2 Inhale as your body relaxes down.

3 As you exhale, drop your chin to your chest and slowly continue to
   release your spine, one vertebra at a time. Do not bounce. Root your
   feet firmly into the ground to keep your legs strong, and open the
   backs of the knees without locking them. Let go of the tension in the
   upper body.

▶ Exhale to release the spine, then the shoulders, arms, fingers, neck,
   face, jaw and eyes. Focus your breath as you hold the posture. Hold
   for 1 minute, then slowly come up to a standing position.

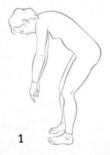

1

2

3

❸ The standing fish

Corrects rounded shoulders • Expands lungs • Tones the arms • Helps to relieve asthma, lethargy and anxiety

1 Standing with your feet hip-width apart, heels turned out slightly, link your fingers together behind your back.

2 Inhale to prepare.

3 As you exhale, slowly lift the centre of the chest and open the shoulders back, pulling the arms down. Root your feet firmly into the ground, keeping your legs strong and the backs of the knees open.

▶ As you focus your breath in the posture, your chest should be lifted and fully open and your arms pulled back. Hold for 1 minute. Then slowly release your arms and allow them to rest by your sides.

 1

 2

 3

❹ The triangle variation

Stimulates the kidneys, liver and intestines • Helps to relieve fatigue, stress, stiffness in the shoulders and indigestion • Stretches the calf muscles and hamstrings • Tones the arms

Caution: Do not attempt this posture if you suffer from high blood pressure or lower back pain.

1 Stand with your feet wide apart, toes pointing forwards. Root your feet firmly into the ground. Position your hands behind your back and link your fingers together. Inhale to prepare.

2 As you exhale, slowly bend forwards with the spine relaxed.

3 Continue to bend, taking your arms over your head.

▶ Focus your breath. Hold the posture for 1 minute. Then slowly return to the standing position and release the arms.

1

2

3

❺ The wide-leg triangle

Stimulates the liver, kidneys and intestines • Helps to relieve indigestion • Improves balance and spinal flexibility • Tones the legs • Stretches the arms • Strengthens the lower back and abdominal muscles

1 Stand with your feet wide apart, toes pointing forwards. Raise your right arm so that it brushes against your ear, fingers pointing to the ceiling. Inhale to prepare.

2 With your face turned into the raised arm, slowly exhale. As you do so, stretch your arm and torso to the left, keeping the left arm straight, by your side.

3 As you stretch, root your right foot firmly into the ground. Ensure that your hips are pointing forwards – do not allow them to twist. If you experience any pain in your sides, stop.

▶ Focus your breath. Hold the posture for 30 seconds. Then slowly return to the standing position and release the arm. Repeat to the other side.

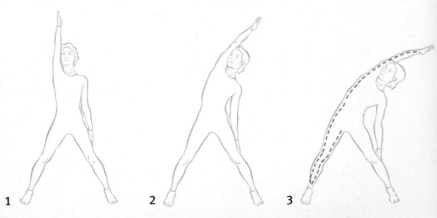

1   2   3

⑥ The dog

Improves circulation to all organs • Stretches the calf muscles, hamstrings, spine, arms and hands • Helps to relieve back pain, headache, fatigue and indigestion

Caution: Do not attempt this posture if you have high blood pressure.

1 On all fours, position your hands in line with the shoulders, knees hip-width apart. Inhale to prepare.

2 As you exhale, bring your weight onto the toes, and slowly lift the knees.

3 Push your tail bone up and out. With your heels turned outwards slightly, extend them to the floor to open out the backs of the knees.

▶ Lengthening the legs fully, relax the neck and face. Focus your breath. Hold the posture for 1 minute. Then slowly return to the starting position.

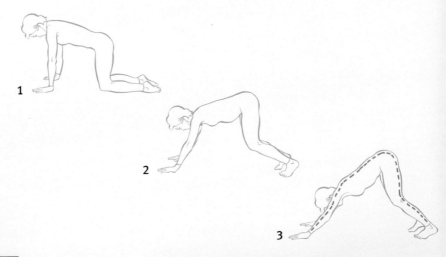

❶ Focus your breath

*Improves circulation to all organs • Relaxes muscles and ligaments •
Relieves stress*

Lie down and gently close your eyes. Slowly inhale through the nose and
focus on your breath as it travels down the throat and into the bottom of
the lungs and ribcage. Be aware of your lungs and ribcage expanding and
your spine lengthening. You will feel the abdomen rise.

Exhale through your nose. Feel the abdomen fall. The out-breath should
be longer than the in-breath.

Surrender the weight of your body into the ground. Let go of your
thoughts. Focus your breathing.

- **The exhalation holds the key to relaxation. The more stale air you
  exhale, the more fresh air you can inhale, the deeper your breathing,
  the quieter the mind.**

  Focus your breath ... relax ... relax.

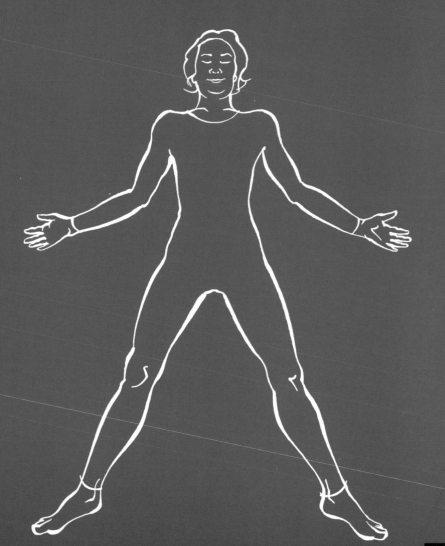

❷ The cobbler

Improves circulation to all organs • Stretches the inner thighs and groin • Opens the chest and shoulders • Helps to relieve asthma and menstrual discomfort

1 Lie on your back and bend your knees up towards the ceiling so that your feet are a few inches away from your buttocks, your feet and ankles together. Spread your arms to an angle of 45 degrees to your body. Keep your head centred and your chin tucked in. Inhale to prepare.

2 As you slowly exhale, begin to open your knees.

3 Continue to open your knees, keeping the lower back pressed into the ground.

▶ Focus your breath as you allow the hips to open fully. Hold for 1 minute. Then slowly bring the knees together.

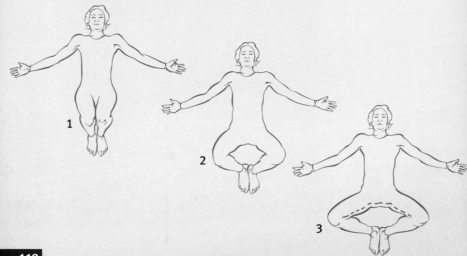

❸ The hip roll

Stimulates the liver, kidneys and intestines • Helps to relieve trapped nerves, indigestion and constipation • Stretches the thighs • Releases tension in the spine • Opens the shoulders and chest • Helps to relieve asthma

Caution: Do not attempt this posture if you are pregnant.

1 Lying on your back, feet together, bend your knees up to the ceiling. Bring your arms out, level with your shoulders, palms facing up. Your head should be centred and your chin tucked in. Inhale to prepare.

2 As you slowly exhale, drop your knees to the left as far as is comfortable. As you do so, turn your head to the right, twisting the spine.

3 Inhale. Then slowly exhale, bringing the knees and head back to centre.

▶ Repeat to the other side. Continue for 2 minutes, twisting to one side then the other. To finish, bring the knees and head back to centre.

❹ The pelvic tilt

Stimulates the thyroid • Expands the lungs • Stretches the neck and thighs • Strengthens the lower back and abdominal muscles • Helps to relieve asthma, menstrual discomfort and back pain

Caution: Avoid this posture if you're pregnant or have a neck injury.

1 Lie on your back with your knees bent and your feet hip-width apart, heels turned out slightly. Place your arms by your sides, palms down. Keep your head centred and your chin tucked in. Inhale to prepare.

2 Slowly exhale, lifting your tail bone off the ground as you do so.

3 Lift each vertebra off the ground one by one until you reach the shoulder blades.

▶ Root your feet firmly into the ground. Become aware of your chest opening as you push the spine up as far as is comfortable. Inhale. Then exhale as you slowly lower the spine, one vertebra at a time – upper spine, central spine, lower spine, tail bone. Repeat the pelvic tilt for 1 minute.

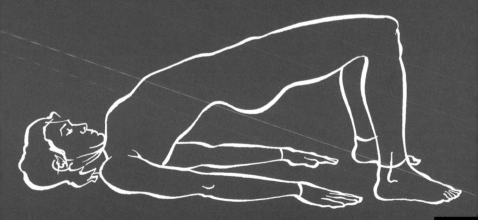

➎ The big toe

Improves circulation to all organs • Stretches the hamstrings and calf muscles • Tones the abdominal muscles • Improves flexibility in the hips • Helps to relieve back pain, indigestion and constipation

1 Lie on your back with your chin tucked into your neck, and your lower back pressed into the ground. Inhale to prepare.

2 Slowly exhale, raising your legs off the ground. Use your hands to support your upper legs.

3 Focusing your breath, raise the legs as far as you can manage, using your hands to guide them. Extend through the heels to open up the backs of the legs.

▶ Grab hold of your toes and gently pull your legs towards you as far as is comfortable, keeping the backs of the knees open. Hold the posture for 1 minute. Slowly lower your legs to the floor.

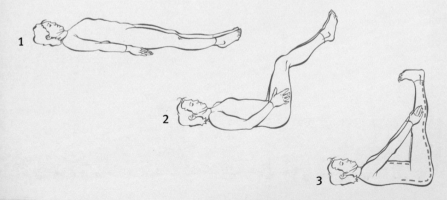

❻ The stork

Improves circulation to all organs • Stretches the thighs and arms •
Expands the lungs • Opens the hips • Helps to relieve asthma and stress
• Improves concentration and balance

1   Stand with your feet hip-width apart, toes pointing forwards, arms by
your sides.

2   Bend your right leg up behind you and take hold of the ankle with your
right hand. Raise your left arm so that your fingers point towards the
ceiling. Your arm should gently brush your ear. Inhale to prepare.

3   Root the left foot firmly into the ground and, as you exhale, slowly lean
forwards and push your right foot up to the ceiling. Make sure your
hips are straight throughout – do not allow them to twist. Keep the
grounded leg strong and straight.

▶   Focus your breath. Hold the posture for 1 minute. Then slowly release
the leg, and relax the arm. Repeat to the other side.

1

2

3

ABOUT THE AUTHOR

Jude Reignier is an experienced yoga teacher living and working in Notting Hill, London. She trained at the Shivananda Yoga Centre in the Catskills, New York, where she was awarded an excellent diploma. During her years of teaching she has developed her own individual style based on the knowledge she has gained working with people on a one-to-one basis, with various groups, with children and those with special needs. Jude is married and has two children.

ABOUT THE CONSULTANT

Sean Durkan has a BSc degree from the London School of Osteopathy, and is a member of the General Osteopathic Council. He has been a practising osteopath for 20 years, and has residency at The Queen's Club, London, where he treats sports professionals; his clients also include many actors and musicians. Sean takes a holistic approach to osteopathy, looking at clients' posture, dietary habits and general lifestyle as a way to improve well-being. His personal interests include Pilates and yoga.

ACKNOWLEDGEMENTS

Very special thanks to my husband Tristan, without whose love and artistic skills I couldn't have done this book. To my son Natty and daughter Dionne for their patience. Thanks to Simon Trewin for recommending Robert Smith Literary Agency and Robert for his continual support. I am very grateful to Eddison Sadd for publishing my book, and especially to Ian Jackson, Elaine Partington, Katie Golsby and Malcolm Smythe for all their hard work. Thanks to Sean Durkan for his advice and support on the introduction and internal organs. To Juliet Percival for the great illustrations, all my clients for their encouragement and inspiration, especially Bertie Newbery (Milk Studios), Ingrid Western, Jackie Hyde and Elaine Maley (Natural Healing Centre). Finally, thank you to my dad, mum and sisters.

ENGLISH
for the IB Diploma

Steven Croft
Helen Cross

Consultant:
Elizabeth Druce,
Senior Examiner

OXFORD
UNIVERSITY PRESS

UNIVERSITY PRESS

Great Clarendon Street, Oxford OX2 6DP

Oxford University Press is a department of the University of Oxford.
It furthers the University's objective of excellence in research, scholarship,
and education by publishing worldwide in

Oxford New York

Auckland Cape Town Dar es Salaam Hong Kong Karachi
Kuala Lumpur Madrid Melbourne Mexico City Nairobi
New Delhi Shanghai Taipei Toronto

With offices in

Argentina Austria Brazil Chile Czech Republic France Greece
Guatemala Hungary Italy Japan Poland Portugal Singapore
South Korea Switzerland Thailand Turkey Ukraine Vietnam

Oxford is a registered trade mark of Oxford University Press
in the UK and in certain other countries

British Library Cataloguing in Publication Data

Data available

ISBN-13: 978 0 19 912416 9
ISBN-10: 0 19 912416 7

5 7 9 10 8 6 4

Designed and typeset by Mike Brain Graphic Design Limited, Oxford

Printed in Great Britain by Ashford Colour Press Ltd, Gosport, Hampshire

Contents

Acknowledgements

The authors and publisher are grateful for permission to reprint the following copyright material:

Simon Armitage: 'I Say, I Say, I Say' from *The Dead Sea Poems* (1995), reprinted by permission of the publishers, Faber & Faber Ltd, and of David Godwin Associates.

Margaret Atwood: extracts from *The Handmaid's Tale* (Jonathan Cape, 1986, Virago, 1997), copyright © O. W. Toad Ltd 1985, reprinted by permission of Curtis Brown Ltd, London, and McClelland and Stewart Ltd, The Canadian Publishers; 'Postcard' from *True Stories* (Jonathan Cape, 1982), reprinted by permission of Curtis Brown Ltd, London.

Iain Banks: extract from *The Crow Road* (Abacus, 1992), copyright Iain Banks 1992, reprinted by permission of Time Warner Books UK and Sheil Land Associates Ltd.

Samuel Beckett: extract from *Waiting for Godot* (1956), reprinted by permission of the publishers, Faber & Faber Ltd, and Grove/Atlantic, Inc.

Laurence Binyon: 'For the Fallen (September 1914)' from *Collected Poems 1869–1943*, 2 vols. (Macmillan), reprinted by permission of The Society of Authors as the Literary Representative of the Estate of Laurence Binyon.

Alison Brackenbury: 'Night Watch' from *Dreams of Power and Other Poems* (1981) reprinted by permission of the publishers, Carcanet Press Ltd.

Vera Brittain: extract from *Testament of Youth*, (Victor Gollancz Ltd, 1933), copyright © the Literary Executors of Vera Brittain 1970, reprinted by permission of Mark Bostridge and Rebecca Williams c/o The Orion Publishing Group Ltd.

Rupert Brooke: letter to Katharine Cox from *The Letters of Rupert Brooke* edited by Geoffrey Keynes (1968), reprinted by permission of the publishers, Faber & Faber Ltd.

Albert Camus: extracts from *The Outsider* translated by Joseph Laredo (Penguin,1983), reprinted by permission of Penguin Books Ltd.

Angela Carter: extract from 'The Snow Pavilion' first published in *New Stories 4* (Hutchinson, 1979), copyright © Angela Carter 1979, reprinted by permission of the Estate of Angela Carter, c/o Rogers, Coleridge & White, 20 Powis Mews, London W11 1JN.

E E Cummings: 'anyone lived in a pretty how town' from *Complete Poems 1904–1962* edited by George J Firmage, copyright © 1991 by the Trustees for the E E Cummings Trust and George J Firmage, reprinted by permission of W W Norton & Company.

Imtiaz Dharker: 'Blessing' from *Postcards from God* (1997), reprinted by permission of the publishers, Bloodaxe Books Ltd.

Margaret Drabble: extract from 'Hassan's Tower' in *Winter's Tales* (Macmillan, 1966), copyright © Margaret Drabble 1966, reprinted by permission of PFD on behalf of Margaret Drabble.

Carol Ann Duffy: 'Mean Time', 'Havisham', 'Confession', 'First Love', and 'Stuffed' from *Mean Time* by Carol Ann Duffy (Anvil Press Poetry, 1993), reprinted by permission of the publisher.

Nissim Ezekiel: 'Night of the Scorpion' from *Poverty Poems* (OUP, India), reprinted by permission of Oxford University Press, New Delhi.

Brian Friel: extract from *Making History* (1989), reprinted by permission of the publishers, Faber & Faber Ltd, and of The Agency (London) Ltd.

Robert Frost: 'The Road Not Taken' from *The Poetry of Robert Frost* edited by Edward Connery Lathem (Jonathan Cape, 1971), copyright 1916, 1928, © 1969 by Henry Holt & Company, copyright 1944, 1956 by Robert Frost, reprinted by permission of the Estate of Robert Frost and the publishers, The Random House Group Ltd, and Henry Holt & Company, LLC.

Paul Fussell: extract from introduction to *The Bloody Game: An Anthology of Modern War*, edited by Paul Fussell (Scribners, London 1991), reprinted by permission of Time Warner Books UK and of W W Norton & Company.

Jane Gardam: extract from 'Stone Trees' from *Pangs of Love and Other Stories* (Hamish Hamilton, 1983), reprinted by permission of David Higham Associates.

Rahila Gupta: 'A Gift', first published in *Don't Ask Me Why: An Anthology of Short Stories by Black Women* edited by Da Choong, Olivette Cole Wilson, Sylvia Parker and Gabriela Pearse (Black Woman Talk, 1991), reprinted by permission of the author.

Joanne Harris: extract from *Chocolat* (Black Swann, 2000), copyright © Joanne Harris 1999, reprinted by permission of Transworld Publishers, a division of The Random House Group Ltd and Viking Penguin, a division of Penguin Group (USA) Inc.

Seamus Heaney: 'Churning Day' from *Death of a Naturalist* (1966), copyright © Seamus Heaney 1966, 1991, reprinted by permission of the publishers, Faber & Faber Ltd and Farrar, Straus & Giroux, LLC.

Ernest Hemingway: extract from 'Indian Camp' from *The Short Stories of Ernest Hemingway* (Scribner Paperback Fiction/Jonathan Cape), copyright 1925 by Charles Scribner's Sons, copyright renewed © 1953 by Ernest Hemingway, reprinted by permission of Simon & Schuster Adult Publishing Group, and The Random House Publishing Group Ltd.

Susan Hill: extracts from 'Missy' and 'Halloran's Child' taken from *A Bit of Singing and Dancing* by Susan Hill, (Hamish Hamilton), copyright © Susan Hill, 1971, 1972, 1973, reprinted by permission of Sheil Land Associates Ltd.

Ted Hughes: 'Swifts' from *New Selected Poems 1957–1994*, (1995) copyright © Ted Hughes 1995, reprinted by permission of the publishers, Faber & Faber Ltd, and Farrar, Straus & Giroux, LLC.

Evan Jones: 'Song of Banana Man' from *The Penguin Book of Caribbean Verse* selected and edited by Paula Burnett (Penguin 1986); copyright holder not traced.

Franz Kafka: extracts from *Metamorphosis* translated by Willa and Edwin Muir in *Metamorphosis and Other Stories* (Martin Secker & Warburg), reprinted by permission of The Random House Group Ltd and Schocken Books, a division of Random House, Inc.

Brian Keenan: extract from *An Evil Cradling* (Hutchinson, 1992), reprinted by permission of The Random House Group and Curtis Brown Ltd, London, on behalf of Brian Keenan.

Philip Larkin: 'Naturally the Foundation Will Pay Your Expenses' from *Collected Poems* (1988), reprinted by permission of the publishers, Faber & Faber Ltd, and Farrar, Straus & Giroux, LLC.

Felicia Hardison Londré: extract from 'A streetcar running fifty years' in *The Cambridge Companion to Tennessee Williams* edited by Matthew C Roudané (Cambridge University Press, 1997), reprinted by permission of the publisher.

Gabriel Garcia Marquez: extract from *Chronicle of a Death Foretold* translated by Gregory Rabassa (Jonathan Cape, 1982), reprinted by permission of The Random House Group Ltd and Carmen Balcells Agencia Literaria SA.

Andrew Motion: 'Dead March' from *Selected Poems 1976–1997* (1998), reprinted by permission of the publishers, Faber & Faber Ltd.

Grace Nichols: 'Hey There Now' and 'Iguana Memory' from *The Fat Black Woman's Poems* (Virago Press, 1984), copyright © Grace Nichols 1984, reprinted by permission of Curtis Brown Ltd, London, on behalf of Grace Nichols.

George Orwell: extract from *Nineteen Eighty Four* (Martin Secker & Warburg, 1949), copyright © George Orwell 1949, reprinted by permission of A M Heath & Co Ltd on behalf of Bill Hamilton as the Literary Executor of the Estate of the late Sonya Brownell Orwell, and of Harcourt, Inc.

Wilfred Owen: letter to Susan Owen from *Wilfred Owen: Collected Letters* edited by Harold Owen and John Bell (1967), copyright © Oxford University Press 1967, reprinted by permission of Oxford University Press.

Sylvia Plath: 'Crossing the Water', 'Blackberrying', 'Mirror', 'Mushrooms' and line from 'Frog Autumn' from *Collected Poems* edited by Ted Hughes (1981), reprinted by permission of the publishers, Faber & Faber Ltd; 'Crossing the Water', 'Blackberrying', and 'Mirror' also reprinted by permission of HarperCollins Publishers, Inc; 'Mushrooms' and line from 'Frog Autumn' also reprinted by permission of Alfred A Knopf, a division of Random House, Inc.

Theodore Roethke: 'The Storm' from *The Collected Poems of Theodore Roethke* (1966), reprinted by permission of the publishers, Faber & Faber Ltd, and Doubleday, a division of Random House, Inc.

Willy Russell: extracts from *Educating Rita* (Methuen, 1985), copyright © 1985 by Willy Russell, reprinted by permission of Methuen Publishing Ltd.

Alexander Solzhenitsyn: extract from *One Day in the Life of Ivan Denisovich* translated by Ralph Parker (Victor Gollancz Ltd, 1963), reprinted by permission of the Orion Publishing Group Ltd.

Wole Soyinka: 'Season' from *Idanre and Other Poems* (Methuen, 1967), copyright © 1967,1995 by Wole Soyinka, reprinted by permission of Methuen Publishing Ltd and Melanie Jackson Agency, LLC.

John Updike: 'Winter Ocean' from *Telephone Poles and Other Poems* (Deutsch, 1963), copyright © John Updike 1963, reprinted by permission of Penguin Books Ltd; also from *Collected Poems 1953–1993*, copyright © John Updike 1993, reprinted by permission of Alfred A Knopf, a division of Random House, Inc.

Elizabeth Walter: extract from 'Dual Control' from *Dead Women and Other Haunting Experiences* by Elizabeth Walter (Collins Harvill, 1975), copyright © Elizabeth Walter 1975, reprinted by permission of A M Heath & Company Ltd.

Tennessee Williams: extracts from *A Streetcar Named Desire* (New Directions), copyright © 1947,1953 by Tennessee Williams, renewed 1975, 1981 The University of the South, reprinted by permission of Casarotto Ramsay Ltd on behalf of The University of the South, Sewanee, Tennessee and New Directions Publishing Corp. All rights whatsoever in this play are strictly reserved and application for performance etc. must be made before rehearsal to Casarotto Ramsay Ltd., National House, 60–66 Wardour Street, London W1V 4ND. No performance may be given unless a licence has been obtained.

We are also grateful to the authors' students for allowing us to use their responses as examples, and to the International Baccalaureate Organization for permission to reproduce material from Language A1 Specification (1999).

We have tried to trace and contact all copyright holders before publication. If notified, the publishers will be pleased to rectify any errors or omissions at the earliest opportunity.

Part 1
The Commentary

1 Approaching Literary Criticism

Objectives

- To establish a strategy of approaching unseen texts
- To practise close reading of poetry and prose texts
- To look at style and structure in literary criticism

Applying the rules

In the play *Educating Rita* by the British playwright Willy Russell, Rita – a young woman from a working-class background – begins to study English Literature through the Open University. She decides that an 'education' will give her more choices in life. After her first unsuccessful attempts at essays, her tutor Frank explains:

Frank: There is a way of answering examination questions that is expected. It's a sort of accepted ritual, it's a game, with rules. And you must observe those rules.

Later, the play suggests that in order to write according to the rules, Rita will have to give up some aspects of herself and her own natural, emotional responses to what she reads. Frank does not believe this will be altogether a good thing. Similarly, the challenge of writing about literature for the Diploma involves adopting particular approaches so as to write in the appropriate way for examination questions without losing the ability to respond in a personal way.

In this unit we will consider those approaches and identify strategies for developing your language of criticism in order to respond successfully to the kinds of unseen literary texts that you will encounter in Paper 1 of the external assessment of the Diploma, the commentary. Although this unit focuses on that purpose, you should bear in mind that learning to analyse language and literature, and understanding how language works, is a very important skill to possess in life.

What is a 'written commentary'?

In Paper 1 of the externally assessed element of the IB Diploma, you will sit an examination in which you will be given an 'unseen' paper. This means that the texts on the paper will be ones that you have not studied or seen before. The paper will contain **two** unseen texts. One of the texts will be a poetry text; the other one may be an extract from a novel or short story, an essay, a biography, or a journalistic piece of writing 'of literary merit'. The texts for commentary may either be complete pieces of writing, or extracts from larger pieces. You will select **one** of the two pieces on which to write your commentary. You must apply 'the techniques of literary criticism'. At Higher Level there will be no accompanying questions or guidelines – you will simply be asked to write your commentary. At Standard Level there will be three or four guiding questions which are intended as prompts to help you structure and organize your commentary. You do not have to respond directly to these questions if you do not wish to, but if you do use them your responses must be integrated into the body of your commentary. You must not simply answer them as individual questions.

What are the 'techniques of literary criticism'?

As the opening quotation of this unit suggests, writing successfully on a piece of literature involves writing to a certain set of 'rules'. These rules are the conventions of literary criticism. However, within these conventions there are a range of approaches you can adopt. It must be stressed that there is no one 'right' way to write a commentary. The term 'criticism', though, is perhaps a little misleading here. The word 'criticizing' suggests some kind of fault-finding, or looking for the bad points in something. In literary terms, however, it really means assessing the quality of the piece of writing, and examining how the writer has written the piece and what effects it creates. In this sense the terms **literary appreciation** or **literary analysis** more closely describe the process. The **techniques** you employ are the methods with which you approach your analysis of the text and the way in which you present this analysis.

As *Educating Rita* also suggests, however, your own personal response to a text is important too and the best pieces of literary analysis are those which blend a personal response with an objective examination of a piece of writing. This objective analysis will look at the various aspects of the piece, analysing the methods the writer has used in order to make the writing effective. These aspects include such elements as the content, theme, style, structure, and language of the piece you are writing about. You can help yourself to prepare for the unseen exam by reading widely, developing your understanding of the techniques of literary criticism and analysis, and developing strategies that you can use to help you approach unseen literary texts.

Close reading

Skills in close reading are essential for literature study in general but they are especially important in writing a commentary on a given text. Whenever you encounter a literary text for the first time – whether it is a text you are reading for coursework, a set text, or a poem or extract you have been asked to analyse in an examination – all the habits and skills of close reading that you have learned will enable you to discover more for yourself about the text. 'Close reading' means exactly what it says: it is the art of reading closely, paying great attention to details of language, in order to come to the best possible understanding of texts and of how writers create meaning.

Developing your skills

The best way to develop your ability to read closely is to practise, by reading and analysing as wide a variety of texts as you possibly can. The more familiar you can become with a broad range of literary texts, the more you will be able to recognize the features of different types of writing and to see the similarities and differences between them.

In the course of your studies you will probably be given opportunities to practise your close reading skills by working on a variety of short texts on a particular theme or by doing what is often called 'practical criticism', 'unseen criticism', or 'critical commentary'. As you know, this means that you are presented with poems or short prose extracts you have not seen before, and asked to discuss them or to write about them, with only a short time to prepare your response.

Here are some of the skills you will need to develop:

- to read and make sense of a text and recognize its most important features quickly – a kind of instant 'research' where you have to 'think on your feet'
- to apply your own literary understanding rather than ideas you have read or been taught
- to know about 'how writers write', in terms of style and structure
- to understand how writers use language to create different effects according to audience and purpose
- to organize your ideas in writing quickly.

Approaching unprepared texts

Some methods of planning your approach can help you feel more confident about the close reading of unprepared texts. First, it is important not to be daunted by a poem or prose extract you are given to analyse. There will be good reasons why a particular piece has been set, and with close reading you will be able to discover them. Texts about which there is nothing to say are not usually chosen!

Once you have the text in front of you, it is helpful to have a strategy that will allow you to examine it in detail. Here is a suggested checklist of the things you need to consider as you read it. As this list suggests, it is a good idea to begin with an overview or general point, such as the theme of the text, and go on to look at the details. This checklist can help you structure your written response.

1 **Subject or theme** What is the text about? (This may seem too obvious, but it is an essential broad starting point.) What other information do you have, for example the writer's name or a date?
2 **Speaker and/or situation** Whose 'voice' do you hear in the text? (For example, in Carol Ann Duffy's poem *Anne Hathaway*, the poet writes using the voice of Shakespeare's widow, Anne Hathaway, remembering the love that she and her husband had for each other.) Is it written in the third person or the first person? If it is first-person writing, is it the voice of the author, or is he or she taking on a role? In poems, in particular, writers sometimes write with the voice of an object (for example a mountain/the wind), an animal, or even a god, as well as with the voices of people or characters. Next, ascertain to whom the text is addressed, and the situation in which it is set.
3 **Form** What is the overall structure of the piece? Is it in a recognizable poetic form? Are there any obvious ways in which it could be divided into sections, either by its layout, its meaning, or by changes in the way language is presented at different points?
4 **Ideas and messages** Look for ideas which are embedded 'below the surface' of the text. Think about the author's aims and purposes. Are there any signs of irony or satire?
5 **Tone and atmosphere** How would you describe the writer's 'tone of voice'? Is there an atmosphere or feeling which pervades the piece, such as sadness, gloom, or joy? If so, what is it about the writing that creates this effect? (For example, long sentences, with soft consonant sounds and repeated use of 'oo' and 'o' vowels, tend to create a sombre effect.) Look at the use of setting in time and place.
6 **Imagery** What kinds of visual images or 'word-pictures' does the text present? How does the writer use simile or metaphor? Comment both on individual examples and on patterns of images which you notice. Be careful to explain and analyse these examples in terms of their contribution to the overall meaning of the text.
7 **Vocabulary or diction** What do you notice about the individual words and phrases the writer has chosen? Are there types of words which recur? (For example, there may be several words relating to death, or fire, or childhood.)

Are there words which seem unexpected or out of place? What effect do they create?

8 **Rhyme, rhythm, and sound effects** If the text is a poem, does it have a rhyme scheme, and what is its effect? (Beware of simply describing a rhyme scheme without going on to say why you think the poet has chosen it and how far this aim is achieved.) Rhythm can be important in prose as well as in poetry. Are the lines/sentences flowing, or short and jerky? Does the rhythm change at key points in the text? Other sound effects or aural images are created through the use of devices like alliteration. Remember to comment on the *effect* of these. If you cannot see any particular effect, it is better not to mention these features at all.

9 **Conclusion** Finally, return to an overview of the text. Sum up how the effects and details of style you have analysed come together to create a 'whole' piece of writing. Do content and style complement each other? What has your reading of it contributed to your understanding of the subject that it deals with? Does it offer a way of looking at things which you had not considered before?

Please note that this is *not* intended as a formula to be applied rigidly in every situation. Not every unseen text requires detailed analysis of every one of these points, but this checklist can act as a starting point and you can easily omit any aspects that are not relevant. See Unit 2 for examples of this checklist used with specific poems.

Planning strategies

Whether you are writing an essay for classwork, in an examination, or beginning a major piece of coursework, it can often be difficult to get started. Students very often find this true of the unseen too. However, there are several measures you can take to make this easier. There are also ways of thinking and planning beforehand that can help you feel more confident and secure about essay writing.

Many students find it best to develop their own preparation and planning methods which feel familiar and which can be used in examinations as well as for less formal pieces of writing. However, it is a good idea to try out several different methods and then choose those that work best for you. Your choice will depend on your 'learning style'. For example, some people naturally find it easier to grasp information when it is presented using pictures and diagrams. These people will sketch out a spider diagram or other visual aid when planning. Others are more comfortable with words, and prefer information written in list or note form. Experiment to find which methods are most helpful to you.

Here are some basic strategies that you might find helpful when approaching a text.

1 Your first task will be to read the text through very carefully at least twice. Check that you understand it fully.

2 What are its key words and ideas? Underline key words and phrases. The underlined words represent the ideas that you will need to keep in mind while you plan and write your answer.

3 In addition to identifying these specific points, look for the underlying meanings that may be present in the text.

4 Annotate the text. When you are preparing to write a commentary, annotating the poem or passage can be very useful. It can help you to remember certain details and enable you to find them again quickly.

5 Write down your responses to the effects created by specific words and phrases.

6 List the key points which you would need to cover in your commentary. Try to arrange them in a logical order, so that you can move easily from one to another as you write. This will help you to structure your commentary in the most effective way.

Although planning is important, we do need to remember that sometimes the process of writing is in itself an exploration. At times we need to throw away all our plans and plunge into the writing before we can find out exactly what our ideas are; some arguments and ideas only take shape when we have worked through them in writing. Some writers always work this way and are not comfortable with planning in advance.

The most important thing is that you discover planning strategies that work for you, and use them so that they become a natural part of your writing process. Then you will have a familiar starting point when faced with the pressure of exam conditions.

Writing a considered essay

Another moment from Willy Russell's play *Educating Rita* will get us thinking about what is meant by a considered essay.

Frank: In response to the question, 'Suggest how you would resolve the staging difficulties inherent in a production of Ibsen's *Peer Gynt*', you have written, quote, 'Do it on the radio', unquote.

Rita: Precisely.

Frank: Well?

Rita: Well what?

Frank: Well I know it's probably quite naïve of me but I did think you might let me have a considered essay.

Rita's answer is not wrong, but as Frank tells her, she has not yet learned the rules she needs to follow in order to write a 'considered essay'.

Activity   Your understanding of essay writing will be far more sophisticated than Rita's is at this stage. From what you have learned so far, create an advice sheet for her about the dos and don'ts of writing literary criticism.

Using evidence from the text effectively

Once you have done some thinking and planning on the text you will be writing about, you will have established the main points that you want to convey in your commentary, and perhaps even feel you have an 'answer', as Rita does. However, as you write, it is essential that you provide some good reasons and evidence to support what you say. Evidence in this sense means examples and quotations from the text. It is not very useful, for example, to write that a poet 'uses a great deal of alliteration' in a poem. That would be to make an assertion without giving any grounds for it. All it would demonstrate is that you can recognize alliteration and that you know the technical term for it. You need to follow this statement with some quotations from the poem which contain alliteration. From there you will need to go on and analyse the quotation and comment on the effect created by the alliteration.

So, broadly speaking, the process of literary comment has three stages.
1 State the point you wish to make.
2 Follow this with your quotation, making sure the context of the quotation is clear, by briefly explaining the situation, or who is speaking and to whom. Quotations should be presented in speech marks or clearly differentiated from the rest of your writing.
3 Analyse the quotation in detail, commenting on individual words or phrases and explaining how and why they are used and with what effect.

For example, *The Laboratory* by Robert Browning is a poem, in the form of a monologue, spoken by a jealous woman who plans to murder the woman who is her rival. At the time she speaks she is in the laboratory of an alchemist who is mixing some arsenic for her to use, and her words are addressed to him. (Apparently this situation was not that uncommon in Renaissance France and Italy!)

1 In stanza 3, as the alchemist works on preparing the poison, she comments on his actions, and seems to be enjoying the process. Her words include some alliteration which heightens this effect:
2 'Grind away, moisten and mash up thy paste,
   Pound at thy powder – I am not in haste.'
3 The repeated 'm' sounds of 'moisten' and 'mash' suggest her almost chewing these words with relish, while the 'p' sounds not only suggest the actual sound of the pestle and mortar, but, because of their explosive quality, express her spiteful pleasure at the thought of her rival's death.

Of course, you will not want to keep rigidly to this three-stage process of Statement, Quotation, Analysis; that would produce rather mechanical essays. However, it is useful to bear it in mind until it becomes integrated into your writing.

Here are two of the most common difficulties that students have with essay-writing.

- **Context:** not providing enough information to make sense of quotations, i.e. sprinkling quotations in essays without providing crucial details about the situation. However, do not fall into the trap of spending all your time paraphrasing the text. It is a fine balance to achieve.

- **Analysis:** students usually find this third stage of the process the most challenging. However, its importance is shown in the IB marking criteria – in two of the five assessment categories, in order to achieve the highest marks the candidate's analysis must be detailed and illustrated by carefully chosen examples.

In any case, you will no doubt find your study of literature more rewarding when you know how to recognize and comment on the important details of how writers use language. It will also help you to become more aware of the language choices you make when you are writing.

Structuring an essay

There is no single structure which will work for every essay. Each will demand a slightly different approach as the following guidelines, using a basic framework, illustrate.

1 Introduction

Briefly outline the subject of the essay. Sometimes it can be useful to give a very concise introduction to the text you are writing about. This might include one or two sentences to establish the context of the piece, for example, in terms of theme or setting. It is vital that you do not simply describe what the poem or prose piece is about at length. All your time and effort should be devoted to commenting on your interpretation of the text and the literary features and the effects they create.

2 Main section

- If you have already thought about how to approach the text and have made a plan, in one of the ways suggested earlier, you can then set about working through the topics in your list or diagram, presenting them in an order which allows you to move easily from one to another.
- Present your ideas, making sure you always support them with evidence from the text, commenting on various elements analytically.

3 Conclusion

Once you have explored all the ideas you want to mention and feel that your analysis of the text is complete, finish by explaining the conclusion you have reached and/or briefly summing up the most important points you have made. Sometimes it is useful to restate the key ideas in your conclusion.

Good commentaries often conclude by suggesting other possible interpretations or making personal comments on the impact of the piece. Try to express your conclusion clearly. An otherwise good essay can be marred by a weak ending, and you want to leave your reader with a good impression!

Adding more sophistication

The above essay structure is quite straightforward. You will often find, however, that in following a particular line of thought, it is necessary to explore a side issue or a related topic before returning to your central theme. It is vital that you can do this without becoming sidetracked and never returning to the main path, and without jumping jarringly from one idea to another.

Practise ways of incorporating related ideas while maintaining a strong sense of direction and flow in your writing. Use connecting words such as 'however', 'although', and 'therefore', and constructions such as 'there are exceptions to this, such as . . . but on the whole . . .'. See page 144 for examples of successful transitions.

Being 'objective'

Until you are familiar with the conventions for writing literary criticism, it may be difficult to grasp exactly what kind of tone or style is appropriate. One way to approach this is to read some good critical writing to get the 'feel' of it. Collections of critical writing which contain essays and reviews relating to a particular author or to specific texts can be useful in this respect. These often illustrate widely differing points of view and so serve as good reminders that there is rarely only one way to interpret a text. As well as introducing you to some different ways of thinking about the texts you are studying, they will help you to develop your awareness of the accepted language of criticism.

Some of these points are brought out in this extract from *Educating Rita*.

Frank: Now the piece you wrote for me on – what was it called . . .?
Rita: *Rubyfruit Jungle.*
Frank: Yes, it was – erm . . .
Rita: Crap?
Frank: No. Erm – the thing is, it was an appreciation, a descriptive piece. What you have to learn is criticism.
Rita: What's the difference?
Frank: Well. You must try to remember that criticism is purely objective. It should be approached almost as a science. It must be supported by reference to established literary critique. Criticism is never subjective and should not be confused with partisan interpretation. In criticism sentiment has no place. (*He picks up the copy of* Howards End) Tell me, what did you think of *Howards End*?
Rita: It was crap.
Frank: What?
Rita: I thought it was crap!
Frank: Crap? And who are you citing in support of your thesis, F. R. Leavis?
Rita: No. Me!
Frank: What have I just said? 'Me' is subjective.
Rita: Well it's what I think.

Perhaps Frank's assertion that literary criticism is 'purely objective', and like a science, is going too far. In studying literature there should be opportunities for you to express your own responses to texts as well as writing objectively about them. However, the more objective approach always needs to form the backbone of your critical writing, and when you do express your opinions or feelings about the effectiveness of a piece of writing, you still need to support them with reasoned evidence. Usually this evidence will take the form of quotations from the text. Beware of writing statements like 'The imagery in stanza 2 is extremely evocative and effective' or 'I found this passage very moving' – and leaving it at that. You need to provide specific examples or quotations and explain how the lines are effective and why.

Examiners will always look for well-supported ideas and interpretations that you have worked out for yourself. They will also look for your understanding of the writer's use of literary techniques and the effects that these create. They will look at how well you have organized and structured your commentary and how accurately you have used language in expressing your ideas. This will include the use of an appropriate choice of register and style for your commentary. Register in this instance refers to how appropriately you have used such features as vocabulary, tone, sentence structure, and expression, given the nature of your task.

Here is a sample of critical writing to give a sense of an appropriate tone and style and to demonstrate the use and analysis of quotations. It is an extract from an essay on Tennessee Williams's *A Streetcar Named Desire* by an American scholar, Felicia Hardison Londre, in which she comments on Scene 3 of the play.

On 'The Poker Night'

Scene 3 stands out from the others in several ways. It has its own title, 'The Poker Night.' Its pictorial atmosphere of 'lurid nocturnal brilliance, the raw colors of childhood's spectrum' is inspired by a picture of Van Gogh's of a billiard parlour at night, which Henry I. Schvey has identified as *All Night Café* (1888). It is one of few ensemble scenes in a play composed largely of two- or three-character sequences. And most importantly, it is the scene in which Blanche and Stanley truly begin to see each other as a threat. The opening line, spoken by one of the men at the card table, serves as a pointer: 'Anything wild in this deal?'

Stanley has been losing at cards and displays a volatile irritability even before Stella and Blanche come in. Mitch sets himself apart from the other card-players by his anxiety over his sick mother. The association with sickness and the dread of loneliness in his comment that 'I'll be alone when she goes' convey a subtle thematic linkage with Blanche, to whom he is introduced by Stella. Blanche quickly senses that Mitch is a prospective conquest. When she changes out of her dress, she deliberately stands in the light so the men can see her through the portieres. When Stella exits into the bathroom, Blanche turns on the radio and sits in a chair . . . as if confident of her power to attract Mitch to her. First, however, it is Stanley who crosses to the bedroom and turns off the radio, but 'stops short at the sight of Blanche in the chair. She returns his look without flinching', and he returns to the poker table. Thus with great economy of means, by a simple dramatic gesture, Williams demonstrates the staking out of territory.

Mitch soon leaves the card game to chat with Blanche. He shows her the inscription on his silver cigarette case, given to him by a girl who knew she was dying. Blanche homes in on his vulnerabilities: 'Sick people have such deep, sincere attachments.' She asks him to cover the light bulb with a paper lantern she bought on Bourbon Street: 'I can't stand a naked light bulb, any more than I can a rude remark or a vulgar action.' Her equation of the naked bulb with vulgarity implies its opposite: the soft glow of filtered light as the refined sensibility by which she identifies herself. It recalls her comment to Stanley in Scene 2: 'I know I fib a good deal. After all, a woman's charm is fifty per cent illusion . . .' Blanche's desire for illusion in opposition to the harsh realities that surround her is probably the play's most obvious thematic value. It is significant that Mitch is the one who both installs the paper lantern and, in Scene 9, removes it, for these actions define the period during which he sees Blanche as she wants him to see her, under the spell of an illusion she creates . . . Blanche . . . is an artist who dramatizes herself as if she were a stage character, playing roles detached from the reality of her situation, costuming herself from the trunk containing fake furs and costume jewelry, designing the lighting effects that will show her to advantage. With Mitch as her enthralled audience, she adds musical underscoring: she turns on the radio and 'waltzes to the music with romantic gestures'.

The radio galvanizes Stanley into aggressive action, though the actual source of his action undoubtedly lies deeper. Here in his own home, where he is cock of the roost and host of the poker party, the intruder Blanche has lured both his wife and his best friend into her orbit. She has appropriated his radio for her kind of music. In a drunken rage, he throws the radio out of the window.

Felicia Hardison Londre

Formality of style

In *Educating Rita*, as well as saying that Rita should be more objective, Frank hints that she needs to develop a more formal style of writing before her essays will be acceptable. This can be difficult to define, but you might have noted that the example above has a certain formality of tone while at the same time still engaging with the reader.

Here are some features to avoid in your writing. If you keep them out of your commentary it will immediately assume a tone more appropriate to the task:

- **The first person** Generally, avoid *over-using* the first person in your responses. For example, rather than saying 'I think Louisa is imaginative because . . .', try to use expressions like 'It appears that Louisa has a vivid imagination, because . . .' or 'Louisa seems to be imaginative because . . .' Having said that, the occasional use of 'I' or 'me' in a piece of critical commentary to reinforce an important point can be most effective, especially in your conclusion.
- **Slang** Avoid using slang expressions (unless, of course, they appear in quotations from your text!). Colloquial language is the language of informal speech. Try to develop your awareness of the differences between spoken English and written English.
- **Dialect and local usage** Some words or expressions may be used only in some parts of the country or world; these are appropriate in some forms

of writing, but in a formal essay Standard English is preferable. Try to develop your awareness of your regional dialect and, if you can, substitute Standard English equivalents in your essays. This will also avoid confusions in meaning.

- **Abbreviations** It is better not to use abbreviated forms in formal writing. For example, write 'did not' rather than 'didn't'; and avoid using 'etc.'.
- **Numbers** These should be written in word form, for example, 'thirty-seven' rather than '37', unless the figure is very large.

However, do use:

- **The present tense** Most literary criticism is written in the present tense. This is because the text itself, whether a novel or a poem, always exists in the same way, even though the narrative may be in the past tense. Aim to keep your writing in the present tense. For example, 'The opening scenes of the play take place in . . .' not '. . . took place in . . .'. It is even more important to be consistent: whether you use present or past tense, make sure you use the same one throughout.

Activity

Here is part of a draft student commentary on 'The Poker Night' where the style needs quite a lot of attention. Redraft it, improving the style in as many ways as possible. Don't worry if you do not know the text. It is not necessary for the purpose of this activity.

In the scene of the poker night the men and women were presented very differently. Stanley seems to me to be presented in a very macho style character. This is shown in the way that Stanley gets very drunk and this is seen to be the manly thing to do. Also the way he mocks Mitch about having to go home and see his Mam. Stanley says 'Hurry back and we'll fix you a sugar-tit'. He's also shown as a hard and nasty character when he hits Stella because she wants them to stop playing poker. This shows Stanley to be a harsh and hard character because he hits his wife because she asks them to stop playing poker.

Whereas in contrast with the other 3 men, Mitch is shown to be a very sensitive and understanding person. This is shown in the fact that he goes home early to see his Mam because she's ill. Mitch says, 'I gotta sick mother. She don't sleep until I come in at night. She says go out, so I do, but I don't enjoy it. I just keep wondering how she is.' I think this shows Mitch is sensitive and caring and thinks about his mother a lot.

Mitch also shows his sensitivity when after Stanley had hit Stella he said, 'This is terrible. Poker should not be played in a house with women.' This showed Mitch felt very sorry and awful about what had happened to Stella.

The craft in your writing

As your study of literature progresses, you will develop an awareness of the variety of ways in which writers use language. You will begin to think of writing as a 'craft', something which most writers think about and work at with great care and attention to detail, rather than something which simply happens.

Try to think about your own writing in the same way.

- Make deliberate choices about the vocabulary you use, choosing the best word for the job, rather than the first one that comes to mind.
- Try out different lengths and types of sentences.
- Think about the different ideas you wish to include in your paragraphs.
- Try to weigh ideas against each other when you are writing argumentatively.

Some fortunate people – usually those who have read very widely – seem to have an innate sense of how to write appropriately for different purposes. Others only develop a sense of style with practice. The aim is to reach the point where you know you can communicate ideas clearly and that you are in complete control of your writing.

Activity

1 Re-read some of your own recent essays. What are the strengths and weaknesses of your written style? Think about this carefully yourself and/or ask a teacher for feedback. Choose one weakness (for example, not putting quotations properly in context; changing tense; poor punctuation) and focus on correcting it in your next essay.

2 If you are working as part of a group, swap essays or other written work. Work together to read and discuss each other's work. Consider these points:
- Is it easy to read and understand?
- Does the tone and style seem to suit the task?
- Are quotations used effectively?
- Is there analytical comment?

Make a note of positive comments and advice about improvements before giving each other feedback.

Assessment

Your commentary will be assessed under five criteria. You should be clear in your mind what these criteria mean and make sure that you carefully take account of them when writing your commentary. The examiner will be looking to see:

1 How well you understand the text
To gain top marks you need to show:
- a perceptive understanding of the thoughts and feelings expressed in the text
- detailed and persuasive references to the text.

2 How effectively you have interpreted the text
To gain top marks you need to show:
- that your ideas are convincing and include a considered and appropriate personal response
- that your analysis is detailed and illustrated by carefully chosen examples.

3 How well you have appreciated the effect of literary features

To gain top marks you need to show:

- a detailed and persuasive appreciation of the effects of the literary features of the text
- a detailed analysis illustrated by carefully chosen examples.

4 How well you have organized your commentary and presented your ideas

To gain top marks you need to show:

- a purposeful and effective structure to your commentary
- supporting examples well integrated into the body of your commentary.

5 How well you have used formal language

To gain top marks you need to show:

- clear, varied, precise, and concise use of language
- accurate use of grammar, spelling, and sentence construction
- the precise use of a wide vocabulary and appropriate style
- an effective choice of register.

In order to achieve the best mark possible for your commentary you will need to bear in mind all these aspects of your own writing. In the next two units we will look in more detail at writing commentaries on poems and on other kinds of text that you might encounter on the examination paper.

2 Analysing Poetry

Objectives

- To establish a strategy of approaching unseen poetry texts
- To practise close reading of poetry texts
- To look at examples of commentaries on poems

In Unit 1 we looked at ways of approaching the commentary and literary analysis in general. In this unit we will look at ways of examining specific poems together with some practical examples of students' work on some of these poems. First it is worth reminding yourself of some points to bear in mind when approaching poetry both in your preparation for the commentary paper and when sitting the examination itself:

- Read the poem through very carefully several times before starting to write about it.
- Avoid rushing into hasty judgements on it – this is not easy under exam conditions, but thinking things through carefully can save you time in the long run.
- In a class, tutorial, or group discussion, the comments of others can help you to find your 'way into' a poem, but in an exam only further reading of the poem for yourself can help.
- An effective pattern of approach might be to read the poem through carefully at least twice and then read it again making notes, marking lines, underlining words, and so on. In the exam you can annotate the printed poem. Twenty minutes or so spent on this can pay dividends when you write your commentary.

- If you need to spend more time reading the poem then take it – it is better to pause and make sure you have something meaningful to say about a poem than to rush into it making cursory and confused comments.
- When writing under exam conditions, remember that the exam is not a race. You are not being tested on your ability to write at speed – what matters is the quality of what you have to say. The examiner will be very aware of the time constraints you are working under, and the time allocated for the exam will be reasonable for you to complete the task.

Now let us consider a poem using the close reading strategy suggested on pages 4–5.

Activity

> **1** Working alone or with a partner, read the poem *Swifts* carefully, making notes under each of the headings 1–9 given on pages 4–5.
> **2** Compare your notes with those that follow the poem below. What are the main similarities and differences in interpretation? You will no doubt have noticed different effects and meanings.

Swifts

Fifteenth of May. Cherry blossom. The swifts
Materialize at the tip of a long scream
Of needle. 'Look! They're back! Look!' And they're gone
On a steep

Controlled scream of skid
Round the house-end and away under the cherries. Gone.
Suddenly flickering in sky summit, three or four together,
Gnat-whisp frail, and hover-searching, and listening

For air-chills – are they too early? With a bowing
Power-thrust to left, then to right, then a flicker they
Tilt into a slide, a tremble for balance,
Then a lashing down disappearance

Behind elms.
They've made it again,
Which means the globe's still working, the Creation's
Still waking refreshed, our summer's
Still all to come –
And here they are, here they are again
Erupting across yard stones
Schrapnel-scatter terror. Frog-gapers,
Speedway goggles, international mobsters –

A bolas of three or four wire screams
Jockeying across each other
On their switchback wheel of death.
They swat past, hard fletched,

Veer on the hard air, toss up over the roof,
And are gone again. Their mole-dark labouring,
Their lunatic limber scramming frenzy
And their whirling blades
Sparkle out into blue –
Not ours any more.
Rats ransacked their nests so now they shun us.
Round luckier houses now
They crowd their evening dirt-track meetings,

Racing their discords, screaming as if speed-burned,
Head-height, clipping the doorway
With their leaden velocity and their butterfly lightness,
Their too much power, their arrow-thwack into the eaves.

Every year a first-fling, nearly-flying
Misfit flopped in our yard,
Groggily somersaulting to get airborne.
He bat-crawled on his tiny useless feet, tangling his flails

Like a broken toy, and shrieking thinly
Till I tossed him up – then suddenly he flowed away under
His bowed shoulders of enormous swimming power,
Slid away along levels wobbling

On the fine wire they have reduced life to,
And crashed among the raspberries.
Then followed fiery hospital hours
In a kitchen. The moustached goblin savage

Nested in a scarf. The bright blank
Blind, like an angel, to my meat-crumbs and flies.
Then eyelids resting. Wasted clingers curled.
The inevitable balsa death.
Finally burial
For the husk
Of my little Apollo –

The charred scream
Folded in its huge power.

Ted Hughes

Here is one interpretation of the poem. Remember, however, that this is just *one* interpretation. Different readers may have different ideas. As long as they can be supported by the text itself, a whole range of ideas may be valid and relevant.

1 **Subject or theme:** As the title tells us, the poem is almost entirely devoted to describing and 'capturing' in writing the appearance, movements, and behaviour of the swifts. (Fast-moving, forked-tailed birds related to swallows and martens, they are summer visitors to Britain.)

2 **Speaker and/or situation:** The poem is written in the first person. There is no reason to question that the poet is writing in his own voice and that he is addressing the reader directly. Although his chief purpose is to convey the characteristics of the birds in words, there are also elements of a 'story' in the poem. Watching and describing the punctual arrival of the swifts in May, Hughes reacts with excitement:

'Look! They're back! Look!'

For him, they signal the beginning of summer. As he puts it:

'. . . our summer's

Still all to come –'

Placing 'Still all to come' on a separate line seems to convey his pleasure in anticipating the summer that lies ahead.

Later in the poem, Hughes reminisces about previous seasons and tells the story of how each year a young bird would fail to manage its first flight, be rescued and cared for, wrapped in a scarf and offered 'meat-crumbs and flies', only to die later and be buried.

3 **Form:** For the most part, four-line stanzas are used, but rather freely. Line lengths vary. Lines are quite frequently broken or interrupted, or run on to the next line, suggesting the fast, erratic flight of the birds.

4 **Ideas and messages:** This poem does not seem to carry a hidden message but it does hold some thought-provoking ideas. For Ted Hughes, the annual arrival of the swifts is a reminder that life goes in cycles; they are a signal that the seasons continue to change and spring and summer will follow winter.

'They've made it again,

Which means the globe's still working, the Creation's

Still waking refreshed . . .'

The phrase 'Which means the globe's still working' contains a touch of humour, suggesting, perhaps, that he had begun to doubt whether summer would come again.

In his description of his vain attempts to keep the helpless small birds alive each year and his tone of resignation as they reach 'The inevitable balsa death', he may be reminding us that there is little point in trying to interfere with the inexorable course of nature. The rule of the survival of the fittest would ensure that the weak bird did not live long.

5 **Tone and atmosphere:** Most of the poem has a tone of excitement and haste. The swifts move with such speed that

'. . . they're gone

On a steep

Controlled scream of skid

Round the house-end and away under the cherries. Gone.'

almost before you have seen them. The way in which they dart in and out of sight is reflected in these short, broken lines. They give the poem an almost breathless quality, enforced by repetitions of 'gone' and 'here they are again'.

The second half of the poem is slightly more subdued, but the feeling of great speed continues whenever Hughes focuses on the movements of the birds. Many lines run into each other without punctuation, adding to the effect of fast, perpetual motion.

6 **Imagery:** As you might expect in a poem whose main aim is descriptive, the use of imagery is particularly powerful here. Most noticeable is the repeated use of metaphors likening the birds to machines (a device typical of Hughes). Many words and phrases suggest the flight of planes – fast fighter-planes in particular – or speedway driving. For example:

'On a steep
Controlled scream of skid'
and
'. . . With a bowing
Power-thrust to left, then to right, then a flicker they
Tilt into a slide . . .'

This would not be out of place in an account of an air display. Words like 'Power-thrust', 'Erupting', and 'Schrapnel-scatter terror' suggest something violent and frightening.

However, there is a contradictory quality to the swifts. As well as making them sound powerful and dangerous, Hughes also draws attention to their delicacy: they 'flicker' and 'tremble' and are 'Gnat-whisp frail'. He repeatedly uses paradox to contrast their speed, which seems blundering and uncontrolled, a 'lunatic limber scramming frenzy', with their tiny size and grace which is very much under control. They have 'leaden velocity' and 'butterfly lightness'.

Another aspect which Hughes captures is the swifts' cry – a high-pitched screaming sound. Somehow he manages to combine their sound with their movement. It is as if the birds are faster than their sounds, which they leave trailing behind them like wires:

'A bolas of three or four wire screams'
When they come into view they:
'Materialize at the tip of a long scream
Of needle . . .'

So conversely sometimes they are heard first and then seen. The word 'needle' conveys the sharp, piercing quality of their cry and their movement.

7 **Vocabulary:** In addition to these metaphors, there are other interesting choices of words. When Hughes describes the injured young bird, he emphasizes its mysterious, wild, and rather awe-inspiring qualities by referring to it as a 'moustached goblin savage' and as 'my little Apollo'. This suggests that he worships it like a little god. Apollo, the sun god, was one of the more powerful gods of Greek mythology; 'goblin' also suggests something supernatural, but rather mischievous too. Hughes refers to the bird's 'balsa death'. Balsa wood is very light and brittle, so this word encapsulates the feel of the bird's corpse, little more than feathers and bones.

8 **Rhyme, rhythm, and sound effects:** Formal rhyme does not feature in this poem. As we have noted, some lines and sentences run on fluently, while others are abrupt and broken. The rhythmic pattern emulates the darting movements of the swifts.

Hughes does also use some sound effects to contribute to his imagery. In particular, when he describes the young bird which fails to fly, it is a 'first-fling, nearly-flying/Misfit' which 'flopped' in the yard. The alliterative repetition of the soft 'f', 'l' and 's' sounds creates an aural image which helps to suggest the bird's floundering as well as representing the fluttering sound of its wings.

9 **Conclusion:** To sum up, Hughes's main concern here is to 'capture' and convey as clearly as possible his impressions of the swifts. Through his use of metaphor and choice of words he gives an impression both of their incredible speed, power, and vivacity and of their tiny lightness of touch.

If you were to omit the headings from these notes and adapt them slightly, you would have a reasonable analysis of the poem in essay form. Of course, not every detail of the poem has been examined here; probably you noted other ideas or other examples of imagery that you would include in an answer. However, with a poem of this length, it is advisable to be selective in the details you choose to analyse.

Activity

Working alone or with a partner, now look at the following student response to *Swifts* and compare it with your own notes and the ideas given above.
- Which aspects of the poem has the student covered thoroughly and which need more attention?
- Has he supported his ideas by quoting details from the text?
- Has he analysed details of the text closely? Can you find places where he needs to do more of this?
- Is his written style clear and appropriate?

Commentary

Ted Hughes begins the poem by describing the time and one aspect of the natural surroundings associated with that time when the birds return:
'Fifteenth of May. Cherry blossom.'

The poet also shows how excited he is to see the returning swifts. This is shown by the use of exclamation marks and the repetition of the word 'Look!' Almost immediately the poet goes on to discuss the speed of the swifts. He does this by saying that by the time a step has been taken the swifts are out of sight. This is a sign of the tone of the poem; the most striking feature is that of the way the poet describes the speed with which the swifts fly. The speed of the swifts is also shown by the poet by the way the different stanzas are written. The sentences are fragmented as they use exclamation marks, dashes, commas, and question marks. This gives the poem a sense of pace which is reflected by the way the swifts fly.

The language the poet uses in the first stanza shows how the swifts use power and agility to fly. This is best described in the lines:
'Power-thrust to left, then to right, then a flicker they
Tilt into a slide'.

The swifts manage to use both power and agility to fly, which is something that man-made machines fail to achieve. A rocket has power but agility is reserved for machines such as gliders.

The poet also uses metaphors of nature to explain how the swifts arrived:
'They've made it again.
Which means the globe's still working'.

This gives the connotation that the arrival of the swifts signifies that nature will continue to develop as long as they arrive after their winter break.

In the next few stanzas sporting metaphors are used and this helps again to highlight the speed at which the swifts fly. Examples of these are 'Speedway goggles', 'Jockeying', and 'Veer on the hard air.' These are used because of the speed associated with them – speedway for fast motorbikes, jockeying as in jockeying for a position in a race, and veering hard as in some other form of motor sport. These all help to give a sense of realism to the reader who may be unfamiliar with the sight of a swift flying.

The poet feels saddened when they have gone. He tries to find something to blame. In this case it is the rats who have destroyed their nests. The poet seems jealous that the swifts have gone. This is shown in the line that says they are:
'Round luckier houses now'.

This also shows the fondness which the poet has for the birds.

The next stanza best highlights the speed of the swifts. Again dashes are used in the sentence structure, which adds to the sense of speed. The way the poet describes how the swifts are
'clipping the doorway'
shows that the birds are flying so quickly that there is hardly any margin for error. They try to take short-cuts to reach their destination quicker and this could prove fatal.

The final few stanzas show the youth of the swift and how frail and vulnerable they can be. This is in great contrast to the agility and power with which they are described early in the poem.

The poet describes how in the early days, swifts, like any other birds, find it hard to fly. He uses language which again is in contrast to the language used earlier. Words such as 'crawled', 'useless feet', and 'tangling' are in vast contrast with the sure and certain movements such as 'erupting' and veering. These also show the power the young swift has to come.

The poet also describes how he once found a swift that had 'crashed among the raspberries'. He attempted to care for it in his kitchen but the bird died. The poet describes the death of the swift as:
'The inevitable balsa death'.

This shows both the benefits and drawbacks of being, as balsa wood is when used for model planes, swift and light through the air but also frail.

The life the swifts lead is best described by:
'the fine wire'.

This shows that they live on the edge, risking their life by flying so quickly through the air.

Activity

Now try applying the same approach to Alison Brackenbury's poem, *Night Watch*. Again, the poet's purpose is to 'capture' the characteristics of an animal in words. Make notes under each of the nine headings before writing a short critical commentary on the poem.

Night Watch

The cat curls in her fur, like a robe,
which is tortoiseshell, bright
black and amber
her paws glow white, she is
the most beautiful cat I have half-owned:
her name is 'Moth': she catches them,
and once, when young, moved lightly.

And I? I am hope, I am fear. In the long grass, we will
watch evening
People are washing their children
eating their food.
It is very still.

When all floors were washed today
(Moth was lost, in sun) I lay
on the bed by the propped window:
by a blue-lit space
where swallows crossed and sank, and rose -
not to own the air but be
so free of it, to turn and fall
through pathless, sun-held sky
instinctive, ending, come so near
on light wind wings softly tear
And close: flash sun: will never fly
through the open window

The sky is quickened: warm with light
always there, withdrawn from sight
to heat.
The clouds bloom slow:
from some distant rubbish ground
the gulls fly in straight lines, nicked wings
dark to tender light
calling harsh and slow, the sea
as distant here, as sky from me,

closed in their freedom, journeying.
Dew rustles through the hidden depths of air:
still, as long grass grows, the earth is moving.
The cat is night, black fur.
I wear the evening.

Alison Brackenbury

Activity Read the following poem, *Blessing* by Imtiaz Dharker, carefully and make your own notes on it. When you have finished your notes compare your ideas with those that follow, also written by a student.

Blessing

The skin cracks like a pod.
There never is enough water.

Imagine the drip of it,
The small splash, echo
in a tin mug,
the voice of a kindly God.

Sometimes, the sudden rush
of fortune. The municipal pipe bursts,
silver crashes to the ground
and the flow has found
a roar of tongues. From the huts,
a congregation: every man woman
child for streets around
butts in, with pots,
brass, copper, aluminium,
plastic buckets,
frantic hands,

and naked children
screaming in the liquid sun,
their highlights polished to perfection,
flashing light,
as the blessing sings
over their small bones.

Imtiaz Dharker

1 Content: The poem tells about how the 'blessing' of water is received in a land where rainfall is sparse. The opening line of the poem 'The skin cracks like a pod' suggests that this is a place with a hot climate, the image of 'skin cracking' showing the effects on a dry, parched land where there 'never is enough water'.

The poem goes on to relate how people celebrate during the times of heavy rainfall and how everyone is affected by the 'blessing'. We are told that all the people in the place present themselves with all different kinds of pots to collect some water and that 'naked children' scream 'in the liquid sun'.

The poem concludes with the reiteration of the idea of rainfall being a 'blessing': 'as the blessing sings/over their small bones'. However, this positive sentiment is accompanied by the inclusion of the image of 'small bones', which presents an idea of fragility.

2 Structure: The structure of the poem is very interesting as the length of the initial three stanzas reflects the amount of rainfall being received. For instance, in the first stanza only two lines are used to describe life without water. This succeeds in giving the poem an initial slow pace which suggests what life is like during a drought period. This pace increases a little in the second, four-lined, stanza, which asks us to imagine the sound of a 'small splash' of water echoing 'in a tin mug'. We see much excitement and activity in the third stanza, which is reflected in the eleven lines. The pace here is very quick, which supports the idea of the activities described. The final stanza has six lines, which suggests that the excitement and pleasure from receiving such a 'blessing' is slowing down and that a return to lack of rainfall is inevitable.

3 Mood: Initially the poem has a mood of desperation. However, by the third stanza a celebratory mood is evident as the place in drought receives a 'sudden rush of fortune' and there is so much water that 'The municipal pipe bursts'. This injects a degree of energy into the poem, which is lacking initially.

4 Imagery: The opening image of 'skin cracking' through lack of water can have two meanings which adds to its power within the poem. It could relate to the cracking of the parched earth or indeed the skin of the people themselves. Both interpretations present negative images in relation to the lack of water. When the rain does arrive in abundance, positive images of 'children/screaming in the liquid sun' present a picture of children dancing in puddles which are bright and golden as they reflect the hot sun's rays. However, at the conclusion of the poem their vulnerability is suggested in the words 'small bones'.

5 Language/vocabulary: The language used in the poem is supportive of the sentiments expressed within it. The preciousness of the long-awaited rainfall is reflected in its description as 'silver'. The 'roar of tongues' suggests fire and heat and we get the impression that the rainfall's presence will quench a great thirst of both the people and the land. When a little water is available in stanza 2, the word 'echo' as the drips fall into the bottom of a 'tin mug' suggests emptiness. The word 'frantic', which is used to describe hands which try to contain water, is powerful and suggests the energy involved in the activity.

6 Rhythm: Devices used to increase the rhythm of the poem when the rainfall comes are effective in increasing the pace. For example, the use of commas towards the end of the third stanza speeds up the pace in line with the activity being described: 'every man woman/child for streets around/butts in, with pots,/brass, copper, aluminium,/plastic buckets,/frantic hands'. This quickened pace is slowed by the end of the poem as the poet uses longer line lengths. This succeeds in emphasizing a sense of relief at the rain's eventual return and suggests a tapering off of the rainfall itself.

7 Poetic devices: The opening line includes the simile 'cracks like a pod'. This induces a feeling of destruction through lack of water – the 'pod' indicating the effect on crops and therefore food sources. When there is limited water available in stanza 2, the onomatopoeic 'drip' is effective in that its repetition could indicate the passing of time. This idea is emphasized in the inclusion of the alliterative 'small splash' used to describe the water as it falls into the mug. The onomatopoeic word 'crashes' used to describe the heavy rainfall in stanza 3 adds a degree of power and sound which enhances the life-giving force of water.

8 Symbolism: There is much religious symbolism in this poem, which suggests the reliance of the people on things spiritual. The title of the poem, 'Blessing', suggests something that is given rather than expected, and words such as 'congregation' and 'kindly God' support this idea.

Activity   Now, using your notes, write a commentary on the poem in the form a complete essay.

The following is a poem by Andrew Motion called *Dead March*, in which the poet reflects on the loss of a loved one.

Activity   Read the poem through several times very carefully, and then:
1 Make a note of the overall idea expressed in the poem.
2 Pick out any words, phrases, or images that strike you as being particularly effective, interesting, or unusual.
3 Make notes on the structure of the poem and how this adds to the overall impact.
4 Write down your own response to the poem and its effectiveness.

Dead March

It's twenty years *It's not, it's twenty-three –*
be accurate since you were whisked away
I wasn't whisked away: I broke my skull
and I was left to contemplate your life.
My life. Ridiculous. You mean my death.

Well, twenty or twenty-three. I can't decide
if that's a long time or no time at all,
or whether everything I've said since then,
and thought, and done, to try and work out how
the way we treat our lives might be involved
with how our lives treat us is more than just
a waste of breath. That's right. A waste of breath.

You see, you're always with me even though
you're nowhere, nothing, dead to all the world
you interrupt me when I start to talk,
you are the shadow dragging at my heels.

This means I can't step far enough away
to get the thing I want you to explain
in focus, and I can't lean close enough
to hear the words you speak and feel their weight.

And if I could, what difference would it make?
It's like I said. I can't decide. It's just
that having you suspended all these years
at some clear mid-point between life and death
has made me think you might have felt your way
along the link between the two, and learnt
how one deserves the other. Or does not.

I feel I'm standing on a frozen pond
entranced by someone else below the ice,
a someone who has found out how to breathe
the water and endure the cold and dark.
I know I ought to turn my back. I can't.
I also know that if I just stay put
and watch the wax-white fingers flop about
I'll start to think they must be beckoning.
I stare and stare and stare and stare and stare.
It's twenty years since you were whisked away,
or twenty-three. That's more than half my life.

Andrew Motion

Activity

> Here is a student commentary on this poem. Read it through carefully and make a note of any ideas, comments, or interpretations that you had not thought of yourself, and think carefully about them.
> Then read the examiner's comments which follow the student's response.

The poem *Dead March* expresses the thoughts of someone who has lost a loved one in tragic circumstances some time ago. As the poem is written in the first person, which promotes the idea that it is a personal experience, it suggests that this loss has been experienced by the poet himself. The poem, therefore, could be seen as an internal monologue, although the italicized utterances in stanza 1 could come from the internal thoughts of the person who has suffered the loss or they could represent a possible imagined response from the one who has died.

The tone of the poem is one of sadness and melancholic desperation as the poet ponders on and debates the reasons for 'life' and 'death' and expresses thoughts of suicide in the final stanza. Words and phrases such as 'A waste of breath', 'shadow', 'frozen', 'cold', 'dark', and the lack of any uplifting sentiments help to create a mood of solitary suffering and highlights the sadness felt through the 'suspension' between the living and deceased experienced by the poet: 'having you suspended all these years/at some clear mid-point between life and death'.

The five-stanza structure of this poem takes us chronologically from the death of a loved one twenty years ago, 'or twenty-three', to the present time in which the poet contemplates a reconciliation by committing suicide. The first stanza is short in comparison which appears to reflect the way in which memory returns to the consciousness – in a short flash of recollection. The stanza length then increases as we see the subject indulge in deliberations and thoughts about the experience and time spent alone; the longest stanza is the concluding one, where the poet considers his present feelings and suicidal thoughts.

There is no set rhythm pattern in this poem and the poem varies in speed throughout, in line with the sentiments being expressed. For instance, as the painful memory of loss returns to the subject in the first stanza, the line length is comparatively short and broken up by italicized utterances in the same way as memory returns in short bursts of recollections and realizations. As the poet relates thoughts about the effect of the loss, the sentence length increases as different feelings are expressed. In the final stanza, in which the poet contemplates suicide, the sentence length increases further, which slows the pace and is reflective of the seriousness of the intention, and this is further emphasized in the line: 'I stare and stare and stare and stare and stare', the rhythm of which appears to mirror a heartbeat.

The language used within the poem is effective in maintaining the melancholy mood. For example, the poet wonders whether trying to work out the connection between 'the way we treat our lives' and 'the way our lives treat us' is pointless, in the phrase 'A waste of breath', which supports the overall tone of the poem – 'A waste of breath' having dual meaning as it could relate both to the deliberations and life of the subject and the 'life cut short'. The poem expresses a feeling of suspension between life and death and this is reflected in words and phrases such as 'shadow', 'mid-point', and 'I can't decide'. The image of the 'frozen pond' also supports this idea by presenting the ice as being a thin, fragile film between the two.

The way in which the death is described in stanza 1 is interesting in that the stark, forthright 'I broke my skull' contrasts with the softer, euphemistic 'whisked away'. This appears to represent the poet's alternating views of how the person died during differing moods, while trying to come to terms with the loss. It could also refer to how the poet imagines the deceased would respond. It could, however, also be the 'voice' of the deceased interrupting the thoughts of the poet as indeed his or her death has interrupted the continuation of life for the subject: 'you interrupt me when I start to talk'. This contrast between the deceased being forgotten and being very much a part of the poet's present is one which is further emphasized in stanza 3, where we are presented with an image of the 'shadow dragging at my heels'. The word 'dragging' is effective in emphasizing how the poet is held back from living life.

The language and images in the final stanza show how, ironically, it is the deceased who manages to carry on and live as: 'someone who has found out how to breathe/the water and endure the cold and dark' while the subject, in contrast, 'just stay[s] put' and his life is just 'A waste of breath'. The description of the deceased's fingers under the water is particularly effective here: 'wax-white' presents an image of lifelessness and absence of colour. A mystical feeling is created in this stanza through the use of words such as 'entranced' and 'beckoning', and this suggests the poet is in a kind of fantasy state and sees suicide as a sort of fairytale conclusion. But the deliberations continue in 'I know I ought to turn my back'.

In conclusion, we can see how the poet has captured the mood of one who has suffered, and who is still suffering, through the tragic loss of a loved one, by using different techniques. Just as confusion is demonstrated throughout the poem through the deliberations of the poet, we are left not knowing whether suicide is really contemplated. The final utterance 'That's more than half my life' could relate to the apparent loss of one half of the unified 'whole' of the relationship or, indeed, it could indicate a final end to the life of the poet himself.

Examiner's comments

The student begins by giving a brief indication of the idea behind the poem and identifies that it is written in the first person. She draws some inference from this and show awareness of interpretations.

The tone of the poem is identified and commented upon and specific examples from the text are given to support ideas. A perceptive point is made here about the 'suspension' between the living and the dead.

Clear awareness of structure is shown, and this is linked to the overall effect of the poem. The student is sensitive to the fact that there is no regular rhythm pattern in the poem but is also aware that the poet does vary pace to achieve particular effects. Again, specific examples are given to illustrate this.

A range of perceptive, well-supported, and illustrated points are made concerning the poet's use of language and imagery.

An effective conclusion sums up the student's overall view of the poem.

In summary, the student shows:
- a perceptive understanding of the thoughts and feelings expressed in the text
- detailed and well-chosen references to support ideas
- clear and relevant ideas and a personal response
- a clear appreciation of the literary features of the text
- detailed and illustrated analysis
- ability to use a purposeful and effective structure for the commentary
- a clear, varied, and precise use of language, with a wide vocabulary and effective choice of register.

The following two poems provide you with further practice on writing commentaries on poems. The first one is accompanied by some guiding questions of the kind that you will be given on the paper if you are sitting the exam at Standard Level. The second one is presented without guiding questions, in the form that your exam will take if you are taking Higher Level.

Activity   Write a commentary on the following poem. It is not compulsory for you to respond directly to the guiding questions provided below. However, you are encouraged to use them as starting points for your commentary.

- What impression do you gain of the mother's experiences from the poem and how are these experiences conveyed?
- How does the narrator of the poem give an impression of the reactions of the other people to the scorpion stinging his mother?
- Consider the representation of the role of the scorpion in the unfolding of the poem.
- What thoughts and feelings are aroused in you by the final sentence?

Night of the Scorpion

I remember the night my mother
was stung by a scorpion. Ten hours
of steady rain had driven him
to crawl beneath a sack of rice.
Parting with his poison – flash
of diabolic tail in the dark room –
he risked the rain again.
The peasants came like swarms of flies
and buzzed the name of God a hundred times
to paralyse the Evil One.
With candles and with lanterns
throwing giant scorpion shadows
on the mud-baked walls
they searched for him: he was not found.
They clicked their tongues.
With every movement that the scorpion made
his poison moved in Mother's blood, they said.
May he sit still, they said.
May the sins of your previous birth
be burned away tonight, they said.
May your suffering decrease
the misfortunes of your next birth, they said.
May the sum of evil
balanced in this unreal world
against the sum of good
become diminished by your pain.
May the poison purify your flesh
of desire, and your spirit of ambition,
they said, and they sat around
on the floor with my mother in the centre,
the peace of understanding on each face.
More candles, more lanterns, more neighbours,
more insects, and the endless rain.

My mother twisted through and through,
groaning on a mat.
My father, sceptic, rationalist,
trying every curse and blessing,
powder, mixture, herb and hybrid.
He even poured a little paraffin
upon the bitten toe and put a match to it.
I watched the flame feeding on my mother.
I watched the holy man perform his rites
to tame the poison with an incantation.
After twenty hours
it lost its sting.

My mother only said
Thank God the scorpion picked on me
and spared my children.

Nissin Ezekiel

Activity   Write a commentary on the following poem.

The Storm

Against the stone breakwater,
Only an ominous lapping,
While the wind whines overhead,
Coming down from the mountain,
Whistling between the arbours, the winding terraces;
A thin whine of wires, a rattling and flapping of leaves,
And the small streetlamp swinging and slamming against
      the lamp-pole.
Where have the people gone?
There is one light on the mountain,
Along the sea-wall a steady sloshing of the swell,
The waves not yet high, but even,
Coming closer and closer upon each other;
A fine fume of rain driving in from the sea,
Riddling the sand, like a wide spray of buckshot,
The wind from the sea and the wind from the
      mountain contending,
Flicking the foam from the whitecaps straight upwards
      into the darkness.
A time to go home!
And a child's dirty shift billows upward out of an alley;
A cat runs from the wind as we do,
Between the whitening trees, up Santa Lucia,
Where the heavy door unlocks
And our breath comes more easy.

Then a crack of thunder, and the black rain runs
    over us, over
The flat-roofed houses, coming down in gusts, beating
The walls, the slatted windows, driving
The last watcher indoors, moving the cardplayers closer
To their cards, their Lachryma Christi.
We creep to our bed and its straw mattress.
We wait, we listen.
The storm lulls off, then redoubles,
Bending the trees halfway down to the ground,
Shaking loose the last wizened oranges in the orchard,
Flattening the limber carnations.
A spider eases himself down from a swaying light bulb,
The bulb goes on and off, weakly.
Water roars in the cistern.
We lie closer on the gritty pillow,
Breathing heavily, hoping –
For the great last leap of the wave over the breakwater.
The flat boom on the beach of the towering sea-swell,
The sudden shudder as the jutting sea-cliff collapses
And the hurricane drives the dead straw into the
    living pine-tree.

Theodore Roethke

The psychologist Carl Jung puts forward the theory that people tend towards being **introverted** (more concerned with the 'inner' world of thought or imagination) or **extraverted** (more grounded in the external world of physical reality and other people). Stemming from this, he maintains that some people are thinking types, most at home with thoughts and ideas and perhaps less comfortable with the experience and expression of emotions; others use their intuition. A third group are feeling types, relying on their feelings more than their thoughts to guide them through life, and a final group are sensation types, experiencing the world via their physical senses.

This is a partial and simplistic explanation of Jung's ideas, and many other people have created models to try to understand the human personality. However, factors like these are bound to influence the choices writers make when they write, in terms of content and style. They may also account for the fact that most of us respond or 'relate' better to some writers than others. We naturally feel more at home with the work of a writer who experiences the world as we do, while reading the work of a writer who experiences it very differently may feel like struggling to understand a foreign culture.

Of course, most writing – the act of putting ideas and experiences into words – involves a rather cerebral or 'thinking' activity. Most writers 'craft' their work carefully even if their aim is to use words to convey emotional or sensual experiences, but there are some who use more intuitive or free-writing techniques, allowing their words to flow without judging or altering them.

Now let us consider how these ideas might help us in gaining a sense of a writer's personal 'style'.

First, read the following passage from *The Rainbow*. This novel by D. H. Lawrence traces the patterns of love and relationships through three generations of the Brangwens, a family of farmers in the East Midlands. Here, in the early part of the book, Tom Brangwen struggles with his sense of being both close to and distant from the woman he will marry.

The Rainbow

Chapter 1

Then, as he sat there, all mused and wondering, she came near to him, looking at him with wide, grey eyes that almost smiled with a low light. But her ugly-beautiful mouth was unmoved and sad. He was afraid.

His eyes, strained and roused with unusedness, quailed a little before her, he felt himself quailing and yet he rose, as if obedient to her, he bent and kissed her heavy, sad, wide mouth, that was kissed, and did not alter. Fear was too strong in him. Again he had not got her.

She turned away. The vicarage kitchen was untidy, and yet to him beautiful with the untidiness of her and her child. Such a wonderful remoteness there was about her, and then something in touch with him, that made his heart knock in his chest. He stood there and waited, suspended.

Again she came to him, as he stood in his black clothes, with blue eyes very bright and puzzled for her, his face tensely alive, his hair dishevelled. She came close up to him, to his intent, black-clothed body, and laid her hand on his arm. He remained unmoved. Her eyes, with a blackness of memory struggling with passion, primitive and electric away at the back of them, rejected him and absorbed him at once. But he remained himself. He breathed with difficulty, and sweat came out at the roots of his hair, on his forehead.

'Do you want to marry me?' she asked slowly, always uncertain.

He was afraid lest he could not speak. He drew breath hard, saying:

'I do.'

Then again, what was agony to him, with one hand lightly resting on his arm, she leaned forward a little, and with a strange, primeval suggestion of embrace, held him her mouth. It was ugly-beautiful, and he could not bear it. He put his mouth on hers, and slowly, slowly the response came, gathering force and passion, till it seemed to him she was thundering at him till he could bear no more. He drew away, white, unbreathing. Only, in his blue eyes was something of himself concentrated. And in her eyes was a little smile upon a black void.

She was drifting away from him again. And he wanted to go away. It was intolerable. He could bear no more. He must go. Yet he was irresolute. But she turned away from him.

With a little pang of anguish, of denial, it was decided.

'I'll come an' speak to the vicar to-morrow,' he said, taking his hat.

She looked at him, her eyes expressionless and full of darkness. He could see no answer.

'That'll do, won't it?' he said.

'Yes,' she answered, mere echo without body or meaning.

'Good night,' he said.

'Good night.'

He left her standing there, expressionless and void as she was. Then she went on laying the tray for the vicar. Needing the table, she put the daffodils aside on the dresser without noticing them. Only their coolness, touching her hand, remained echoing there a long while.

They were such strangers, they must for ever be such strangers, that his passion was a clanging torment to him. Such intimacy of embrace, and such utter foreignness of contact! It was unbearable. He could not bear to be near her, and know the utter foreignness between them, know how entirely they were strangers to each other. He went out into the wind. Big holes were blown into the sky, the moonlight blew about. Sometimes a high moon, liquid-brilliant, scudded across a hollow space and took cover under electric, brown-irridescent cloud-edges. Then there was a blot of cloud and shadow. Then somewhere in the night a radiance again, like a vapour. And all the sky was teeming and tearing along, a vast disorder of flying shapes and darkness and ragged fumes of light and a great brown circling halo, then the terror of a moon running liquid-brilliant into the open for a moment, hurting the eyes before she plunged under cover of cloud again.

D. H. Lawrence

Activity

> Having read the passage carefully, make notes on the following questions.
>
> **1** To what extent is Lawrence concerned with:
> - his character's thoughts and ideas
> - his character's feelings and emotions
> - his character's experience of the physical world around him
> - relationships?
>
> **2** What choices does Lawrence make relating to:
> - theme
> - vocabulary
> - sentence structures
> - rhythm
> - sound?

Lawrence is a writer deeply concerned with human relationships, particularly those between men and women. He tries to articulate the effect people have on each other and presents an ambivalent view of close relationships, which can bring great happiness, but may also be very threatening or destructive.

You will probably have noticed in this extract that he seems to be chiefly aiming to convey Brangwen's feelings, both in a physical and in an emotional sense. Brangwen feels sexual desire for the woman, but is also fearful of losing himself in love, of being 'absorbed' by it. Lawrence sometimes describes this in terms of the actual physical sensations in his body:

'He breathed with difficulty, and sweat came out at the roots of his hair, on his forehead.'

However, when he describes their kiss, he can no longer be quite so concrete. To convey the emotional and physical sensations Brangwen feels here, Lawrence uses the image of her seeming to be 'thundering' at him, which suggests something both powerful and threatening, but is much less direct. It is the nearest he can get to an impression of his character's feelings.

Some of Lawrence's work was originally banned for being too sexually explicit, but often, as he tries to convey his characters' experiences of love and sex, his descriptions have this rather impressionistic quality. Powerful images and metaphors from nature are used to portray emotional and sexual needs as something almost mystical. Something of this is present in the final paragraph of the extract above, where his description of the stormy night sky mirrors Brangwen's experience with the woman. The moon, which scuds behind the clouds, appearing intermittently, 'hurting the eyes' and causing 'terror', reminds us of the moments when he fully feels the presence of the woman and their mutual desire, or looks into her eyes and sees 'a little smile upon a black void'. Both are elusive, beautiful, and frightening.

Having recognized that Lawrence's 'style' has its basis in the emotional, physical, and sensual exploration of life, we can go on to examine in detail some of the choices he makes in using language. You may have noticed some of these.

- Predictably, perhaps, he uses 'feeling' words in almost every sentence: 'unmoved and sad', 'afraid', 'fear', 'agony', and 'anguish' are just a few.
- Although this is a third-person narrative, everything is filtered through Brangwen's emotional responses.
- Colours, and other adjectives, are sometimes used repeatedly, reinforcing their effect, creating patterns, or even giving a ritualistic effect. His eyes are blue and very bright, while hers are grey, black, or 'full of darkness' and her 'sad, wide' mouth is 'ugly-beautiful'.
- Sentence lengths are varied. This too contributes to the portrayal of Brangwen's feelings. Moments of tension and uncertainty are made up of short or incomplete sentences, which give a sense of pain, urgency, and indecision:
  'She was drifting away from him again. And he wanted to go away. It was intolerable. He could bear no more. He must go. Yet he was irresolute.'
- The description of the ragged sky is similarly broken up, but there are other moments when the sentences flow more freely, usually when the two characters seem more connected. The use of sentence patterns to enhance a sense of drama is typical of Lawrence.
- The sound qualities of the words are fairly varied, with a few alliterative patterns. Hard consonants are used and, in the case of the image of the disordered sky 'teeming and tearing along', add to the sense of confusion.

Now we will look at some more extracts and some of the commentaries that students have written on them.

The first piece we will look at is the opening of a novel, *The Crow Road*, by Iain Banks.

Activity

First, read the following extract carefully. Working either on your own or with a partner, make notes in preparation for answering this question:

Write a commentary on the beginning of *The Crow Road* by Iain Banks. Here are some questions that you might like to think about as the starting point for your commentary:
- Show how character is conveyed through use of detail.
- What kind of style does the writer use and what kinds of effects does he achieve? How does Banks create humorous effects?

The Crow Road

It was the day my grandmother exploded. I sat in the crematorium, listening to my Uncle Hamish quietly snoring in harmony to Bach's Mass in B Minor, and I reflected that it always seemed to be death that drew me back to Gallanach.

I looked at my father, sitting two rows away in the front line of seats in the cold, echoing chapel. His broad, greying-brown head was massive above his tweed jacket (a black arm-band was his concession to the solemnity of the occasion). His ears were moving in a slow oscillatory manner, rather in the way John Wayne's shoulders moved when he walked; my father was grinding his teeth. Probably he was annoyed that my grandmother had chosen religious music for her funeral ceremony. I didn't think she had done it to upset him; doubtless she had simply liked the tune, and had not anticipated the effect its non-secular nature might have on her eldest son.

My younger brother, James, sat to my father's left. It was the first time in years I'd seen him without his Walkman, and he looked distinctly uncomfortable, fiddling with his single earring. To my father's right my mother sat, upright and trim, neatly filling a black coat and sporting a dramatic black hat shaped like a flying saucer. The UFO dipped briefly to one side as she whispered something to my father. In that movement and that moment, I felt a pang of loss that did not entirely belong to my recently departed grandmother, yet was connected with her memory. How her moles would be itching today if she was somehow suddenly reborn!

'Prentice!' My Aunt Antonia, sitting next to me, with Uncle Hamish snoring mellifluously on her other side, tapped my sleeve and pointed at my feet as she murmured my name. I looked down.

I had dressed in black that morning, in the cold high room of my aunt and uncle's house. The floorboards had creaked and my breath had smoked. There had been ice inside the small dormer window, obscuring the view over Gallanach in a crystalline mist. I'd pulled on a pair of black underpants I'd brought especially from Glasgow, a white shirt (fresh from Marks and Sparks, the pack-lines still ridging the cold, crisp cotton) and my black 501s. I'd shivered, and sat on the bed, looking at two pairs of socks; one black, one white. I'd intended to wear the black pair under my nine-eye Docs with the twin ankle buckles, but suddenly I had felt that the boots were wrong. Maybe it was because they were matt finish . . .

The last funeral I'd been to here – also the first funeral I'd ever been to – this gear had all seemed pretty appropriate, but now I was pondering the propriety of the Docs, the 501s, and the black biker's jacket. I'd hauled my white trainers out of the bag, tried one Nike on and one boot (unlaced); I'd stood in front of the tilted full-length mirror, shivering, my breath going out in clouds, while the floorboards creaked and a smell of cooking bacon and burned toast insinuated its way up from the kitchen.

The trainers, I'd decided.

So I peered down at them in the crematorium; they looked crumpled and tea-stained on the severe black granite of the chapel floor. Oh-oh; one black sock, one white. I wriggled in my seat, pulled my jeans down to cover my oddly-packaged ankles. 'Hell's teeth,' I whispered. 'Sorry, Aunt Tone.'

My Aunt Antonia – a ball of pink-rinse hair above the bulk of her black coat, like candy floss stuck upon a hearse – patted my leather jacket. 'Never mind, dear,' she sighed. 'I doubt old Margot would have minded.'

'No,' I nodded. My gaze fell back to the trainers. It struck me that on the toe of the right one there was still discernible the tyre mark from Grandma Margot's wheelchair. I lifted the left trainer onto the right, and rubbed without enthusiasm at the black herring-bone pattern the oily wheel had left. I remembered the day, six months earlier, when I had pushed old Margot out of the house and through the courtyard, past the outhouses and down the drive under the trees towards the loch and the sea.

Iain Banks

Activity   **Read this student's response to the question and then study the comments on its strengths and weaknesses which follow.**

Commentary

The extract from the novel *The Crow Road* by Iain Banks is rather unusual. The passage describes his family at his grandmother's cremation in his home town of Gallanach. The piece is unusual as it is written in a jovial style which is not often connected with death except in black comedy. However, this is not a comedy so is unusual. The opening sentence, 'It was the day my grandmother exploded' is so surprising when put in context with the rest of the passage.

The narrator does not dwell on the grief of losing a member of his family, but more so on his isolation from his parents. In a movement his mother makes to his father he feels 'a pang of loss that did not entirely belong to my recently departed grandmother'.

The fact he has had to stay at his aunt and uncle's house and is sitting with them shows his isolation from his parents. The narrator does not seem to 'fit in' with the rest of his family. His clothes are different and his whole attitude towards the funeral is distracted.

This distraction of the narrator is shown in his digressions from the funeral. He notices his father's ears move, as he grinds his teeth, like 'John Wayne's shoulders when he walks'. He notices his brother James is not wearing his Walkman for the first time in years and that his mother's dramatic hat is shaped like a UFO. There do not seem to be many emotions shown by the narrator, nor any of the other characters. He remarks how his father is probably angry his grandmother had chosen religious music for her funeral ceremony instead of secular, as he would have wanted. His Uncle Hamish has fallen asleep and is snoring 'in harmony to Bach's Mass in B Minor'; he is obviously oblivious or uncaring of the situation around him.

The narrator tries to create a cold atmosphere, one traditionally associated with death. They are sitting in the cold 'echoing chapel' which emulates a feeling of emptiness and loss. The cold temperature of his bedroom, however, which the author embellishes upon, seems to be more related to his isolation from his family. The fact he is not in his parents' home shows how they have excluded him from their lives. Also that they do not sit with him at the chapel. The atmosphere is not maintained as the author makes comical asides which are more light-hearted, for example the references to John Wayne and the UFO and the fact his boots didn't look right because they had a matt finish. Also, how he has odd socks on and his description of his Aunt Antonia being like 'candy floss stuck upon a hearse'.

From this passage, the narrator shows himself to be a young man who has moved away from his home town, possibly without his parents' blessing as they have become disassociated. The narrator shows that he did love his grandmother Margot as he describes a fond memory of her at the end of the passage, yet shows no real signs of grief.

This passage is quite effective as the opening of a novel as it makes me want to read on. It provides details of what are, presumably, the main characters (his family) and it would be interesting to find out what happens next. His jovial style is easy to read and understand, being quite light-hearted.

Examiner's comments

The student provides a clear introductory paragraph, giving enough information to put the passage in context without wasting time on paraphrasing.

She describes the style as 'jovial'. This may be a good way to describe it, but she will need to clarify what she means by explaining fully later in the essay. Perhaps a more accurate word to express what she means would be 'humorous'. The reference to black comedy is very useful. Again she needs to pick out examples of this later, even though she has stated that the passage as a whole is not comedy.

She comments on the surprising first sentence in relation to the rest of the passage. A fuller analysis would improve this. For example, she could point out the strangely matter-of-fact tone of the sentence and the shocking effect of the word 'exploded' when applied to a 'grandmother'.

Her point in paragraph 3 about the narrator seeming isolated from his parents is a good one. We have to be careful, though, not to speculate too far. From this extract, we do not know that the whole family were not staying with the aunt and uncle! It's best to keep to points for which you can find evidence in the passage. However, within the extract, there is a sense of his distance from his parents.

The student has pointed out that the narrator's clothes are different, but could expand on this. What do the details of his clothes tell us about him? They could suggest an image or stereotype: 'Nine-eye Docs, 501s and the black biker's jacket'.

She makes a good point about the narrator's 'digressions' in paragraph 4, giving examples of how his attention wanders to dwell on the people around him. Again, she could comment more analytically about these, on what they tell us about the members of his family and also, through his choice of words, about himself. For example, the similes he uses, referring to John Wayne and UFOs, suggest the popular culture of film stars and science fiction, which contrasts with the sombre music his grandmother has chosen. It seems that his brother, too, with his earring, but without his Walkman, has made concessions for the occasion.

In paragraph 5, the student's remarks on atmosphere are apt, the quotation is helpful, and she has added some further comment. She could also go on to say something about the use of colour in the passage. Repeated 'black' and 'white' are appropriate for cold and death. Having mentioned the aunt's pink hair, she could go on to explain why this is humorous: its inappropriateness among all the black, which is captured by the candy-floss/hearse image.

The penultimate paragraph is disappointing. The student is rather too concerned with inventing theories about the young man's background at the expense of paying close attention to the details that are provided.

This highlights a broader point. The texts chosen for the commentary are specially selected so that there is as little chance as possible that students will have already read them or be familiar with them. However, if you are familiar with the whole text from which the extract has been set, although your previous knowledge of the text may help you to understand it and the way it is written more readily, you will need to avoid letting your wider knowledge distract you from focusing on and making deductions from the details of the passage itself. Remember, the whole focus on the commentary is only on the text you are given on the exam paper.

The student begins to explore the narrator's reference to his grandmother at the end; however, we are not given any evidence in the extract that the memory is a 'fond' one, as she claims.

The passage has obviously captured the student's interest, and her final paragraph provides a fair summing up of her response, but overall the paragraphing and general organization of the commentary could have been improved.

However, there is more to notice about the young man in relation to his family and the scene at the crematorium. Here are some suggestions:

- His outward 'style' and image, which suggest rebellious youth, could lead to his being labelled uncaring. It contrasts with the conventional dress of his older relatives. As the student's commentary above points out, he does not overtly declare his emotions or much sense of loss, although we do not detect much emotion in the other characters either.

- In opposition to this is his painful preoccupation with 'getting it right'. He is very concerned that his dress should be appropriate, so he does care. In a strange sense, what seemed inappropriate is in fact fitting: the white trainers carry the mark of his grandmother's wheelchair, and serve as a record of their last meeting, and of his having shown his care of her. The adults, on the other hand, may be dressed more conventionally, but seem, if anything, less involved in the proceedings.

Activity

Now look at another student's commentary, which has different qualities. Read this carefully, noting its strengths and suggesting some ways in which the work could be improved. In particular, look at:

- major points the student has noticed about the passage
- how well his ideas are supported with evidence
- the appropriateness of quotations from the text
- his analysis of the writer's style
- clarity of expression: is it easy to follow? Is the writing well organized or chaotic?
- technical accuracy: punctuation, paragraphing, and spelling.

Commentary

This passage is an effective opening to the novel, as the first sentence 'It was the day my grandmother exploded' grabs the reader's attention instantly. This opening line also establishes the mood of the piece, a quite darkly humorous style – the various family members present at the crematorium are described in a lot of detail – the images created of them are expanded upon (the narrator's mother is said to be wearing a hat that looks like a flying saucer – this is furthered when we are given the image of it 'dipping' to the side when she talks). There is a very sarcastic tone to the passage in places, such as when the narrator tells us his father is probably 'annoyed that my grandmother had chosen religious music for her funeral ceremony', and the constant references to Uncle Hamish snoring in the background – this style of humor fits in quite well with the proceedings as it isn't (for want of a better term) 'Har-de-har-har' humor – it is subtle, and certain points about it are written in such a way, that they could just be taken as extra description of the events (the flashback to the narrator getting dressed is a good example – with him rattling off precise descriptions of his clothes, and where they are from). The atmosphere, despite the humor, is retained: the formal mood is (kind of) still there, and there are references to the cold atmosphere to add to this (although this refers to the morning, it still has an effect on the scene at hand). Also, a lot of the comments from the narrator (who seems to be taking the event as a sort of 'family reunion' – or a freak show, depending) are linked with death, even if in an obscure way such as referring to somebody as looking like candy floss stuck on a hearse – which in itself, is mixing something associated with fun & something associated with death – much like the whole passage.

PS – is the 'smell of cooking bacon & burned toast' line a really sick reference to the cremation taking place?

Activity

Now read carefully the following extract, which is from the beginning of a short story. Think about how you might approach this extract and make notes on the key elements of it that you would discuss if you were planning a commentary on it. You can use whatever approach you choose.

Stone Trees

So now that he is dead so now that he is dead I am to spend the day with them. The Robertsons.

On the Isle of Wight. Train journey from London. There and back in a day.

So now that he is dead –

They were at the funeral. Not their children. Too little. So good so good they were to me. She – Anna – she cried a lot. Tom held my arm tight. Strong. I liked it. In the place even the place where your coffin was, I liked it, his strong arm. Never having liked Tom that much, I liked his strong arm.

And they stayed over. Slept at the house a night or two. Did the telephone. Some gran or someone was with their children. Thank God we had no children. Think of Tom/Anna dying and those two children left –

So now that you are dead –

It's nice of them isn't it now that you are dead? Well, you'd have expected it. You aren't surprised by it. I'm not surprised by it. After all there has to be somewhere to go. All clean all clean at home. Back work soon someday. Very soon now for it's a week. They broke their two week holiday for the funeral. Holiday Isle of Wight where you/I went once. There was a dip, a big-dipper dip, a wavy line of cliffs along the shore, and in this dip of the cliffs a hotel – a long beach and the waves moving in shallow.

Over stone trees.

But it was long ago and what can stone trees have been? Fantasy.

So now that you are dead so now –

Sweetie love so now that you are dead I am to spend the day with the Robertsons alone and we shall talk you/I later. So now –

The boat crosses. Has crossed. Already. Criss-cross deck. Criss-cross water. Splashy sea and look – ! Lovely clouds flying (now that you are dead) and here's the pier. A long, long pier into the sea and gulls shouting and children yelling here and there and here's my ticket and there they stand. All in a row – Tom, Anna, the two children solemn. And smiles now – Tom and Anna. Tom and Anna look too large to be quite true. Too good. Anna who never did anything wrong. Arms stretch too far forward for a simple day.

They stretch because they want. They would not stretch to me if you were obvious and not just dead. Then it would have been, hullo, easy crossing? Good. Wonderful day. Let's get back and down on the beach. Great to see you both.

So now that you are dead –

We paced last week. Three.

Tom. Anna. I.

And other black figures wood-faced outside the crematorium in blazing sun, examining shiny black-edged tickets on blazing bouquets. 'How good of Marjorie – fancy old Marjorie. I didn't even know she – ' There was that woman who ran out of the so-called service with handkerchief at her eyes. But who was there except you my darling and I and the Robertsons and the shiny cards and did they do it then? Were they doing it then as we read the flowers? Do they do it at once or stack it up with other coffins and was it still inside waiting as I paced with portly Tom? Christian Tom – Tom we laughed at so often and oh my darling now that you are dead –

Cambridge. You can't say that Tom has precisely changed since Cambridge. Thickened. More solid. Unshaken still, quite unshaken and – well, wonderful of course. Anna hasn't changed. Small, specs, curly hair, straight-laced. Dear Anna how we sat and worked out all. Analysed. Girton. We talked about how many men it was decent to do it with without being wild and when you should decide to start and Anna said none and never. Not before marriage you said. Anna always in that church where Tom preached and Tom never looking Anna's way, and how she ached. So now that –

Sweet I miss you so. Now that you are –. My darling oh my God!

In the train two young women. (Yes thanks Anna, I'm fine. Nice journey. First time out. It's doing me good. Isn't it a lovely day?) There were these two women talking about their rights. They were reading about all that was due to them. In a magazine.

'Well, it's only right isn't it?'

'What?'

'Having your own life. Doing your thing.'

'Well – '

'Not – you know. Men and that. Not letting them have all the freedom and that. You have to stand up for yourself and get free of men.'

Jane Gardam

Activity   Here are the notes made by one student working on this text. Look at them carefully and compare them with your own ideas, making a note of any key similarities and differences in your interpretations.

1 Content
The extract from *Stone Trees* describes the thoughts of a woman whose husband has died. This impression is gained right at the very beginning of the extract in the words: 'So now that he is dead'. As the extract progresses, we learn that the

woman and her dead husband had a long-standing, close friendship with another family, the Robertsons. It becomes clear in the extract that the Robertsons were a great support following the death of her husband – 'They were at the funeral . . . So good so good they were to me' – and that they have invited the woman to spend the day with them on the Isle of Wight. The extract concludes on a note of irony in the utterance 'You have to stand up for yourself and get free of men'.

2 Structure
The structure of the story appears to be somewhat disjointed as the narrative alternates between the past and the present. This appears to reflect the way memory is recalled and how thought processes do not conform to a rigid chronological order. For example, after describing her plans to spend the day with the Robertsons, the narrative jumps back to describe events at the funeral and goes on to relate events in the woman's youth: 'Dear Anna how we sat and worked out all'. In addition, just as memory is often recalled in short glimpses, the narrative, in parts, reflects this through the use of short, concise sentences: 'They were at the funeral. Not their children. Too little.'

The whole of the narrative is interrupted by the woman's thoughts of her husband – particularly his death: 'So now that you are dead so now – '. This again reflects how painful experiences can return repeatedly through memory – a torment which the woman is obviously experiencing.

3 Voice
The piece is written in the first person in a 'stream-of-consciousness' style. This is supported in the way that the extract is structured. It is interesting to note that the opening 'So now that he is dead' transforms into 'So now that you are dead' as the piece progresses, the woman's internal 'conversation' transforming into a direct conversation with her dead husband. This reflects the fact that the sense of loss is felt greatly by the woman who continues to view her husband as being very much a part of the present. It could also be a sign of the emotional confusion felt by the woman, a point emphasized further by the inclusion of 'you/I' – 'and we shall talk you/I later'. At the end of the extract we also get a sense of hearing Anna speaking when we read the responses made by the woman: '(Yes thanks Anna, I'm fine...)'.

4 Characters
Like her husband, we appear to learn very little about the woman from the extract apart from her reaction to the death of her husband and the fact that she has been invited to spend the day with friends. However, the characters of Tom and Anna appear to be more rounded through the woman's descriptions of them. For example, we learn that Tom is 'portly', a 'preacher' who does not appear to have 'changed since Cambridge', only 'Thickened. More solid. Unshaken still' and that the woman views him as 'wonderful'. Anna is described by the woman as someone who 'never did anything wrong', and like her husband she 'hasn't changed. Small, specs, curly hair, straight-laced'. We also learn of Anna's views regarding sex before marriage – 'none and never' – but how she 'ached' for Tom to look her way in church. The fact that both Tom and Anna have not 'changed' emphasizes the changes that the woman herself is going through on the death of her husband.

5 Language

Jane Gardam uses language to great effect in this extract. For example, the repetition of the phrase 'he is dead' interrupts the flow of the narrative like a recurring nightmare, highlighting the effect that the loss has had on the woman. In parts the language used is somewhat poetic – especially when used in describing the journey to the Isle of Wight: 'Criss-cross deck. Criss-cross water. Splashy sea and . . . Lovely clouds flying (now that you are dead).' The number of effective adjectives used injects a degree of richness to the piece, but again, this is interrupted by thoughts of her husband's death. The inclusion of adjectives, however, is not only reserved for the more pleasant parts of the extract. As Gardam relates a picture of the funeral through the eyes of the woman, she includes words and phrases such as 'black figures wood-faced', 'blazing sun', 'shiny black-edged tickets', 'blazing bouquets', and 'shiny cards'. The adjectives used help to create a more rounded picture of the event as well as indicating what images struck the woman on such a sad occasion.

Activity

Now write your own commentary on the following extract from *Chocolat* by Joanne Harris. Some guiding questions are given of the type that you would see if you were sitting the Diploma at Standard Level. The passage is followed by a student's response. After you have finished writing your own response, read this student's commentary carefully, together with the examiner's comments that follow it.

Write a commentary on the passage. It is not compulsory for you to respond directly to the guiding questions provided. However, you are encouraged to use them as starting points for your commentary.

- What do we learn about the narrator and the young girl?
- How does the writer use language to appeal to the senses?
- How does she use description to create a sense of the atmosphere of the place?
- What is the importance of the carnival as a connecting thread in the passage?

February 11, Shrove Tuesday

We came on the wind of the carnival. A warm wind for February, laden with the hot greasy scents of frying pancakes and sausages and powdery-sweet waffles cooked on the hotplate right there by the roadside, with the confetti sleeting down collars and cuffs and rolling in the gutters like an idiot antidote to winter. There is a febrile excitement in the crowds which line the narrow main street, necks craning to catch sight of the crêpe-covered *char* with its trailing ribbons and paper rosettes. Anouk watches, eyes wide, a yellow balloon in one hand and a toy trumpet in the other, from between a shopping-basket and a sad brown dog. We have seen carnivals before, she and I; a procession of two hundred and fifty of the decorated *chars* in Paris last Mardi Gras, a hundred and eighty in New York, two dozen marching bands in Vienna, clowns on stilts, the *Grosses Têtes* with their lolling papier-mâché heads, drum majorettes with batons spinning and sparkling. But at six the world retains a special lustre. A wooden cart, hastily decorated with gilt and crêpe and scenes from fairy tales. A dragon's head on a shield, Rapunzel in a woollen wig, a mermaid with a Cellophane tail, a gingerbread house all icing and gilded cardboard, a witch in the doorway, waggling extravagant green fingernails at a group of silent children . . . At six it is possible to perceive subtleties which a year later are already out of reach. Behind the papier-mâché, the icing, the plastic, she can still see the real witch, the real magic. She looks up at me, her eyes, which are the blue-green of the Earth seen from a great height, shining.

'Are we staying? Are we staying here?' I have to remind her to speak French. 'But are we? Are we?' She clings to my sleeve. Her hair is a candyfloss tangle in the wind.

I consider. It's as good a place as any. Lansquenet-sous-Tannes, two hundred souls at most, no more than a blip on the fast road between Toulouse and Bordeaux. Blink once and it's gone. One main street, a double row of dun-coloured half-timbered houses leaning secretively together, a few laterals running parallel like the tines of a bent fork. A church, aggressively whitewashed, in a square of little shops. Farms scattered across the watchful land. Orchards, vineyards, strips of earth enclosed and regimented according to the strict apartheid of country farming: here apples, there kiwis, melons, endives beneath their black plastic shells, vines looking blighted and dead in the thin February sun but awaiting triumphant resurrection by March . . . Behind that, the Tannes, small tributary of the Garonne, fingers its way across the marshy pasture. And the people? They look much like all others we have known; a little pale perhaps in the unaccustomed sunlight, a little drab. Headscarves and berets are the colour of the hair beneath, brown, black or grey. Faces are lined like last summer's apples, eyes pushed into wrinkled flesh like marbles into old dough. A few children, flying colours of red and lime-green and yellow, seem like a different race. As the *char* advances ponderously along the street behind the old tractor which pulls it, a large woman with a square, unhappy face clutches a tartan coat about her shoulders and shouts something in the half-comprehensible local dialect; on the wagon a squat Santa Claus, out-of-season amongst the fairies and sirens and goblins, hurls sweets at the crowd with barely restrained aggression. An elderly small-featured man, wearing a felt hat rather than the round beret more common to the region, picks up the sad brown dog from between my legs with a look of polite apology. I see his thin graceful fingers moving in the dog's fur; the dog whines; the master's expression becomes complex with love, concern, guilt. No-one looks at us. We might as well be invisible; our clothing marks us as strangers, transients. They are polite, so polite; no-one stares at us. The woman, her long silk scarf fluttering at her throat; the child in yellow wellingtons and sky-blue mac. Their colouring marks them. Their clothes are exotic, their faces – are they too pale or too dark? – their hair marks them other, foreign, indefinably strange. The people of Lansquenet have learned the art of observation without eye contact. I feel their gaze like a breath on the nape of my neck, strangely without hostility but cold nevertheless. We are a curiosity to them, a part of the carnival, a whiff of the outlands. I feel their eyes upon us as I turn to buy a *galette* from the vendor. The paper is hot and greasy, the dark wheat pancake crispy at the edges but thick and good in the centre. I break off a piece and give it to Anouk, wiping melted butter from her chin. The vendor is a plump, balding man with thick glasses, his face slick with the steam from the hot plate. He winks at her. With the other eye he takes in every detail, knowing there will be questions later.

'On holiday, Madame?' Village etiquette allows him to ask; behind his tradesman's indifference I see a real hunger. Knowledge is currency here; with Agen and Montauban so close, tourists are a rarity.

'For a while.'

'From Paris, then?' It must be our clothes. In this garish land the people are drab. Colour is a luxury; it wears badly. The bright blossoms of the roadside are weeds, invasive, useless.

'No, no, not Paris.'

The *char* is almost at the end of the street. A small band – two fifes, two trumpets, a trombone and a side drum – follows it, playing a thin unidentifiable march. A dozen children scamper in its wake, picking up the unclaimed sweets. Some are in costume; I see Little Red Riding Hood and a shaggy person who might be the wolf squabbling companionably over possession of a handful of streamers.

A black figure brings up the rear. At first I take him for a part of the parade – the Plague Doctor, maybe – but as he approaches I recognize the old-fashioned soutane of the country priest. He is in his thirties, though from a distance his rigid stance makes him seem older. He turns towards me, and I see that he too is a stranger, with the high cheekbones and pale eyes of the North and long pianist's fingers resting on the silver cross which hangs from his neck. Perhaps this is what gives him the right to stare at me, this alienness; but I see no welcome in his cold, light eyes. Only the measuring, feline look of one who is uncertain of his territory. I smile at him; he looks away, startled, beckons the two children towards him. A gesture indicates the litter which now lines the road; reluctantly the pair begin to clear it, scooping up spent streamers and sweet-wrappers in their arms and into a nearby bin. I catch the priest staring at me again as I turn away, a look which in another man might have been of appraisal.

There is no police station at Lansquenet-sous-Tannes, therefore no crime. I try to be like Anouk, to see beneath the disguise to the truth, but for now everything is blurred.

'Are we staying? Are we, *Maman*?' she tugs at my arm, insistently. 'I like it, I like it here. Are we staying?'

I catch her up into my arms and kiss the top of her head. She smells of smoke and frying pancakes and warm bedclothes on a winter's morning.

Why not? It's as good a place as any.

'Yes, of course,' I tell her, my mouth in her hair. 'Of course we are.'

Not quite a lie. This time it may even be true.

Joanne Harris

Commentary

This extract, the opening of the novel *Chocolat* by Joanne Harris, tells how a mother and her young daughter, Anouk, arrive at a small rural town in France with a possibility that they might settle there.

In the town, Lansquenet-sous-Tannes, a carnival is taking place when the two arrive and it is interesting to see how some of the participants are described: 'Rapunzel in a woollen wig, a mermaid with a Cellophane tail, a gingerbread house all icing and gilded cardboard . . .' These descriptions are a mixture of the fantasy and the ordinary, even the carnival float is merely 'A wooden cart, hastily decorated with gilt and crêpe'. They suggest a strong degree of transparency – perhaps a symbolic indication of what is to come further in the novel. Indeed, the carnival itself appears to be a weak attempt to impress when compared, by Anouk's mother, with other carnivals both she and her daughter have seen: 'a procession of two hundred and fifty of the decorated *chars* in Paris, a hundred and eighty in New York, two dozen marching bands in Vienna, clowns on stilts . . . drum majorettes with batons spinning and sparkling'.

The small town itself is described in a less than favourable light. Some of the descriptions used, such as 'a blip on the fast road . . .', 'Blink once and it's gone', rather than implying a quaint rural village appear to emphasize its insignificance. There is also the suggestion of something secretive and sinister about the place. For example, the 'main street' is described as a 'double row of dun-coloured houses leaning secretively together' and this is surrounded by 'Farms scattered across the watchful land'. These descriptions are not only effective in portraying an isolated, tight-knit community but they also arouse a degree of curiosity in the reader as to why they might be considering settling there.

There is obviously a strong religious presence within the community, although from the way both the church and the priest are described, this appears to be a restricting, dominating force in the town. For instance, the church is described as being 'aggressively whitewashed' and the priest himself, 'a black figure' who could be mistaken for a character from the procession, 'the Plague Doctor', appears to be not only a spoilsport but a dominant figure as he insists on making the playing children clean up carnival debris by just 'a gesture'. Later in the piece the priest is described in greater detail, which reinforces the idea that he is a dominant but unpleasant figure, with a 'rigid stance', 'pale eyes', and his 'high cheekbones' suggest a degree of superciliousness, especially with his 'fingers resting on the silver cross which hangs from his neck.' In addition, his look is described as 'measuring', which implies that he is somewhat judgmental in an unchristian way.

The adult residents are also described in an unfavourable manner, which contrasts markedly with the descriptions of the children of the village. For instance, the adults are described as being somewhat insignificant: 'They look much like all others we have known' and are 'a little drab', and the colours used to describe their clothing and hair project 'dull' images: 'brown, black or grey.' Their faces are described as being 'lined like last summer's apples', which gives a wizened impression and suggests a sense of lifelessness which is also emphasized by their eyes being 'pushed into wrinkled flesh like marbles into old dough'. The descriptions of the children, on the other hand, contain life and vivid colour: 'A few children, flying colours of red and lime-green and yellow'. Indeed, they 'seem like a different race' and they appear to inject a degree of energy in a town where even the dog is described as 'sad'.

The residents seem to be quite insular and suspicious of 'outsiders', and although the mother in the story tells us that 'No-one looks at us' she gets the impression that 'We are a curiosity to them'. This seems not to be surprising considering how the mother's appearance contrasts with that of the villagers, 'her long silk scarf fluttering at her throat . . .' and with her 'exotic' clothes. However, it is interesting to see that the daughter's appearance, although she too wears 'exotic' clothes, is as colourful as the other children in the village. Perhaps this is an indication that she will be accepted more easily than her mother. Indeed the daughter appears to like the place: 'I like it, I like it here. Are we staying?'

There is an indication that the unwelcoming feel of the place might alter later in the novel, in the line 'Vines looking blighted and dead . . . but awaiting triumphant resurrection by March.' This appears to be supported by the sense of magic induced into the writing in the opening line 'We came on the wind of the carnival', the phrase being reminiscent of 'the winds of change'. Indeed, it would appear that magic is needed if the rural town with its 'strips of earth enclosed and regimented according to the strict apartheid of country farming' is to become anything else but 'drab'.

Harris uses language to great effect in this piece. The many sensory inclusions, such as 'hot greasy scents of frying pancakes and sausages and powdery-sweet waffles', helps us to share the carnival experience, and the simile used to describe the confetti falling is particularly effective here: 'like an idiot antidote to winter', especially considering the weak attempts made to dress up for the carnival. She also uses an abundance of adjectives in her similes, which add a richness to the narrative. For instance, she describes her daughter's eyes as being 'the blue-green of the Earth seen from a great height, shining.' Harris also includes a degree of ambiguity which succeeds in arousing curiosity. For example, at the beginning of this piece, the line 'but at six the world retains a special lustre' seems a little out of place and its meaning is unclear. A little later, the line 'At six it is possible to perceive subtleties which a year later are already out of reach' also appears to be unconnected, but the meaning will become clear later in the novel. In addition, some of the words are written in French and their meaning can be tentatively assumed. For example, the word '*char*' is unusual but, through the reading of the passage, can be assumed to be a carnival float. This technique adds a degree of interest and colour to the extract.

The piece is definitely an effective opening. The ambiguity created and the curiosity raised by Harris makes the reader want to find out whether such a well-travelled pair who have visited Paris, New York, and Vienna will stay in such a 'drab' town – indeed, why they have ever gone there in the first place.

Examiner's comments

This is a perceptive commentary in which the student includes attention to:

- the vocabulary used by the writer
- the effect of imagery
- the way language is used to appeal to the senses
- the sense of atmosphere created by the setting
- the use of the carnival in the narrative
- an understanding of the portrayal of the girl and her mother.

Activity   The final passage is a complete short story. Read it carefully and write a commentary on it.

A Gift

I am gifting you an experience, were your parting words. You ultimate egoist. Whichever way I look at it that sentiment yields no other meaning. And who are you to make this gift? In an artist, such detachment might be forgivable, an act of generosity even.

My experience is of my own making, thank you, my own perceptions. You can impinge on it only if I will it. Will-power, that limp uninflatable thing that hung around my self-hood, making its presence felt as the missing dimension . . . from the moment that you first entered that crowded room and diminished everyone by your appearance, your personality clearing a path for you. I thought at the time that I noticed you because you had such a fiery commitment to your politics, because you spoke not fluently but in a rush as if you had a pact with silence, and because somewhere deep down stirred an old memory about the romance of a French accent.

The party, to which we owed varying degrees of loyalty, threw us together with a determinism that left no room for dialectics. You had entered my consciousness like air in my lungs – essential but unfelt, gossamer like, even insubstantial. And when you entered again and again, my skin thinned, like a balloon overblown, replete at the point of rupture.

We found ourselves together on the same Saturday morning outside the same supermarkets to get guilty shoppers to help prolong the miners' strike, distributing leaflets outside the same tube stations to advertise a public meeting, holding either pole of the same banner at the same demo and rolling cigarettes for each other with fingers turned to stone by the February chill. Was it surprising then that we took turns to buy each other drinks when the day's work was done? And that the emptiness of our stomachs drove us to the fish and chips shop or a sit down Chinese meal, depending on the fullness of our pockets.

I enjoyed your presence like an old and deep friendship with an affection which made up in intensity what it lacked in maturity. And from the political, we moved to the personal. You asked, if your nose was prominent? (Do you really care?) How can I tell? Each time my eyes travel to make a judgement, they are drawn upwards by the power of your eyes and consumed, slithering sideways and away to a confused middle distance. I could not trust myself on personal grounds. And yet I could not keep politics forever on the agenda. So I tried to counter that by asking, do you like the shape of my shoulders? From where you stand, you have to look at them so often that you must have an opinion about them. Your eyes admitted the frivolity of your concern with your nose. Touché. I won that round. Now maybe we can go back into the safer waters of the impersonal.

But again, you chose to discuss the political implications of one person's passion for another. Studying the hairs on the barman's fingers, I talked passionately about the destructiveness of passion and how I would personally choose to steer clear. And you agreed and said you were good at that too. We stopped talking. We were interrupted by the silence that fell around us.

Your loyalty to silence proved to be your preservation. Being uncomfortable with silence, became my undoing – my self-respect lay in shreds like a soaring kite grounded. Only on Sunday afternoons, when you liked to unwind by playing Scrabble, would words that choked on your vocal chords come pouring out of your fingers. On one such afternoon, my words shrank on the Scrabble board as they grew and rioted inside my mouth, tumbling from my lips in cascades of incoherence. You must've known then. I wiped my mouth. Perhaps I had overcreamed my lips to preserve them from winter's chafing touch and words ungripped slipped out or was it, pure and simple, nervousness? I talked about how you filled the room, about my mother, about my past loves and the present vacuum as I placed the word 'cue' on the board.

Your turn, I said. You continued to shuffle and clink the letters, the noise crowding out your silence. It was the first time your silence felt cold, a refusal to communicate. This was the first time I had been first to make a declaration of love. My incoherence and your silence. My head began to ache with an infinite series of interpretations. My heart throbbed through my eyes and my vision came in diastolic and systolic rhythms.

Through your lowered lids, your eyes bounced off the board and reduced my confusion to cinders. Then, grasping their victory for one split second, they smiled warmly. I don't believe in possession, she said, but basically I am a one-woman woman. I met her last summer. But don't let this put you off, she said, allowing her fingers to stray off the board and locking my hand in hers, 'loving women is much better for your sanity than loving men.' She swept all my crumbling certainties aside in that fleeting touch which brought heaven vibrating through my blood. I had never been attracted to other women and never would be again. Never, she mocked, tchtu, tchtu, that's a dangerous word. I felt myself drowning and tried to hold on to some understanding of the situation. I was trying to elicit the essence of it, I was writing about it even as I was living it – men, power, etiquette, women, warmth, arrogance, honesty, conquest, bitterness, humiliation – words asserting their identity, refusing to come together and make sense.

Our game of Scrabble was to remain unfinished. It had become too internalised, I reflected as the letters rattled back into the box – some face up, some hiding their mystery. Misreading the signals – a painful self-reckoning.

Loss and desire merged when I kissed her goodbye, my lips scrambling across her faced unfocused. This experience is yours for the keeping, she said. Make good use of it.

Rahila Gupta

Part 2
Literary Genres

4 Studying Prose

Objectives

- To find ways of gaining an overview when studying a novel, short story, and other prose writing
- To discuss approaches to analysing aspects of novels, short stories, and other prose writing
- To develop your own responses to novels, short stories, and other prose writing
- To prepare for studying a set text

As part of your IB Diploma you will study a number of novels and possibly some short stories and other prose writings, depending on the choices that have been made for your English A1 course. You will also encounter prose writings as part of your work for the unseen commentary. This chapter will introduce you to ways in which you can approach the study of a variety of prose works.

Studying novels

What is a novel?

The adjective 'novel' usually means that something is new – a novelty. Some of the earliest novels, written in the seventeenth and eighteenth centuries, would have been just that. One dictionary definition describes a novel as:

'a fictitious prose narrative or tale presenting a picture of real life, especially of the emotional crises in the life-history of the men and women portrayed.'

Jane Austen's view was that a novel was:

' . . . only some work in which the greatest powers of the mind are displayed, in which the most thorough knowledge of human nature, the happiest delineation of its varieties, the liveliest effusions of wit and humour, are conveyed to the world in the best chosen language.'

A 'novelty' suggests something fairly lightweight, entertaining, and perhaps not of lasting significance. Early novels such as those of Samuel Richardson were sometimes serious and carried strong moral messages, but could often be rather sentimental. Nowadays we tend to make a distinction between 'literary' novels and popular fiction – but this dividing line can be blurred. As part of your Diploma course, you will be expected to study novels which are 'literary', and to develop the ability to recognize the differences. However, it can also be interesting to study popular, mass market novels and to consider how the conventions of writing fiction are applied in them.

Studying the novel

At the outset, studying a novel as a set text can seem a daunting prospect. If yours happens to be Dickens's *Great Expectations*, or Hardy's *Tess of the D'Urbervilles*, it may well be the longest book you have ever read. If it is a twentieth-century novel which does not follow realistic conventions or a novel from an earlier period where the language is unfamiliar, you may feel that you will struggle to master it. Some novels are difficult, but usually they are rewarding and a 'good read' too, once you become engaged with the plot and characters and more familiar with the author's language and ideas. In this unit we will develop strategies for approaching them and identify the most important things to pay attention to.

It is very easy, when studying a novel, to begin to talk about the characters and situations as if they were real. After all, one of the writer's intentions is to create convincing characters which the reader can believe in and to create a world into which the reader can enter through the imagination. However, when studying literature it is important that we see the novel as a 'text', as a created work of art, and look at it in a much more detached and analytical way. Characters are devices which the author uses and manipulates to create a particular effect. Their only existence is in the precise words on the page. Studying with this attitude, we will be more likely to consider what a character's role is in the construction of a plot, or the effect of using particular language to describe a place or person.

When studying a novel, there are several aspects which you will need to know well. Most examination questions, though they may be worded in different ways, will focus on one of these.

- **An overview** You need to have a clear understanding of the plot and central ideas, how events follow on and are related, and how the novel is structured. Questions might ask you to show how the novel's structure affects the reader's response, particularly if it is not a straightforward chronological narrative.
- **Narrative viewpoint** Who tells the story? Why has the writer chosen this viewpoint? How does this affect the reader's response? Is there more than one narrator?
- **Characters** Questions often focus on one or more characters and the ways in which the writer presents them.
- **Themes, issues, and ideas** that the novel raises and deals with.
- **The society, setting, or world** in which the action of the novel takes place. Questions may centre on this, or may ask about the relationship between a character and the society in which he or she lives.
- **Language and style** There may be distinctive qualities in the writer's choice of language, for example in the use of imagery or comic exaggeration. Questions may ask you to consider why the writer has made these choices. What is their purpose and effect?

Approaching the text

With a large text like a novel, we need to become familiar enough with it to 'find our way around' easily. We need to be able to locate incidents and important passages quickly. Here are some strategies that will help you to gain this familiarity.

- If you have time, read through the novel fairly quickly before you begin to study it. This gives you the opportunity to gain an overall impression of the novel and to read it, as it was intended, for entertainment. It will also help you to see how different aspects of the novel fit together when you begin to study it in depth. You will see how the plot is constructed and have an idea of what form of novel it is.
- Do some research. Find out what you can about the author and what was going on when the novel was written. Knowing something about the historical and social background and about the conventions and beliefs of the time can help you to understand things which may otherwise seem strange or incomprehensible.
- Keep a separate journal or 'log' for your work on each text. Try dividing a notebook into sections, one for each important aspect of the novel. You will need pages for each of the main characters, the setting, the narrator, themes and ideas, and language and style. As you work through the novel, jot down your observations about each aspect in the appropriate places. Include important quotations and page references. Then, when

you need the information for a discussion or an essay on one of these topics, it will be easy to locate.

- You may find it helpful to annotate your copy of the text, if you have your own copy, marking important passages so that you can find them again easily.

Let us turn now to exploring some texts. As we examine different aspects of novels in this chapter, we will look at examples from these three very different novels from the English A1 Prescribed Book List.

- *Emma* by Jane Austen
- *Hard Times* by Charles Dickens
- *The Handmaid's Tale* by Margaret Atwood.

Activity

Use reference books and/or information provided in editions of these novels to find out what you can about each of these authors and their eras.

An overview

Novels come in many shapes and sizes, from short novellas (more like long short stories) with a few characters and fairly simple plots, to enormously large and complex works, with numerous characters, plots, and subplots and with many different strands which may or may not be interconnected.

There are also different types or forms of novel. For example:

- **Fictional biography or autobiography** focuses on the life and development of one character.
- **Picaresque novels** follow a central character on a journey through life in which he or she encounters a series of 'adventures' which form separate episodes.
- **Social or 'protest' novels** use the characters and the world they inhabit as a way of criticizing or protesting about social or political issues.

Novelists sometimes choose to combine more than one of these types.

The plot, or storyline, of a novel can also be constructed in different ways. The simplest plots relate events in straightforward chronological order, from the point of view of a single narrator, but there have been many variations on this. For example:

- In *Hard Times*, Dickens moves from one group of people in Coketown to another. The connections between them all are not completely clear until the end, when we realize he has constructed a network of threads which link them.
- In *The Handmaid's Tale*, the narrative alternates between chapters which tell the story in the 'present' of the novel and others which are flashbacks. Entitled *Night* or *Nap*, these are times when the narrator has a chance to reminisce, dream, or daydream about the past.

- Emily Brontë, in *Wuthering Heights*, uses two main narrators but there are others too, so that there is sometimes narration within narration. Brontë also departs from chronological order by plunging us into the middle of a mysterious situation and then going back in time to explain how it has come about. She then repeats this process to show how the situation is resolved.

Activity

1 Discuss the structure of your set novel. Is it simply chronological or does it operate in some other way? What do you think is the effect of this structure?
2 Widen your discussion to cover any other novels you have read which have interesting structures.

Opening pages

Usually, we can learn quite a lot about a novel by looking closely at the first few pages. The writer will be trying to engage our attention so that we want to read on. So it is quite likely that some of the important situations, characters, and themes will be presented right from the start.

Activity

1 Here are the opening pages of the three novels listed above. Read them carefully.
2 Working with a partner, choose one of these and discuss it in detail, making notes on the following points.
   - Who is the narrator and what, if anything, can you find out about him or her? Is the narrative in the third person or the first person?
   - What characters (including the narrators) are introduced? What do you learn about them?
   - What situation is presented? Does the story begin in a particular place? If so, how is it described? What atmosphere is generated?
   - Does the writer begin by explaining clearly who is who and what is what? Or are you plunged into the middle of a situation and left to work out what is going on from hints the writer gives you?
   - Can you get a sense of the author's tone? Is the writing straightforward? Might there be hidden messages or other levels of meaning?
   - What do you notice about the writer's style? What sort of imagery, vocabulary, and sentence structures are used?
   - What do you think this novel is going to be 'about'? Can you get a sense of any important ideas or themes that may be central to it?
   - In what ways does the writer arouse your curiosity? Do you want to read further? Why?
3 Present and compare your notes with the whole group. What similarities and differences are there between the three passages?
4 Try working on the opening pages of any other novel which you are studying in the same way.

Emma

Chapter 1

Emma Woodhouse, handsome, clever, and rich, with a comfortable home and happy disposition, seemed to unite some of the best blessings of existence; and had lived nearly twenty-one years in the world with very little to distress or vex her.

She was the youngest of the two daughters of a most affectionate, indulgent father, and had, in consequence of her sister's marriage, been mistress of his house from a very early period. Her mother had died too long ago for her to have more than an indistinct remembrance of her caresses; and her place had been supplied by an excellent woman as governess, who had fallen little short of a mother in affection.

Sixteen years had Miss Taylor been in Mr Woodhouse's family, less as a governess than a friend, very fond of both daughters, but particularly of Emma. Between *them* it was more the intimacy of sisters. Even before Miss Taylor had ceased to hold the nominal office of governess, the mildness of her temper had hardly allowed her to impose any restraint; and the shadow of authority being now long passed away, they had been living together as friend and friend very mutually attached, and Emma doing just what she liked; highly esteeming Miss Taylor's judgement, but directed chiefly by her own.

The real evils, indeed, of Emma's situation were the power of having rather too much her own way, and a disposition to think a little too well of herself; these were the disadvantages which threatened alloy to her many enjoyments. The danger, however, was at present so unperceived, that they did not by any means rank as misfortunes with her.

Sorrow came – a gentle sorrow – but not at all in the shape of any disagreeable consciousness. Miss Taylor married. It was Miss Taylor's loss which first brought grief. It was on the wedding-day of this beloved friend that Emma first sat in mournful thought of any continuance. The wedding over, and the bride-people gone, her father and herself were left to dine together, with no prospect of a third to cheer a long evening. Her father composed himself to sleep after dinner, as usual, and she had then only to sit and think of what she had lost.

Jane Austen

Hard Times

Chapter 1
The One Thing Needful

'Now, what I want is, Facts. Teach these boys and girls nothing but Facts. Facts alone are wanted in life. Plant nothing else, and root out everything else. You can only form the minds of reasoning animals upon Facts: nothing else will ever be of any service to them. This is the principle on which I bring up these children. Stick to Facts, sir!'

The scene was a plain, bare, monotonous vault of a schoolroom, and the speaker's square forefinger emphasized his observations by underscoring every sentence with a line on the schoolmaster's sleeve. The emphasis was helped by the speaker's square wall of a forehead, which had his eyebrows for its base, while his eyes found commodious cellarage in two dark caves, overshadowed by the wall. The emphasis was helped by the speaker's mouth, which was wide, thin, and hard set. The emphasis was helped by the speaker's voice, which was inflexible, dry, and dictatorial. The emphasis was helped by the speaker's hair, which bristled on the skirts of his bald head, a plantation of firs to keep the wind from its shining surface, all covered with knobs, like the crust of a plum pie, as if the head had scarcely warehouse-room for the hard facts stored inside. The speaker's obstinate carriage, square coat, square legs, square shoulders – nay, his very neckcloth, trained to take him by the throat with an unaccommodating grasp, like a stubborn fact, as it was – all helped the emphasis.

'In this life, we want nothing but Facts, sir; nothing but Facts!'

The speaker, and the schoolmaster, and the third grown person present, all backed a little, and swept with their eyes the inclined plane of little vessels then and there arranged in order, ready to have imperial gallons of facts poured into them until they were full to the brim.

Charles Dickens

The Handmaid's Tale

Chapter 1

We slept in what had once been the gymnasium. The floor was of varnished wood, with stripes and circles painted on it, for the games that were formerly played there; the hoops for the basketball nets were still in place, though the nets were gone. A balcony ran around the room, for the spectators, and I thought I could smell, faintly like an after image, the pungent scent of sweat, shot through with the sweet taste of chewing gum and perfume from the watching girls, felt-skirted as I knew from pictures, later in mini-skirts, then pants, then in one ear-ring, spiky green-streaked hair. Dances would have been held there; the music lingered, a palimpsest of unheard sound, style upon style, an undercurrent of drums, a forlorn wail, garlands made of tissue-paper flowers, cardboard devils, a revolving ball of mirrors, powdering the dancers with a snow of light.

There was old sex in the room and loneliness, and expectation, of something without a shape or name. I remember that yearning, for something that was always about to happen and was never the same as the hands that were on us there and then, in the small of the back, or out back, in the parking lot, or in the television room with the sound turned down and only the pictures flickering over lifting flesh.

We yearned for the future. How did we learn it, that talent for insatiability? It was in the air; and it was still in the air, an afterthought, as we tried to sleep, in the army cots that had been set up in rows, with spaces between so we could not talk. We had flannelette sheets, like children's, and army-issue blankets, old ones that still said U.S. We folded our clothes neatly and laid them on the stools at the ends of the beds. The lights were turned down but not out. Aunt Sara and Aunt Elizabeth patrolled; they had electric cattle prods slung on thongs from their leather belts.

Margaret Atwood

Narrative viewpoint

You will have noticed that in *Emma* and *Hard Times* the authors have chosen to use third-person narrative, while Margaret Atwood uses a first-person narrator for *The Handmaid's Tale*. There are advantages and disadvantages, and different possibilities in each.

Writing in the first person, the author takes on the role of a character (or characters) and tells the story 'from the inside'. This can strengthen the illusion that the novel is 'real', by making us, the readers, feel involved and able to empathize with the character. However, this usually also limits our perspective to this one character's perceptions: we only see other characters through his or her eyes. We cannot know of events the narrator does not witness unless they are reported by another character, for example in conversation.

As we have only this narrator's words to go on, we need to ask how far we can trust the narrator. He or she might be biased, deluded, blind to the true significance of events, or even deliberately deceiving the reader. Often, this very question adds interest to a first-person narrative.

The narrator in *The Handmaid's Tale* is Offred, a woman living in a future society in which people are restricted to very narrow, specific roles. Offred is a handmaid. Her job is to 'breed' to ensure the survival of her nation, while other women are responsible for domestic chores and some carry out the formal duties of a wife. Much of her narrative is in **stream-of-consciousness** form, where the writer aims to give a sense of how a character's mind works by tracking her thoughts as they flow from one topic to another. We have to piece together our impressions of Offred from what she reveals of her thoughts and feelings, her actions, and her attitudes to other characters.

Activity

Here, early in the novel, Offred describes her living quarters and ponders her situation. Read the extract and make a note of everything that you learn about her as a person and as a storyteller. How does Atwood try to engage your sympathy for Offred? Is she successful?

The Handmaid's Tale

Chapter 2
A window, two white curtains. Under the window, a window seat with a little cushion. When the window is partly open – it only opens partly – the air can come in and make the curtains move. I can sit in the chair, or on the window seat, hands folded, and watch this. Sunlight comes in through the window too, and falls on the floor, which is made of wood, in narrow strips, highly polished. I can smell the polish. There's a rug on the floor, oval, of braided rags. This is the kind of touch they like: folk art, archaic, made by women, in their spare time, from things that have no further use. A return to traditional values. Waste not want not. I am not being wasted. Why do I want?

A bed. Single, mattress medium-hard, covered with a flocked white spread. Nothing takes place in the bed but sleep; or no sleep. I try not to think too much. Like other things now, thought must be rationed. There's a lot that doesn't bear thinking about. Thinking can hurt your chances, and I intend to last. I know why there is no glass, in front of the water-colour picture of blue irises, and why the window only opens partly and why the glass in it is shatterproof. It isn't running away they're afraid of. We wouldn't get far. It's those other escapes, the ones you can open in yourself, given a cutting edge.

So. Apart from these details, this could be a college guest room, for the less distinguished visitors; or a room in a rooming-house, of former times, for ladies in reduced circumstances. That is what we are now. The circumstances have been reduced; for those of us who still have circumstances.

But a chair, sunlight, flowers: these are not to be dismissed. I am alive, I live, I breathe, I put my hand out, unfolded, into the sunlight. Where I am is not a prison but a privilege, as Aunt Lydia said, who was in love with either/or.

Margaret Atwood

Summary   Probably you will have noted the following points.
- She notices and describes her surroundings in detail and specific details spark off trains of thought about her life in an interior monologue. She pays attention to these things because there is plenty of time to do so and nothing else to occupy her.
- She separates herself from the people in authority by referring rather anonymously to 'they' and 'them'.
- She feels limited by her life and is not satisfied living by the maxims she has been taught. She longs for something more – 'Waste not want not. I am not being wasted. Why do I want?'
- She is determined to survive, even if this means denying the truth sometimes – 'Thinking can hurt your chances, and I intend to last.'
- She is optimistic enough to recognize what is good in her surroundings – 'But a chair, sunlight, flowers: these are not to be dismissed.'
- Her language is usually simple and she does not use specific imagery. Many of her sentences are short or incomplete. Their confiding quality suggests we already know what she is talking about and who 'they' are, when in fact we know nothing about the regime in which she lives. She likes to play with words and double meanings in a wry, humorous way – 'The circumstances have been reduced; for those of us who still have circumstances.'

Third-person narrative offers different possibilities. The author or narrator adopts a position which is 'godlike', or becomes a 'fly on the wall' reporting everything to us, the readers. This omniscient (all-knowing) narrator, from a vantage point outside the action, can relate events which may occur in different places, at different times, or even simultaneously. Often we are told how different characters feel so we see things from more than one perspective.

Sometimes the author might tell the story dispassionately, without commenting or judging. Usually, however, authors make their presence felt. This might be through obvious authorial intrusion, where the writer butts into the narrative to express an opinion or comment on a situation, or it might be more subtle. For example, a character may be described in language we recognize as sarcastic, 'tongue-in-cheek', or ironic, making it clear that the author is critical or mocking; or positive or negative judgements may simply be revealed by the writer's choice of vocabulary.

We can easily detect Dickens's opinion of 'the speaker' in the opening page of *Hard Times*: describing his forehead as a 'square wall' and his voice as 'inflexible, dry, and dictatorial' is only the beginning of his portrait of the rigid Mr Gradgrind. A few pages later, he is concluding his description of Stone Lodge, Mr Gradgrind's 'matter of fact home' and his fact-ridden 'model' children. His bitter sarcasm is clear:

Iron clamps and girders . . . mechanical lifts . . . everything that heart could wish for.

A moment later Dickens 'intrudes' in his own voice to express his doubts:

Everything? Well I suppose so.

Jane Austen does something similar, but rather more gently. Primarily, her opening paragraphs in *Emma* introduce her central character. Little in the way of judgement can be detected except where she informs us that:

The real evils indeed of Emma's situation were the power of having rather too much her own way, and a disposition to think a little too well of herself.

She does create characters who are 'types', such as Emma's father Mr Woodhouse, the anxious hypochondriac, and Miss Bates, the non-stop talker. Their traits are exaggerated, but her mockery of them tends to be affectionate, without the ferocity of Dickens. Often, she comments ironically with the voice of 'society', when it is clear that her own intention is to question or poke fun at the conventional view, as she does in the famous opening lines of *Pride and Prejudice*:

It is a truth universally acknowledged, that a single man in possession of a good fortune must be in want of a wife.

This question of the writer's stance towards characters or situations can be quite complex. Even in third-person narrative, things are often filtered through the perceptions of one particular character. We may need to consider carefully whether the author's views match those of this character or not. Alternatively, the author may choose to write with a 'voice' which is neither his or her own nor that of one of the characters in the novel.

Most of *Emma* is told from Emma's point of view, with her values and prejudices, but it is also possible to detect that Jane Austen shares some of her views and not others. Emma disapproves of two characters whose social status is inferior to her own. First, the self-satisfied Mrs Elton, who fails to recognize Emma's position in Hartfield society and is much too familiar with her and her friends. Emma finds that she is:

a vain woman, extremely well satisfied with herself, and thinking much of her own importance; that she meant to shine and be very superior, but with manners which had been formed in a bad school, pert and familiar; that all her notions were drawn from one set of people, and one style of living; that if not foolish she was ignorant, and that her society would certainly do Mr Elton no good . . .

Happily it was now time to be gone. They were off; and Emma could breathe.

On the other hand, Emma also disapproves of respectable young farmer Robert Martin, whom she considers a bad match for her young protégé, Harriet Smith:

His appearance was very neat, and he looked like a sensible young man, but his person had no other advantage; and when he came to be contrasted with gentlemen, she thought he must lose all the ground he had gained in Harriet's inclination . . .

'He is very plain, undoubtedly – remarkably plain: – but that is nothing, compared with his entire want of gentility. I had no right to expect much, and I did not expect much; but I had no idea that he could be so very clownish, so totally without air. I had imagined him, I confess, a degree or two nearer gentility.'

In the novel, it is clear that we are expected to agree with Emma about Mrs Elton. She is indeed an awful woman. However, where Robert Martin is concerned, we come to see that Emma is snobbish and misguided and that Jane Austen intends us to question her opinion.

Activity

1 Look once more at the openings of *Emma* and *The Handmaid's Tale* on pages 60–61. Working with a partner, rewrite the first paragraph of *The Handmaid's Tale* in the third person and the first two paragraphs of *Emma* in the first person (with Emma as the narrator). Discuss the results. What is lost and what gained from changing the narrative viewpoint?

2 Think carefully about the narrative viewpoint in the novel you are studying. Who is the narrator? Can you trust the narrative? How aware are you of the author's presence? Look for examples of authorial intrusion.

Characters

Much of the interest in a novel lies in the characters whose world we enter and in whose lives we share. We usually respond to them first as people. We can analyse their personalities, trace how they are affected by events and empathize or disapprove of them. However, we do need to remember that they do not have lives outside the pages of the novel and so it is rarely useful to speculate about their past or future experiences. More importantly, we need to pay attention to how they are presented.

It has already been suggested that it is useful to keep a journal or 'log' to record key passages and quotations for each important character which can be built up as you work through the text.

Summary

Characters are revealed to us in various ways.

- **Description** The author often provides an introductory 'pen-portrait' and then builds up our knowledge with details as the narrative proceeds. Key passages describe main characters or make us aware of how they change and develop.
- **Dialogue** Other characters often give important clues when they discuss the character concerned. We may also find out a lot about someone from his or her own speech.
- **Thoughts and feelings** The 'inner life' of a character can be revealed directly, particularly in a first-person narrative.
- **Actions and reactions** How characters behave in various situations will inform our view of them.
- **Imagery and symbols** Characters may be described using simile and metaphor, or may be associated symbolically with, for example, a colour or an element. In Emily Brontë's *Wuthering Heights*, Heathcliff is frequently linked with fire and with the colour black. Similarly, in Thomas Hardy's *Tess of the D'Urbervilles*, Tess is associated with the colour red, which suggests danger or marks her out as a 'fallen woman' from the beginning. She is also associated with white, traditionally a symbol of purity – Hardy's sub-title for the novel is 'A Pure Woman'.

Activity

Here are some introductory character sketches from *Emma*, *The Handmaid's Tale*, and *Hard Times*. Working alone or in a small group, make notes on these points.
- What kind of information does each author provide about the character in question?
- Do you learn anything of the character's inner life, or just factual or superficial information?
- How does the writer use language in each case? Consider sentence structure, vocabulary, use of imagery, and other effects.
- What can you detect of the author's attitude to the character?

1

Mr John Knightley was a tall, gentleman-like, and very clever man; rising in his profession, domestic, and respectable in his private character; but with reserved manners which prevented his being generally pleasing; and capable of being sometimes out of humour. He was not an ill-tempered man, not so often unreasonably cross as to deserve such a reproach; but his temper was not his great perfection; and indeed, with such a worshipping wife, it was hardly possible that any natural defects in it would not be increased.

Jane Austen

2

The Commander has on his black uniform, in which he looks like a museum guard. A semi-retired man, genial but wary, killing time. But only at first glance. After that he looks like a midwestern bank president, with his straight neatly brushed silver hair, his sober posture, shoulders a little stooped. And after that there is his moustache, silver also, and after that his chin, which really you can't miss. When you get down as far as the chin he looks like a vodka ad, in a glossy magazine, of times gone by.

His manner is mild, his hands large, with thick fingers and acquisitive thumbs, his blue eyes uncommunicative, falsely innocuous.

Margaret Atwood

3

[Mr Bounderby] was a rich man: banker, merchant, manufacturer, and what not. A big, loud man, with a stare and a metallic laugh. A man made out of a coarse material, which seemed to have been stretched to make so much of him. A man with a great puffed head and forehead, swelled veins in his temples, and such a strained skin to his face that it seemed to hold his eyes open and lift his eyebrows up. A man with a pervading appearance on him of being inflated like a balloon, and ready to start. A man who could never sufficiently vaunt himself a self-made man. A man who was always proclaiming, through that brassy speaking-trumpet of a voice of his, his old ignorance and his old poverty. A man who was the Bully of humility.

Charles Dickens

Development of character and relationships

Now let us look at a character in more detail. If you are asked to explore the way a character is presented and how he or she changes and develops in the course of a novel, it is a good idea to choose a few passages or episodes from different parts of the novel, which feature the character, to examine in detail. These may be descriptive passages, moments of dramatic action, episodes where the character contrasts or is in conflict with others, or where he or she faces a decision.

Louisa Gradgrind

Dickens created the bleak world of Coketown, the setting of *Hard Times*, to expose and mock the philosophy of Utilitarianism. This set of beliefs saw people only in terms of their usefulness as workers or tools for industry and wealth-creation. No allowances were made for people having imaginations or emotional lives.

Many of Dickens's characters, such as Mr Bounderby, are caricatures whose traits are exaggerated in the extreme. The effect is comic, but they also allow Dickens to make serious points and express his anger. Sometimes, he is accused of creating only caricatures, unrealistic people without depth, but this is by no means the case. In *Hard Times*, the caricatures are usually recognizable by their comical names, while the central characters who develop as 'real' people are allowed to have ordinary names. Louisa Gradgrind, a victim of her father's belief that facts are 'The one thing needful', is one of these. The account of how her life and development are distorted, and of how her father learns to regret his rigid methods, is moving.

Activity

> We first meet Louisa when her father is appalled to have discovered her with her brother Tom, spying on the local circus, a forbidden entertainment. Study the passage closely, and make notes on how Dickens presents her and her relationship with her father. Consider in particular:
> - the imagery used to describe Louisa's manner
> - what is revealed about each of them by the dialogue.

Hard Times

Chapter 3
A Loophole
'In the name of wonder, idleness, and folly!' said Mr Gradgrind, leading each away by a hand; 'what do you do here?'

'Wanted to see what it was like,' returned Louisa shortly.

'What it was like?'

'Yes, father.'

There was an air of jaded sullenness in them both, and particularly in the girl: yet, struggling through the dissatisfaction of her face, there was a light with nothing to rest upon, a fire with nothing to burn, a starved imagination keeping life in itself somehow, which brightened its expression. Not with the brightness natural to cheerful youth, but with uncertain, eager, doubtful flashes, which had something painful in them, analogous to the changes on a blind face groping its way.

She was a child now, of fifteen or sixteen; but at no distant day would seem to become a woman all at once. Her father thought so as he looked at her. She was pretty. Would have been self-willed (he thought in his eminently practical way), but for her bringing-up.

'Thomas, though I have the fact before me, I find it difficult to believe that you, with your education and resources, should have brought your sister to a scene like this.'

'I brought him, father,' said Louisa quickly. 'I asked him to come.'

'I am sorry to hear it. I am very sorry indeed to hear it. It makes Thomas no better, and it makes you worse, Louisa.'

She looked at her father again, but no tear fell down her cheek.

'You! Thomas and you, to whom the circle of the sciences is open; Thomas and you, who may be said to be replete with facts; Thomas and you, who have been trained to mathematical exactness; Thomas and you here!' cried Mr Gradgrind. 'In this degraded position! I am amazed.'

'I was tired. I have been tired a long time,' said Louisa.

'Tired? Of what?' asked the astonished father.

'I don't know of what – of everything I think.'

'Say not another word,' returned Mr Gradgrind. 'You are childish. I will hear no more.'

Charles Dickens

Louisa is presented in opposition to her father and his world of facts, but as yet the conflict is mostly within her, as her thwarted imagination fights for life. The images of light and an inward 'fire with nothing to burn' will recur frequently. She often gazes at the smoking chimneys of the Coketown factories which she knows must contain flames which have been suppressed, like her own imagination, and which burst out when darkness falls.

The dialogue reveals just how little capacity Gradgrind has for understanding his children. Notice the contrast between Louisa's short answers and her father's pompous, wordy style. She seems sullen, but also honest and very self-controlled. Her dry education has rendered her incapable of tears or emotional displays. His final accusation, that she is childish, is ironic. She has never been allowed to be a child. The passage does mark the first time Gradgrind is surprised by his children. Later it will be Louisa's tragedy which jolts him out of his complacency.

Activity

1 Choose a character from a novel you are studying. Then select three or four passages from different parts of the novel which show 'key' moments for that character.

2 Analyse the passages carefully, paying close attention to how language and imagery are used to present the character at different times.

3 Using examples from these passages, write a short essay about the development of your chosen character.

4 Alternatively, choose an important relationship from a novel you are working on and follow steps 1 to 3.

The setting

The imaginary 'world' of a novel, into which the reader is invited, is often more than simply 'the place where the story happens'. The physical environment may be important in itself or as a backdrop to the action but it can also be used to reflect the characters and their experiences. It can also be symbolic of the ideas the writer wishes to convey. However, the 'world' of a novel will also portray a society with its own culture, politics, and values. Characters may exist comfortably in their worlds, but often, the whole thrust of a novel depends on the central character being a misfit, or being in conflict with some aspect of their 'society', whether this is their family, their social class, a religious group, or a state.

The world of a novel can be as small as a household or as large as a nation. Jane Austen set herself tight limits, saying that 'Three or four families in a country village is the very thing to work on.' *Emma* is set in Highbury, a 'large and populous village almost amounting to a town'. London is only sixteen miles distant, but far enough in those days to seem out of easy reach. The action concerns only a few of the 'best' families in the village – those with whom the Woodhouses, at the top of their social ladder, can associate, and one or two others of lower status who provide material for comedy.

Although Jane Austen is quick to make fun of hypocrisy and snobbery, she does not challenge the rigid class boundaries of Highbury; in fact in this novel she endorses them. Emma's attempts to disregard them are definitely seen as misguided. Her matchmaking with Mr Elton on behalf of her 'friend' Harriet Smith, who is pretty but illegitimate and penniless, causes only pain and embarrassment.

In *Hard Times*, the world Dickens creates is that of a northern English industrial town, a larger world than Jane Austen's Highbury. Like some of his characters, the setting is a caricature. It is based on a real town, but has exaggerated features. His intention of protesting against the deadening effects of Utilitarianism is never clearer than when he introduces us to Coketown. He presents us with an environment where the physical surroundings reflect the social conditions. Read his description and then consider it through the activity which follows.

Hard Times

Chapter 5
The Key-note
Coketown, to which Messrs Bounderby and Gradgrind now walked, was a triumph of fact; it had no greater taint of fancy in it than Mrs Gradgrind herself. Let us strike the key-note, Coketown, before pursuing our tune.

It was a town of red brick, or of brick that would have been red if the smoke and ashes had allowed it; but, as matters stood it was a town of unnatural red and black like the painted face of a savage. It was a town of machinery and tall chimneys, out of which interminable serpents of smoke trailed themselves for ever and ever, and never got uncoiled. It had a black canal in it, and a river that ran purple with ill-smelling dye, and vast piles of building full of windows where there was a rattling and a trembling all day long, and where the piston of the steam-engine worked monotonously up and down, like the head of an elephant in a state of melancholy madness. It contained several large streets all very like one another, and many small streets still more like one another, inhabited by people equally like one another, who all went in and out at the same hours, with the same sound upon the same pavements, to do the same work, and to whom every day was the same as yesterday and tomorrow, and every year the counterpart of the last and the next.

Charles Dickens

Activity

How does Dickens present Coketown? Make notes on his use of:
- simile and metaphor
- colour and the senses
- the rhythm of the passage
- sentence construction.

The world of *The Handmaid's Tale* is very different. It is set in the future, in an imaginary state in America, The Republic of Gilead. Fearful about declining population, due to man-made environmental disaster, a dictatorship has assigned roles to all people, but particularly to women. Wives are idealized, non-sexual beings. They wear virginal blue, while those women capable of the all-important child-bearing are assigned to men as handmaids or breeders, dressed in red. This symbolizes blood, sex, and childbirth. It marks them out as 'fallen women'. Gilead is a state ruled by terror, in which it is highly dangerous to ask questions or to assert one's individuality in any way. We do not even discover the narrator's real name: she is merely the handmaid 'Of-Fred'.

None of this is made clear to us at the start of the novel. Only gradually as we read Offred's stream-of-consciousness narrative do we piece together enough information to understand what is going on. It is quite a way into the text before we are provided with some 'historical background'. Here, Offred, waiting to assist at a birth, remembers some of the teaching she received at the Red Centre, where the handmaids are trained.

The Handmaid's Tale

Chapter 19
The siren goes on and on. That used to be the sound of death, for ambulances or fires. Possibly it will be the sound of death today also. We will soon know. What will Ofwarren give birth to? A baby, as we all hope? Or something else, an Unbaby, with a pinhead or a snout like a dog's, or two bodies, or a hole in its heart or no arms, or webbed hands and feet? There's no telling. They could tell once, with machines, but that is now outlawed. What would be the point of knowing, anyway? You can't have them taken out; whatever it is must be carried to term.

The chances are one in four, we learned that at the Centre. The air got too full, once, of chemicals, rays, radiation, the water swarmed with toxic molecules, all of that takes years to clean up, and meanwhile they creep into your body, camp out in your fatty cells. Who knows, your very flesh may be polluted, dirty as an oily beach, sure death to shore birds and unborn babies. Maybe a vulture would die of eating you. Maybe you light up in the dark, like an old-fashioned watch. Death-watch. That's a kind of beetle, it buries carrion.

I can't think of myself, my body, sometimes, without seeing the skeleton: how I must appear to an electron. A cradle of life, made of bones; and within, hazards, warped proteins, bad crystals, jagged as glass. Women took medicines, pills, men sprayed trees, cows ate grass, all that souped-up piss flowed into the rivers. Not to mention the exploding atomic power plants, along the San Andreas fault, nobody's fault, during the earthquakes, and the mutant strain of syphilis no mould could touch. Some did it themselves, had themselves tied shut with catgut or scarred with chemicals. How could they, said Aunt Lydia, O how could they have done such a thing? Jezebels! Scorning God's gifts! Wringing her hands.

It's a risk you're taking, said Aunt Lydia, but you are the shock troops, you will march out in advance, into dangerous territory. The greater the risk, the greater the glory. She clasped her hands, radiant with our phony courage. We looked down at the tops of our desks. To go through all that and give birth to a shredder: it wasn't a fine thought. We didn't know exactly what would happen to the babies that didn't get passed, that were declared Unbabies. But we knew they were put somewhere, quickly, away.

Margaret Atwood

Activity   Read the passage carefully and discuss in a small group what you learn about the following points.
• What has happened in Gilead in the past.
• What conditions are like in Gilead now.
• The laws and customs of Gilead in respect of pregnancy and childbirth.
• How propaganda and religion are used to ensure the women fit in with the needs of the regime.

In *Hard Times* and *The Handmaid's Tale*, the settings are very important. In both cases the writers have presented aspects they dislike about their own societies in an exaggerated form. This enables them to draw attention to these and to protest in an indirect way while being thought-provoking and entertaining. While Dickens demonstrates in Coketown the terrible results of extreme Utilitarianism, Margaret Atwood writes as a feminist, concerned about the environment and about women being defined and limited by their traditional roles. Both writers create worlds where people are reduced to particular functions. However, both have a hopeful note in that the 'human spirit' is not entirely crushed despite such repressive regimes. 'Fancy' and imagination may be buried and distorted in *Hard Times*, but they do not die completely. Similarly, through the very telling of her story we know that Offred is far more than just her 'viable ovaries'.

Activity

> Study and make notes on the setting of the novel you are studying.
> - What sort of 'world' is it? How large or small, open or restrictive? What are its rules, values, beliefs, and customs?
> - Locate passages where the author describes the physical surroundings, comments on the social order, or where characters act or speak in a way which represents their society.
> - Do the characters fit comfortably in their world or are they in opposition to it? Is this shown to be a good or bad thing?

Language and style

Unless we are studying linguistics, we do not usually discuss a writer's use of language in isolation from the content. What we are concerned with is how effectively language is used to create worlds or present characters, situations, and ideas. So you probably will have noticed that as we have looked at each of these aspects of the novel, we have always examined the writer's language and style at the same time.

Now we will look at how a very different writer, Henry James, presents a scene of courtship. In his novel *Washington Square*, Catherine Sloper, a likeable, but rather plain and naïve young woman who is heiress to a great fortune, receives a visit from her 'lover' Morris Townsend, of whom her father disapproves. Mrs Penniman is her sentimental, meddling aunt.

Washington Square

Chapter 10
Catherine received the young man the next day on the ground she had chosen – amidst the chaste upholstery of a New York drawing-room furnished in the fashion of fifty years ago. Morris had swallowed his pride, and made the effort necessary to cross the threshold of her too derisive parent – an act of magnanimity which could not fail to render him doubly interesting.

'We must settle something – we must take a line,' he declared, passing his hand through his hair and giving a glance at the long narrow mirror which adorned the space between the two windows . . . If Morris had been pleased to describe the master of the house as a heartless scoffer, it is because he thought him too much on his guard, and this was the easiest way to express his own dissatisfaction – a dissatisfaction which he had made a point of concealing from the Doctor. It will probably seem to the reader, however, that the Doctor's vigilance was by no means excessive, and that these two young people had an open field. Their intimacy was now considerable, and it may appear that, for a shrinking and retiring person, our heroine had been liberal of her favours. The young man, within a few days, had made her listen to things for which she had not supposed that she was prepared; having a lively foreboding of difficulties, he proceeded to gain as much ground as possible in the present. He remembered that fortune favours the brave, and even if he had forgotten it, Mrs Penniman would have remembered it for him. Mrs Penniman delighted of all things in a drama, and she flattered herself that a drama would now be enacted. Combining as she did the zeal of the prompter with the impatience of the spectator, she had long since done her utmost to pull up the curtain. She, too, expected to figure in the performance – to be the confidante, the Chorus, to speak the epilogue. It may even be said that there were times when she lost sight altogether of the modest heroine of the play in the contemplation of certain great scenes which would naturally occur between the hero and herself.

What Morris had told Catherine at last was simply that he loved her, or rather adored her. Virtually, he had made known as much already – his visits had been a series of eloquent intimations of it. But now he had affirmed it in lover's vows, and, as a memorable sign of it, he had passed his arm round the girl's waist and taken a kiss. This happy certitude had come sooner than Catherine expected, and she had regarded it, very naturally, as a priceless treasure. It may even be doubted whether she had ever definitely expected to possess it; she had not been waiting for it, and she had never said to herself that at a given moment it must come. As I have tried to explain, she was not eager and exacting; she took what was given her from day to day; and if the delightful custom of her lover's visits, which yielded her a happiness in which confidence and timidity were strangely blended, had suddenly come to an end, she would not only not have spoken of herself as one of the forsaken, but she would not have thought of herself as one of the disappointed. After Morris had kissed her the last time he was with her, as a ripe assurance of his devotion, she begged him to go away, to leave her alone, to let her think. Morris went away, taking another kiss first. But Catherine's meditations had lacked a certain coherence. She felt his kisses on her lips and on her cheeks for a long time afterward; the sensation was rather an obstacle than an aid to reflection. She would have liked to see her situation all clearly before her, to make up her mind what she should do if, as she feared, her father should tell her that he disapproved of Morris Townsend.

Henry James

> **Activity**   Now ask yourself these questions about the style of this extract.
> 1 To what extent, would you say, is James concerned with:
>   • his characters' thoughts and ideas
>   • his characters' feelings and emotions?
> 2 Where do you think he stands in relation to his characters? What is his attitude towards them?

Probably you will have noticed the enormous difference between this extract and the one from *The Rainbow* on pages 35–37 in Unit 3. Both depict an encounter between a man and a woman where marriage is in question, yet the writers are poles apart in the ways they approach this subject. Where Lawrence is so intent on conveying a sense of his characters' emotions and sensations, James is much more concerned with what they are thinking, or with analysing what is going on.

The effect is that reading Lawrence can be a powerful emotional experience:

we are presented with such a close view of the characters that it can almost feel as if we are 'inside' their skins. Reading James, however, is often more of an intellectual challenge. It is not that his characters do not have feelings, but rather that they stop and think about them – or James does – often for several pages at a time. Situations are weighed up and the rights and wrongs of their responses are pondered. James maintains a distance between himself and his characters, leaving himself space to comment and judge, to use irony, or to gently mock. (It is almost impossible, incidentally, to imagine Lawrence being ironic or mocking his characters.) As a result, we as readers also feel more remote from James's characters.

There are other factors in James's writing which contribute to this very different 'style'. Asking some further questions about the details of how he uses language should reveal these.

Activity

> Look again at the passage from Washington Square.
> **1** What are James's choices with respect to:
> - vocabulary
> - imagery
> - sentence structures
> - sound?
>
> What do these choices contribute to his 'style'?
> **2** What words would you use to describe his 'style'?

These are some of the points you may have noted.

- James's vocabulary tends to be demanding or 'inflated': he often deliberately chooses words which are complex or latinate (derived from Latin), when simpler words would convey his meaning equally well. Morris is not 'worried', for example, but has 'a lively foreboding of difficulties'. And this extract is a relatively straightforward example! This gives a sense of formality, and adds to the feeling of distance mentioned earlier: only someone who steps back and weighs his words would make these choices. Also, James's tone becomes ironic or mocking as he uses long words when his characters and subjects do not really merit them. They may be foolish, like Mrs Penniman, or dishonest or ordinary, but they think themselves grander than they really are.
- There is little imagery in the extract, but what there is is deliberately clever. For example, the extended metaphor which describes Mrs Penniman's propensity for acting as if life is a stage drama ('Combining as she did the zeal of the prompter . . .') goes on a bit, as we may imagine Mrs Penniman herself does.
- On the whole, James's sentence structures also tend to be complex. (More extreme examples can be found elsewhere in his work.) He is renowned for producing sentences with multiple clauses which temporarily digress from their subject. These require us to hold several ideas in mind simultaneously, which demands concentration. You will find this aspect of his style particularly noticeable if you try to read the passage aloud.

- There is no evidence that James chooses words in order to create deliberate sound effects. The complex and latinate vocabulary does perhaps give a rather dry, crisp effect to his style, but precision in meaning is his chief aim.
- There can be little doubt that James's main purpose is to present us with something to think about. It is the meanings and ideas contained in his long, precisely constructed sentences, carefully chosen vocabulary, and clever metaphors which are important, never sensual effects like alliteration or visual imagery. It is as difficult to imagine James writing to appeal to the senses as it is to imagine Lawrence being ironic.

Summary

Here are some of the features of language we have considered.
- **Narrative voice**: the choice of first-person or third-person narrative.
- **Imagery**: the use of simile and metaphor. Look particularly for recurring images or patterns of imagery.
- **Sentence/paragraph structure**: the use of sentences which are long or short, complete or incomplete, complex or simple.
- **Vocabulary**: the selection of one word or group of words rather than another.

The short story

What is a short story?

In one sense the answer to this question is so obvious it hardly seems worth a thought. A 'short story' is clearly a story that is short! Perhaps we need to rephrase the question and pose the one that the critic, Norman Friedman, once asked – 'What makes a short story?'

Friedman answers this question by identifying two key features.

- A short story may be short because the material itself is narrow in its range or area of interest.
- A short story may be short because although the material has a potentially broad range, the writer cuts it down to focus on one aspect and maximize the story's impact or artistic effect.

Activity

Think carefully about the short stories that you have read. Make a list of the differences between these stories and novels that you have studied (apart from the obvious point to do with length!).

Many short stories do focus on a single incident, moment in time, or experience, but that is not always the case. Not all short stories are deliberately crafted by the writer as a vehicle for a single effect. In fact some stories gain their impact because they do not operate on a 'single effect' structure. Indeed, in some instances the 'single effect' type of story can appear contrived.

For many years the short story suffered a good deal of critical neglect and it has been regarded as an academically lightweight genre when measured against the much 'weightier' and prestigious novel form. However, in more recent years there has been a recognition that the short story is something more than the novel's poor relation, and a number of different short story options are included on the English A1 Prescribed Book List. If you are studying a short story text there are a number of areas that you will need to have some ideas about. Examination questions can be phrased in different ways, but it is likely that they will focus on one or more of the following.

- **Plot and structure** You will need a clear understanding of what happens in the story, the basic ideas that it deals with, how it is structured, and how the various elements of it relate to one another. How the story is structured can be of particular interest if it varies from a straightforward chronological pattern.
- **Narrative viewpoint** The question of who is telling the story is a very important one and raises questions about why the writer has chosen to present the story from this particular viewpoint and what effect this has on the reader's response.
- **Characters** Questions often focus on one or more of the characters in the story or stories and may ask you to examine how the writer presents or develops the characters or to explore how they relate to each other.
- **Language and style** You will also need a clear idea about the distinctive qualities of the writer's style. This will involve focusing closely on the specific detail and the writer's choice of language (the way this is used, and the effects that it creates).

Plot and structure

Activity Think carefully about a short story that you have read and make a list of the features that you think are important in terms of making this story 'work'.

One thing you may have noted about short stories is that very often the story focuses on a single character in a single situation rather than tracing a range of characters through a variety of situations and phases of development, as novels often do. However, often the focus for the story is a moment at which one or more of the central characters undergo some important experience which represents a significant moment in their personal development. It can be seen as a 'moment of truth' (or 'epiphany', as James Joyce calls it) in which something or some perception, large or small, changes within the character. In some stories, though, this 'moment of truth' is evident only to the reader and not the character(s).

Not all stories reach a climax. Some stories may offer a kind of 'snapshot' of a period of time or an experience – a 'day in the life of. . .' story might be like this. Other stories end inconclusively, leaving the reader with feelings of uncertainty, while yet other stories do not seem to have a discernible plot at all. This may lead the reader to feel completely baffled by what he or she has read and subsequently to tentatively explore a range of possible interpretations in his or her head. This might, of course, have been exactly the response that the writer intended.

This diagram presents one way of thinking about how alternative plots and structures of short stories work:

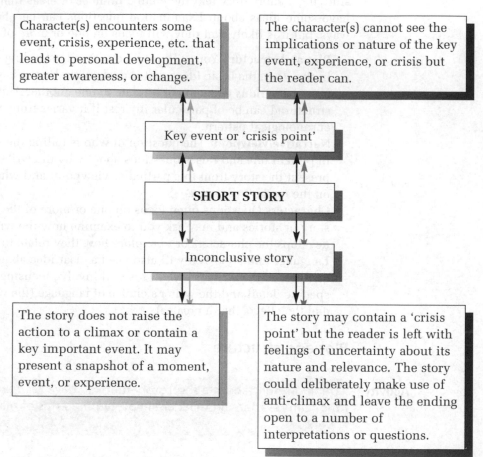

Character(s) encounters some event, crisis, experience, etc. that leads to personal development, greater awareness, or change.

The character(s) cannot see the implications or nature of the key event, experience, or crisis but the reader can.

Key event or 'crisis point'

SHORT STORY

Inconclusive story

The story does not raise the action to a climax or contain a key important event. It may present a snapshot of a moment, event, or experience.

The story may contain a 'crisis point' but the reader is left with feelings of uncertainty about its nature and relevance. The story could deliberately make use of anti-climax and leave the ending open to a number of interpretations or questions.

Beginnings

Our very earliest experiences of stories (the fairy tales we listen to, and then the vast range of stories that we hear, read, and see presented in film and television) teach us one thing – stories have a 'beginning', a 'middle', and an 'end'. Strictly speaking, however, it is not entirely true. There are stories that do not seem to have a beginning or an ending in the conventional sense. The vast majority of stories, however, do have some kind of beginning or opening section; a middle, where the characters, situation, and ideas are developed; and an ending that draws the story to a conclusion.

Here are some possible ways in which stories can open:
   • the writer launches straight into the narrative
   • the writer sets the scene by giving explicit background information

- the writer informs the reader using suggestion or implication rather than direct description
- the opening is direct and holds the reader's attention, perhaps capturing attention with a word or short phrase.

Activity

Read the following openings to three short stories. Then, on your own or in a small group, consider your responses to them. Think carefully about how each writer approaches the opening to the story and try to identify the techniques used. Make a list of what you learn about setting and characters from each opening.

1 Indian Camp

At the lake shore there was another rowboat drawn up. The two Indians stood waiting.

Nick and his father got in the stern of the boat and the Indians shoved it off and one of them got in to row. Uncle George sat in the stern of the camp rowboat. The young Indian shoved the camp boat off and got in to row Uncle George.

The two boats started off in the dark. Nick heard the oar-locks of the other boat quite a way ahead of them in the mist. The Indians rowed with quick choppy strokes. Nick lay back with his father's arm around him. It was cold on the water. The Indian who was rowing them was working very hard, but the other boat moved farther ahead in the mist all the time.

'Where are we going, Dad?' Nick asked.

'Over to the Indian camp. There is an old Indian lady very sick.'

'Oh,' said Nick.

Across the bay they found the other boat beached. Uncle George was smoking a cigar in the dark. The young Indian pulled the boat way up on the beach. Uncle George gave both the Indians cigars.

They walked up from the beach through a meadow that was soaking wet with dew, following the young Indian who carried a lantern. Then they went into the woods and followed a trail that led to the logging road that ran back into the hills. It was much lighter on the logging road as the timber was cut away on both sides. The young Indian stopped and blew out his lantern and they all walked on along the road.

Ernest Hemingway

2 The Snow Pavilion

The motor stalled in the middle of a snowy landscape, lodged in a rut, wouldn't budge an inch. How I swore! I'd planned to be snug in front of a roaring fire by now, a single malt on the mahogany wine-table (a connoisseur's piece) beside me, the five courses of Melissa's dinner savourously aromatizing the kitchen; to complete the décor, a labrador retriever's head laid on my knee as trustingly as if

I were indeed a country gentleman and lolled by rights among the chintz. After dinner, before I read our customary pre-coital poetry aloud to her, my elegant and accomplished mistress, also a connoisseur's piece, might play the piano for her part-time pasha while I sipped black, acrid coffee from her precious little cups.

Angela Carter

3 Dual Control

'You ought to have stopped.'

'For God's sake, shut up, Freda.'

'Well, you should have. You ought to have made sure she was alright.'

'Of course she's alright.'

'How do you know? You didn't stop to find out, did you?'

'Do you want me to go back? We're late enough as it is, thanks to your fooling about getting ready, but I don't suppose the Bradys'll notice if we're late. I don't suppose they'll notice if we never turn up, though after the way you angled for the invitation . . .'

'That's right, blame it all on me. We could have left half an hour ago if you hadn't been late home from the office.'

'How often do I have to tell you that business isn't a matter of nine to five?'

'No it's a matter of the Bradys, isn't it? You were keen enough we should get asked. Where were you anyway? Drinking with the boys? Or smooching with some floozie?'

Elizabeth Walter

Obviously the opening of a story is vital. If readers' attention is not captured immediately the story contains no initial impact to encourage them to continue, or to draw them into the story. However, bearing in mind the constraints of length under which the short story operates, it is also important that the opening compresses information that might have taken some time to explain, so that the reader quickly and effectively gains a picture of what is going on. Short story writers are often faced with this question of how much they can omit while at the same time creating the impression of completeness and continuity in their stories.

Going back to the extracts you have just discussed, you may have noticed that Extract 2 launches straight into the narrative. The car getting stuck in the snow captures the reader's attention straight away. This opening paragraph goes on to give quite a bit of information to set the scene very economically, as the narrator reflects on the plans he had made for his evening.

In Extract 3, on the other hand, we are told very little directly and we have to work out for ourselves what is happening or what has happened using clues suggested through the narrative. This approach can provide us with just as much information as straightforward description. In this instance we learn about the characters – what they are doing and what has happened – through the dialogue, but it leaves a good deal to the reader's imagination too. (In fact, this story is told entirely through dialogue with no direct description.)

In contrast, Extract 1 begins with a straightforward narrative style in which Hemingway simply describes the action without any use of imagery or overly descriptive language. After the narrative opening he then introduces direct speech, which both gives further information and allows the reader to begin to get a sense of the characters involved.

Narrative line

Short stories, like other fictional works, order the events that they describe in a particular way. Through the story-line the writer can create a wide range of effects, such as creating suspense, raising the action to a climax point, resolving problems, leading (or misleading) the reader in particular ways, and leaving endings open to a variety of interpretations.

Very often the narrative structure is a straightforward progression with one event following another and moving towards a conclusion where all is resolved. However, sometimes a writer might play around with this structure to create particular effects. Here are some points to consider when you focus on the narrative structure of a story.

- Make a list of the key events in the story.
- Look at the order in which these events are related by the writer.
- Look at the time structure of the story – is it told in simple chronological order or is there use of flashbacks or cutting back and forth?
- Are there any details or pieces of information that the writer omits or particular points that are emphasized?

Short stories often have a moment in the plot upon which the whole structure of the story turns and which affects the outcome of the tale. Sometimes this trigger can be a quite trivial incident or experience but it signifies a moment of revelation to the central character. *Hassan's Tower* by Margaret Drabble contains just such a moment for newly-married Kenneth on honeymoon with his wife, Chloë, in Morocco. They are a wealthy couple who appear to have everything that they could want in life but Kenneth is disappointed in his new wife and disillusioned with life in general. He is ill-at-ease in Morocco and goes about in constant fear of being robbed. Against his will his wife takes him to Hassan's Tower and wants to climb to the top to see the view. Reluctantly, he accompanies her and during the course of this seemingly unremarkable excursion he experiences a revelation that changes his whole outlook on his wife, his life, and those around him.

Hassan's Tower

The more he looked, the more he realized that the people on top of the tower were in their own way as astonishing a view as the more evidently panoramic vistas. The whole of the top of the tower was thick and covered with people: small children were crawling about, mothers were feeding their babies, young men were holding the hands of girls and indeed the hands of other young men, boys were sitting on the very edge and dangling their feet into space, and old women who would need a day to recover from the climb were lying back in the sun, for all the world as though they were grandmothers on a beach in England . . . and as he gazed he felt growing within him a sense of extraordinary familiarity that was in its own way a kind of illumination . . . He saw these people, quite suddenly, for what they were, for people, for nothing other than people; their clothes filled out with bodies, their faces took on expression, their relations became dazzlingly clear, as though the details of their strangeness had dropped away, as though the terms of common humanity (always before credited in principle, but never before perceived) had become facts before his eyes.

Margaret Drabble

Endings

There are as many ways of ending a story as there are of beginning it and the ending is clearly a very important element in the overall structure of a piece. In a short story it is often the ending which reveals meaning, points up a significant theme, or provides a resolution. This kind of ending should leave the reader contented and satisfied with a sense of a tale completed.

Equally, a writer might create an 'open' ending, one that does not provide answers, an ending that might leave the reader pondering on what it all means, or unsettle him or her. This could be, of course, just the kind of response that the writer is aiming for.

The ending with 'a sting in the tail', a technique often used by Maupassant, has become very popular in recent years, being popularized through the short stories of Roald Dahl. It is worth noting, however, that with this kind of ending we need to distinguish between a device which is merely used as a kind of 'trick', and a twist at the end which causes us to see something fundamental in the story as a whole.

Activity

Choose three short stories that you know and reread them. Discuss the ending of each with a partner, thinking about the following questions.
- Does the story have what you would recognize as a definite ending?
- How does the ending relate to the rest of the story?
- Does the writer draw attention to any specific points in the ending?
- How would you have ended the story?

Narrative viewpoint

You will already be familiar with the term viewpoint in the sense of 'from whose point of view we see the events of the story'. However, it is perhaps worth bearing in mind that this term can encompass two related but distinct ideas. In addressing viewpoint we need to consider the question of who is actually seeing the events described and who is narrating them. They may be one and the same or quite separate, and the question is rather more complex than it might first appear.

It may be possible to approach the question of viewpoint by distinguishing between narrators who seem to address the reader directly from within the story (**internal narrators**) and those who have a more 'external' narrative viewpoint. As readers you need to be aware of how writers use viewpoint within their stories, be sensitive to subtle shifts and aware of the effects this can have on the narrative and your perception of it.

Activity   Look at these three extracts and think about the narrative viewpoints used in each.

1 A Tradition of Eighteen Hundred and Four, Christmas 1882

The widely discussed possibility of an invasion of England through a Channel Tunnel has more than once recalled old Solomon Selby's story to my mind.

The occasion on which I numbered myself among his audience was one evening when he was sitting in the yawning chimney-corner of the inn-kitchen, with some others who had gathered there, and I entered for shelter from the rain. Withdrawing the stem of his pipe from the dental notch in which it habitually rested, he leaned back in the recess behind him and smiled into the fire. The smile was neither mirthful nor sad, not precisely humorous nor altogether thoughtful. We who knew him recognized it in a moment: it was his narrative smile. Breaking off our few desultory remarks we drew up closer, and he thus began:

'My father, as you mid know, was a shepherd all his life, and lived out by the Cove four miles yonder, where I was born and lived likewise, till I moved here shortly afore I was married . . .'

Thomas Hardy

2 Her First Ball

Exactly when the ball began Leila would have found it hard to say. Perhaps her first real partner was the cab. It did not matter that she shared the cab with the Sheridan girls and their brother. She sat back in her own little corner of it, and the bolster on which her hand rested felt like the sleeve of an unknown young man's suit; and away they bowled, past waltzing lamp-posts and houses and fences and trees.

'Have you really never been to a ball before, Leila? But, my child, how too weird – ' cried the Sheridan girls.

'Our nearest neighbour was fifteen miles,' said Leila softly, gently opening and shutting her fan.

Oh, dear, how hard it was to be indifferent like the others! She tried not to smile too much; she tried not to care. But every single thing was so new and exciting . . .

Meg's tuberoses, Jose's long loop of amber, Laura's little dark head, pushing above her white fur like a flower through snow. She would remember for ever. It even gave her a pang to see her cousin Laurie throw away the wisps of tissue paper he pulled from the fastenings of his new gloves. She would like to have kept those wisps as a keepsake, as a remembrance. Laurie leaned forward and put his hand on Laura's knee.

Katherine Mansfield

3 Missy

'There you are, Mrs Ebbs, hold the cup steady. Can you manage, dear? Whoops! That's it. Now sit up properly, you'll slip down in the bed again, sit up against your pillows. That's it. Don't nod off again, will you? Now careful, Mrs Ebbs, I haven't got all day, dear. That's it, good girl.'

The voice came roaring towards her. The face was bland as suet. The face was a cow's face. An ox.

'Ox-face,' she said, but she had not said it.

She tipped the spoon and sucked in her soup, little bits of carrot and soft lentil sieving through the spaces between her teeth.

'All right now, Mrs Ebbs?'

Ox-face.

'I'm not deaf.'

Was she?

Susan Hill

In Extract 1 you will notice immediately that Hardy is writing in the first person here. He is recounting a particular evening when he heard a story told by Solomon Selby. You obviously cannot tell from this brief opening but the bulk of the story is told as if by Solomon Selby as reported by Hardy. Think about what effect this has on the narrative. Notice too how Hardy economically sets the context of the story through implication – the title providing the date, 1804, which coupled with the idea of an invasion through a 'Channel Tunnel' clearly sets the story against the background of the Napoleonic Wars. Hardy also economically sets the story in its more immediate context – the cosy inn of 1882, sheltering from the rain with others gathered round the fire, and the anticipation of a good story well told. All these details help to set the mood and draw the reader into the narrative.

In Extract 2 Mansfield writes in the third person, which allows her to reveal the thoughts and feelings that run through the mind of her character. The third-person narrative is interspersed with direct speech, which allows Mansfield to begin to build up a sense of her characters and encourage the reader to engage with them.

Compare this with the approach adopted by Hill in Extract 3. She chooses a quite different way of telling her story. It is written in the third person and we are launched, without any preamble, into a 'situation'. It is not immediately clear what that situation is, but it seems that someone, perhaps a nurse, is feeding soup to Mrs Ebbs. Although Hill partially adopts the stance of external narrator, some of the narrative views the scene through the eyes of Mrs Ebbs as she sees the face of the nurse peering towards her.

Activity Look at three or four short stories that you have studied. With a partner, discuss the narrative viewpoint that the writer adopts in each. Now write a short essay, illustrated by examples, on the way in which narrative viewpoint contributes to the overall effect of these stories.

Character

Although some critics argue that it is absurd to consider fictitious characters as if they were 'real' people, on the other hand when we read stories we do create our own mental image of them based on our experiences of real life. However, we must not lose sight of the fact that they are creations of the writer and do not have an existence outside the text. In many cases writers create their characters to serve particular functions within the narrative and present them in ways that give particular impressions. Therefore, we should look carefully at the kinds of characters the writer portrays, how they are presented, which of their features are stressed, and what role they perform. We must also think about how the characters interlock with all the other elements of the story to create a unified whole, and how we respond to them as readers.

Activity Think about the ways in which the characters are presented in a short story you have read.
1 What kind of characters are presented?
2 How does the writer give you details about the characters?
3 How effectively and convincingly are they portrayed?
4 Select one character and consider the role he or she plays in the story.

Language and imagery

The style in which a story is written – the choices that writers make in the language they use and the ways in which they use it – is a key element in the overall effect that is created by a story in the mind of the reader. It might be written quite plainly using little figurative language, or the writer might use imagery to help create the desired effect.

In *Halloran's Child*, Susan Hill very often uses groups of images to build up a particular effect. Look at this passage, for example, which describes the Hallorans' daughter, Jenny.

Activity Read the extract carefully and pick out any images that are particularly effective. Describe what impressions are created by each of these and then compare your ideas with the suggestions which follow.

Halloran's Child

They had only one child, the daughter, Jenny. She had never been truly well since the day she was born, and when she was a year old and began to walk her limbs seemed incapable of holding her up, she was unsteady and sickly. At the age of four she had rheumatic fever and almost died, and Halloran had said in public hearing that he wished for it, wished to have it over with, for who wanted an invalid for a child and how could he bear the anxiety? She had been forbidden to run or even walk far, though she went to school when she was five and there was treated like a fragile doll by the others, who had been put in awe of her. She played with no one, though sometimes, as she sat in a corner of the playground, one of them would take pity on her and bring pick-sticks or a jigsaw and do it with her for a little while. But she seemed to be separated from them, almost to be less than human, because of the transparency of her skin and her thin, delicate bones, because of the fine blueness tinging her lips and the flesh below her nervous eyes.

Susan Hill

Notice how Hill emphasizes the frailty of Jenny through a variety of images that build up to create a vivid impression of the sick child. She tells us that Jenny 'was treated like a fragile doll', that she seemed 'almost to be less than human, because of the transparency of her skin and her thin, delicate bones, because of the fine blueness tinging her lips and the flesh below her nervous eyes'. This creates an image of a fragile, young, featherless baby bird and gives an impression of vulnerability, of someone with a tenuous grip on life.

Later on in the story Jenny goes into hospital, and when she comes out the fragility of her body is re-emphasized by Hill, who describes her 'small legs poking out like sticks', her 'neck bent like a stalk', and introduces the idea that she is dying as another character, Nate, sees 'the deadness within the child's eyes'.

Nate goes to visit Jenny, and again Hill uses description relating to skin and eyes and bones to show the child's deteriorating condition:

she seemed to have shrunk, her flesh was thinner, scarcely covering her bones, and the skin was tight and shiny. Her eyes were very bright and yet dead, too.

Again Hill uses imagery suggestive of a helpless creature:

He looked down at her hand, resting on the sheet. It was like a small claw.

and again images that hint of death:

Her lips moved and there was no blood in them, they were thin and dry and oddly transparent, like the skin of a chrysalis.

This technique of using recurring images to build up a picture or atmosphere is a feature typical of Hill's style.

Activity
> Choose two or three stories that you have studied and think carefully about how they are written. Note down what seem to you to be particular features of the style of each. Include examples to illustrate your points.

Prose other than the novel and short story

As part of your A1 English programme you might also encounter non-fiction prose texts.

Prose texts can take many different forms but very often many of the techniques of the novelist are also used by the non-fiction writer, and much of what has been discussed so far in this chapter is also applicable to non-fiction writing. For example, non-fiction writers often portray characters, and although their characters really existed they still need to be recreated in words. Similarly, they often describe scenes and settings, create moods and atmospheres, and their texts often contain themes, ideas, or messages that the writer wants to convey to the reader. Some texts, of course, also combine factual information with that which comes from the imagination of the writer. When studying non-fiction texts, then, our approach is not necessarily any different from when we study novels, or even drama or poetry.

We still need to ask the key questions:

- What is this text about?
- How has the author chosen to write about it?
- What is the purpose in writing it?

Here are some forms of non-fiction writing you might encounter:

- the essay
- autobiographical or biographical writing
- the diary
- the documentary
- journalism.

Now look at the following extract. It is taken from *Testament of Youth*, the autobiography of Vera Brittain. She left Oxford University during the First Word War, in 1916, and volunteered to go to France as a V.A.D. (Voluntary Aid Detachment) nurse. Here she describes her arrival at a camp hospital at Etaples.

Testament of Youth

A heavy shower had only just ceased as I arrived at Etaples with three other

V.A.D.s ordered to the same hospital, and the roads were liquid with such mud as only wartime France could produce after a few days of rain.

Leaving our camp-kit to be picked up by an ambulance, we squelched through the littered, grimy square and along a narrow, straggling street where the sole repositories for household rubbish appeared to be the pavement and the gutter. We finally emerged into open country and the huge area of camps, in which, at one time or another, practically every soldier in the British Army was dumped to await further orders for a still less agreeable destination. The main railway line from Boulogne to Paris ran between the hospitals and the distant sea, and amongst the camps, and along the sides of the road to Camiers, the humped sandhills bristled with tufts of spiky grass.

The noise of the distant guns was a sense rather than a sound; sometimes a quiver shook the earth, a vibration trembled upon the wind, when I could actually hear nothing. But that sense made any feeling of complete peace impossible; in the atmosphere was always the tenseness, the restlessness, the slight rustling, that comes before an earthquake or with imminent thunder. The glamour of the place was even more compelling, though less delirious, than the enchantment of Malta's beauty; it could not be banished though one feared and resisted it, knowing that it had to be bought at the cost of loss and frustration. France was the scene of titanic, illimitable death, and for this very reason it had become the heart of the fiercest living ever known to any generation. Nothing was permanent; everyone and everything was always on the move; friendships were temporary, appointments were temporary, life itself was the most temporary of all. Never, in any time or place, had been so appropriate the lament of 'James Lee's Wife';

To draw one beauty into our heart's core,
And keep it changeless! Such our claim;
So answered, – Never more!

Whenever I think of the War today, it is not as summer but always as winter; always as cold and darkness and discomfort, and an intermittent warmth of exhilarating excitement which made us irrationally exult in all three. Its permanent symbol, for me, is a candle stuck in the neck of a bottle, the tiny flame flickering in an ice-cold draught, yet creating a miniature illusion of light against an opaque infinity of blackness.

Vera Brittain

Activity   Look at the extract carefully and answer the following questions:
1 What techniques does Brittain use to give the reader an impression of her surroundings? Does her account seem biased?
2 Do her methods have anything in common with those of the novelist?
3 Are there any differences?

Brittain uses vivid and detailed description to give the reader an impression of her surroundings. Note how she brings in the various senses to strengthen the impression of the place – 'The noise of the distant guns was a sense rather than a sound; sometimes a quiver shook the earth, a vibration trembled upon the wind, when I could actually hear nothing.' Clearly she is using here the same techniques as a novelist would to set the scene and create a sense of atmosphere. As far as this extract is concerned there are no differences between her writing and that of a novelist or short story writer. We happen to know that Brittain was writing from first-hand experience here, but it could equally be a piece of prose written in the first person and created purely from the writer's imagination.

Activity

> Now read this extract from Brian Keenan's *An Evil Cradling*, which recounts his experiences of being kidnapped and held hostage by terrorists in Beirut.
> 1 How does he draw you into the narrative at the beginning of the passage?
> 2 How does he give you a vivid impression of what his life was like?
> 3 Pick out particular details that he uses and comment on their effectiveness.
> 4 How does he convey the thoughts that run through his mind?
> 5 How effective do you find his writing overall? Why?

An Evil Cradling

Come now into the cell with me and stay here and feel if you can and if you will that time, whatever time it was, for however long, for time means nothing in this cell. Come, come in.

I am back from my daily ablutions. I hear the padlock slam behind me and I lift the towel which has draped my head from my face. I look at the food on the floor. The round of Arab bread, a boiled egg, the jam I will not eat, the slice or two of processed cheese and perhaps some houmus. Every day I look to see if it will change, if there will be some new morsel of food that will make this day different from all the other days, but there is no change. This day is the same as all the days in the past and as all the days to come. It will always be the same food sitting on the floor in the same place.

I set down my plastic bottle of drinking water and the other empty bottle. From bottle to bottle, through me, this fluid will daily run. I set the urine bottle at the far corner away from the food. This I put in a plastic bag to keep it fresh. In this heat the bread rapidly turns stale and hard. It is like eating cardboard. I pace my four paces backwards and forwards, slowly feeling my mind empty, wondering where it will go today. Will I go with it or will I try to hold it back, like a father and an unruly child? There is a greasy patch on the wall where I lay my head. Like a dog I sniff it.

I begin as I have always begun these days to think of something, anything upon which I can concentrate. Something I can think about and so try to push away the crushing emptiness of this tiny, tiny cell and the day's long silence. I try with desperation to recall the dream of the night before or perhaps to push away the horror of it. The nights are filled with dreaming. The cinema of the mind, the reels flashing and flashing by and suddenly stopping at some point when with strange contortions it throws up some absurd drama that I cannot understand. I try to block it out. Strange how in the daytime the dreams that we do not wish to remember come flickering back into the conscious mind. Those dreams that we desperately want to have with us in the daylight will not come to us but have gone and cannot be enticed back. It is as if we are running down a long empty tunnel looking for something that we left behind but cannot see in the blackness.

The guards are gone. I have not heard a noise for several hours now. It must be time to eat. I tear off a quarter of the unleavened bread and begin to peel the shell from the egg. The word 'albumen' intrigues me for a while and I wonder where the name came from. How someone decided once to call that part of the egg 'albumen'. The shape of an egg has lost its fascination for me. I have exhausted thinking about the form of an egg. A boiled egg with dry bread is doubly tasteless. I make this meaningless remark to myself every day and don't know why.

I must ration my drinking water for I am always fearful that I might finish it and then wake in the middle of the night with a raging thirst that I cannot satiate. I think of rabies and the raging thirst of mad dogs and I know how easy it would be to go mad from thirst. Now I know the full meaning of the expression so frequently used in our daily lives: 'He was mad with thirst.' If I were to knock over this water-bottle there would be nothing I could do because there is no-one here. Until tomorrow there will be silence in this tomb of a place so far down under the ground.

Then it begins, I feel it coming from out of nowhere. I recognize it now, and I shrink into the corner to await its pleasure. What will it be today? That slow down-dragging slide and pull into hopeless depression and weariness. The waters of the sea of despair are heavy and thick and I think I cannot swim through them. But today is a day of euphoria. A day in which I will not walk my four paces but in which I will glide, my feet hardly touching the ground. Up snakes and down ladders my mind is manically playing games with me and I cannot escape. Today it is teasing me, threatening me, so far without the full blast of its fury. I squat and rock backwards and forwards reciting a half-remembered nursery rhyme like a religious mantra. I am determined I will make myself more mad than my mind.

Blackness, the light has gone. There will be none for ten hours. They have given me candles. Small, stubby candles. I will not light them. I fear the dark so I save the candles. It's stupid, it's ridiculous. There are a dozen or so hidden in my bed. I will not light them, yet I hate the dark and cannot abide its thick palpable blackness. I can feel it against my skin.

I am going crazier by the day. In the thick sticky darkness I lie naked on the mattress. The blanket reeks, full of filth. It is pointless to try to shield myself from the mosquitoes drooling and humming, their constant buzz, buzz, buzz everywhere, as if it is inside my ears and inside my head. In the thick black invisibility it is foolishness to hope to kill what you cannot see but only feel when it is too late, upon your flesh.

Always in the morning I see the marks of the night's battle. Red lumps like chicken pox, all raging to be itched and scratched. I sit trying to prevent myself from scratching. The more I try to resist, the more difficult it becomes and the more demanding is my body for the exquisite pain of my nails tearing my own flesh. For some reason I do not understand, the feet and the backs of my fingers suffer the most from these insistent fleas. The pain of the bites on these tender areas can be excruciating. At times I exchange one pain for another. Deciding feverishly to tear and scratch the skin from my feet, and with it the pain of the bite, knowing that in the morning my feet will be a bloody mess and I will be unable to walk on this filthy floor. It's all so purposeless. I am naked in the dark and I try to wipe the perspiration from my skin. The night noise of these insects is insidious. I cannot bear much more. I thrust my body back upon the mattress and pull the filthy curtain over it to keep these things from feeding on my flesh. I cannot bear the heat and smell of this rag over my body like a shroud. I must content myself, let the mosquitoes feed and hope that having had a fill of me they will leave me alone to find some sleep.

Brian Keenan

Joseph Conrad

Joseph Conrad, whose real name was Joseph Teodor Konrad Nalecz Korzeniowski, was born in Poland in 1857 into an aristocratic family. His parents died when he was a child and he was brought up by his uncle. As a Polish aristocrat, Conrad's cultural background was Western and he spoke and read in French. However, his father, who had himself been a poet and dramatist, had been a great admirer of English literature and so, as a child, Conrad read much Shakespeare and Dickens in translation. Formal schooling did not appeal to him and by 1872 he wanted to go to sea. He was finally allowed to go at the age of seventeen, although his family were not happy with this idea of his becoming an ordinary sailor or with what seemed, to them, the rejection of his cultural and social background.

During the years that followed he led a colourful and adventurous life and came to England when he was twenty-one. At that time he knew very little English and taught himself the language. He spent the next twenty years or so at sea and rose to the rank of Captain. In 1886 he became a British citizen.

As a writer, Conrad acknowledged his debt to the French author Guy de Maupassant, but he wrote his own stories in English, attracted by the qualities and potential of that language. He began writing as early as 1886 and continued until his death in 1924, producing a total of 31 books as well as a large number of letters. His novels and stories include: *The Nigger of the Narcissus* (1897), *Lord Jim* (1900), *Typhoon* (1902), *Heart of Darkness* (1902), *Nostromo* (1904), and *The Secret Agent* (1907).

For the purpose of this Detailed Study we will focus on one of Conrad's best-known and most studied novels, *Heart of Darkness*.

In this short novel Conrad reveals the depths of human corruptibility, as the central character, Marlow (a seaman), voyages up the Congo river, in search of the enigmatic Kurtz, a European and a man of many talents. Travelling into the heart of Africa, Marlow discovers how Kurtz has gained his power and influence over the local people – a discovery which leads him to 'the heart of darkness'.

Themes and ideas

Heart of Darkness is a novel which contains a complex mesh of themes and ideas concerning the individual, social, political, and metaphorical aspects of human existence:

- civilization/savagery
- colonialism/imperialism

- the journey
- the self and the unconscious.

Activity

> Read the following extract taken from early in the novel. In the opening part of the novel Conrad introduces, in a symbolic or metaphorical way, some of the key themes that he goes on to explore in the book. Look carefully at the extract and see if you can see in it suggestions of any of the themes mentioned above. Marlow is speaking.

'I was thinking of very old times, when the Romans first came here, nineteen hundred years ago – the other day . . . Light came out of this river since – you say Knights? Yes; but it is like a running blaze on a plain, like a flash of lightning in the clouds. We live in the flicker – may it last as long as the old earth keeps rolling! But darkness was here yesterday. Imagine the feelings of a commander of a fine – what d'ye call 'em? – trireme in the Mediterranean, ordered suddenly to the north; run overland across the Gauls in a hurry; put in charge of one of these craft the legionaries – a wonderful lot of handy men they must have been too – used to build, apparently by the hundred, in a month or two, if we may believe what we read. Imagine him here – the very end of the world, a sea the colour of lead, a sky the colour of smoke, a kind of ship about as rigid as a concertina – and going up this river with stores, or orders, or what you like. Sandbanks, marshes, forests, savages – precious little to eat fit for a civilized man, nothing but Thames water to drink. No Falernian wine here, no going ashore. Here and there a military camp lost in a wilderness, like a needle in a bundle of hay – cold, fog, tempests, disease, exile, and death – death skulking in the air, in the water, in the bush. They must have been dying like flies here. Oh yes – he did it. Did it very well, too, no doubt, and without thinking much about it either, except afterwards to brag of what he had gone through in his time, perhaps. They were men enough to face the darkness. And perhaps he was cheered by keeping his eye on a chance of promotion to the fleet at Ravenna by and by, if he had good friends in Rome and survived the awful climate. Or think of a decent young citizen in a toga – perhaps too much dice, you know – coming out here in the train of some prefect, or tax-gatherer, or trader, even, to mend his fortunes. Land in a swamp, march through the woods, and in some inland post feel the savagery, the utter savagery, had closed round him – all that mysterious life of the wilderness that stirs in the forest, in the jungles, in the hearts of wild men. There's no initiation either into such mysteries. He has to live in the midst of the incomprehensible, which is also detestable. And it has a fascination, too, that goes to work upon him. The fascination of the abomination – you know, imagine the growing regrets, the longing to escape, the powerless disgust, the surrender, the hate.'

He paused.

'Mind,' he began again, lifting one arm from the elbow, the palm of the hand outwards, so that, with his legs folded before him, he had the pose of a Buddha preaching in European clothes and without a lotus-flower – 'Mind, none of us would feel exactly like this. What saves us is efficiency – the devotion to efficiency. But these chaps were not much account, really. They were no colonists; their administration was merely a squeeze, and nothing more, I suspect. They were conquerors, and for that you want only brute force – nothing to boast of, when you have it, since your strength is just an accident arising from the weakness of others. They grabbed what they could get for the sake of what was to be got. It was just robbery with violence, aggravated murder on a great scale, and men going at it blind – as is very proper for those who tackle a darkness. The conquest of the earth, which mostly means the taking it away from those who have a different complexion or slightly flatter noses than ourselves, is not a pretty thing when you look into it too much. What redeems it is the idea only. An idea at the back of it; not a sentimental pretence but an idea; and an unselfish belief in the idea – something you can set up, and bow down before, and offer a sacrifice to . . .'

Here are some possible ideas:

- The theme of imperialism can be seen in the reference to the Roman invasion of Britain and the 'conquest of the earth'.
- His reference to the 'growing regrets, the longing to escape, the powerless disgust, the surrender, the hate' that the Roman invaders experienced can be seen to have parallels in the journey that Kurtz undertakes in the novel.
- The reference to the Roman invasion also creates a sense of contrast between the 'civilization' that their empire represented and the 'savagery' which surrounded the Roman soldier – 'Land in a swamp, march through the woods, and in some inland post feel the savagery, the utter savagery, had closed round him – all that mysterious life of the wilderness that stirs in the forest, in the jungles, in the hearts of wild men.'
- The words in the previous quotation foreshadow later descriptions of Marlow's experiences as he travels up the Congo.
- The reference to the Roman invasion up the River Thames suggests the idea that they have made a journey, again paralleling Marlow's journey up the Congo.

Conrad's use of symbols and motifs

Symbols are objects, colours, or characters that are used to represent ideas or themes or concepts. Motifs are recurring images, symbols, structures or patterns which are repeated at various points in the novel in order to create particular effects or to emphasize major themes. In this novel Conrad uses a number of symbols and motifs such as:

- The title itself, which holds a symbolic meaning in that it represents both the heart of the wilderness and the central darkness within Kurtz himself.
- The image of the journey, which metaphorically represents a journey into the unconscious part of the human mind.
- The characters, who can hold symbolic meanings – for example, Marlow can be seen as a shadow of Kurtz.

- The derelict machinery at the outer station, which can represent the destructive influence of white 'civilization' on Africa.
- Light and darkness, which are referred to frequently throughout the novel. Normally we associate 'light' and 'white' with good, and 'black' and 'darkness' with evil. However, Conrad often uses these images in a different way. For example he sometimes gives 'light' the connotation of destruction, and 'white' connotations of death.
- Fog, which is used to suggest distorting or obscuring the truth. For example, Marlow's steamer is caught in the fog, meaning that he has no idea where he is going or whether danger or safety lie ahead.

Activity   Read the following passage, which describes Marlow's journey up the river to Kurtz's station. Examine the ways in which Conrad uses language here to achieve his effects. Pay particular attention to his use of imagery, and symbolism. Make a note of any images you can identify, and analyse the effects that Conrad creates through their use.

'Towards the evening of the second day we judged ourselves about eight miles from Kurtz's station. I wanted to push on; but the manager looked grave, and told me the navigation up there was so dangerous that it would be advisable, the sun being very low already, to wait where we were till next morning. Moreover, he pointed out that if the warning to approach cautiously were to be followed, we must approach in daylight – not at dusk, or in the dark. This was sensible enough. Eight miles meant nearly three hours' steaming for us, and I could also see suspicious ripples at the upper end of the reach. Nevertheless, I was annoyed beyond expression at the delay, and most unreasonably too, since one night more could not matter much after so many months. As we had plenty of wood, and caution was the word, I brought up in the middle of the stream. The reach was narrow, straight, with high sides like a railway cutting. The dusk came gliding into it long before the sun had set. The current ran smooth and swift, but a dumb immobility sat on the banks. The living trees, lashed together by the creepers and every living bush of the undergrowth, might have been changed into stone, even to the slenderest twig, to the lightest leaf. It was not sleep – it seemed unnatural, like a state of trance. Not the faintest sound of any kind could be heard. You looked on amazed, and began to suspect yourself of being deaf – then the night came suddenly, and struck you blind as well. About three in the morning some large fish leaped, and the loud splash made me jump as though a gun had been fired. When the sun rose there was a white fog, very warm and clammy, and more blinding than the night. It did not shift or drive; it was just there, standing all around you like something solid. At eight or nine, perhaps, it lifted as a shutter lifts. We had a glimpse of the towering multitude of trees, of the immense matted jungle, with the blazing little ball of the sun hanging over it – all perfectly still – and then the white shutter came down again, smoothly, as if sliding in greased grooves. I ordered the chain, which we had begun to heave in, to be paid out again. Before it stopped running with a muffled rattle, a cry, a very loud cry, as of infinite desolation, soared slowly in the opaque air. It ceased. A complaining clamour, modulated in savage discords, filled our ears. The sheer unexpectedness of it made my hair stir under my cap. I don't know how it struck the others; to me it seemed as though the mist itself had screamed, so suddenly, and apparently from all sides at once, did this tumultuous and mournful uproar arise. It culminated in a hurried outbreak of almost intolerably excessive shrieking, which stopped short, leaving us stiffened in a variety of silly attitudes, and obstinately listening to the nearly as appalling and excessive silence. "Good God! What is the meaning – ?" stammered at my elbow one of the pilgrims – a little fat man, with sandy hair and red whiskers, who wore side-spring boots, and pink pyjamas tucked into his socks. Two others remained open-mouthed a whole minute, then dashed into the little cabin, to rush out incontinently and stand darting scared glances, with Winchesters at "ready" in their hands. What we could see was just the steamer we were on, her outlines blurred as though she had been on the point of dissolving, and a misty strip of water, perhaps two feet broad, around her – and that was all. The rest of the world was nowhere, as far as our eyes and ears were concerned. Just nowhere. Gone, disappeared; swept off without leaving a whisper or a shadow behind.

Here are some points you might have noted:

- The dusk makes it dangerous to go on – they must continue in daylight.
- When daylight comes, their vision is obscured by fog, which carries with it a psychological as well as a practical effect.
- There is a striking description of the forest on either side of the river, the 'living trees' and 'every living bush of the undergrowth, might have been changed into stone, even to the slenderest twig, to the lightest leaf. It was not sleep – it seemed unnatural, like a state of trance.' Conrad suggests here that nature, usually thought of as living and vibrant, has become dead, like stone. This can be seen as symbolic of the deadness that overcomes the white men as they approach the Inner Station.
- The next sentences – 'not the faintest sound of any kind could be heard. You looked on amazed, and began to suspect yourself of being deaf – then the night came suddenly, and struck you blind as well' – emphasize the symbolic importance of this.
- This idea of blindness connects with the image of the fog, which is 'more blinding than the night'.

Activity   Now read this section from towards the end of the novel. Kurtz is dead and Marlow thinks about his own attitude towards death compared with the moment of truth experienced by Kurtz just before he dies. Analyse this passage, commenting on its content and on the ways in which Conrad uses language here to achieve his effects.

'However, as you see, I did not go to join Kurtz there and then. I did not. I remained to dream the nightmare out to the end, and to show my loyalty to Kurtz once more. Destiny. My destiny! Droll thing life is – that mysterious arrangement of merciless logic for a futile purpose. The most you can hope for from it is some knowledge of yourself – that comes too late – a crop of unextinguishable regrets. I have wrestled with death. It is the most unexciting contest you can imagine. It takes place in an impalpable greyness, with nothing underfoot, with nothing around, without spectators, without clamour, without glory, without the great desire of victory, without the great fear of defeat, in a sickly atmosphere of tepid scepticism, without much belief in your own right, and still less in that of your adversary. If such is the form of ultimate wisdom, then life is a greater riddle than some of us think it to be. I was within a hair's breadth of the last opportunity for pronouncement, and I found with humiliation that probably I would have nothing to say. This is the reason why I affirm that Kurtz was a remarkable man. He had something to say. He said it. Since I had peeped over the edge myself, I understand better the meaning of his stare, that could not see the flame of the candle, but was wide enough to embrace the whole universe, piercing enough to penetrate all the hearts that beat in the darkness. He had summed up – he had judged. "The horror!" He was a remarkable man. After all, this was the expression of some sort of belief; it had candour, it had conviction, it had a vibrating note of revolt in its whisper, it had the appalling face of a glimpsed truth – the strange commingling of desire and hate. And it is not my own extremity I remember best – a vision of greyness without form filled with physical pain, and a careless contempt for the evanescence of all things – even of this pain itself. No! It is his extremity that I seem to have lived through. True, he had made that last stride, he had stepped over the edge, while I had been permitted to draw back my hesitating foot. And perhaps in this is the whole difference; perhaps all the wisdom, and all truth, and all sincerity, are just compressed into that inappreciable moment of time in which we step over the threshold of the invisible. Perhaps! I like to think my summing-up would not have been a word of careless contempt. Better his cry – much better. It was an affirmation, a moral victory paid for by innumerable defeats, by abominable terrors, by abominable satisfactions. But it was a victory! That is why I have remained loyal to Kurtz to the last, and even beyond, when a long time after I heard once more, not his own voice, but the echo of his magnificent eloquence thrown to me from a soul as translucently pure as a cliff of crystal.'

Cultural and thematic issues

Colonialism

The colonization of the Congo and the brutality which accompanied this is a key element in the book. In recent years there has been increasing interest in the nature and effects of early imperialism. Conrad's presentation of colonization in *Heart of Darkness* not only examines its effects but raises fundamental questions about the nature of 'white' civilization and its imposition on what were then considered 'primitive' cultures. We have already seen how the novel opens with a consideration of the impact of colonialism from early times, through reference to the Roman conquest of Britain. Conrad's exploration extends beyond that of the political to look at the impact of colonization in terms of its cultural, social, and economic aspects as well as the consequences of an individual's lust for power.

In examining the novel in terms of its presentation of colonialism, you should look at various critical views. Not all regard Conrad's presentation favourably, and it is worth reading one of the best-known negative responses, which was written by Chinua Achebe in 1977. In his article 'An Image of Africa', he makes reference to the derogatory images of Africans presented in the novel. He reaches the conclusion that Conrad was a racist and that *Heart of Darkness* is full of the prejudices that for many years and in many ways called into question the very humanity of black people. Other critics, however, express different views. You should try to read as many views as you can in order to inform your own judgement.

Self-discovery

As well as the socio-political theme, the novel also explores a more personal theme as it traces Marlow's journey through the Congo and his journey to discover himself. Marlow is confronted by the reality of colonialism but also experiences another kind of journey, through his own mind. He embarks on his travels feeling distanced from Africa and with vague ideas of 'adventure'. He witnesses the destruction that the Europeans have brought to Africa. He is repelled by the greed he sees in the white men, and the brutality that they display towards their fellow human beings, but at the same time he wants to find evidence that the Europeans can act as agents of good in Africa. His journey of self-discovery leads him not to the discovery of a compassionate and benign influence, however, but to the realization that there is nothing morally substantial behind the colonization of Africa. At its heart, all he finds is 'darkness'.

Any study you undertake of the novel should recognize that Conrad presents the physical and metaphorical journey Marlow undertakes not as separate issues but as integral to one another. In a sense, the novel is not simply about what people do, but addresses the idea that their collective actions express what each person is individually and inwardly.

5 Studying Poetry

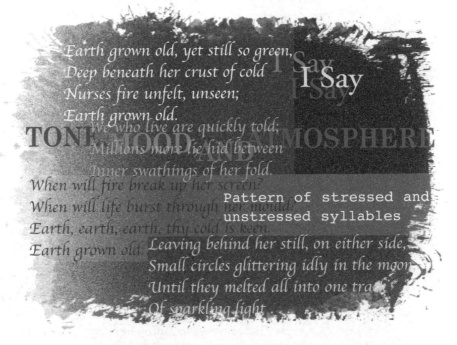

Earth grown old, yet still so green,
Deep beneath her crust of cold
Nurses fire unfelt, unseen;
Earth grown old.

We who live are quickly told;
Millions more lie hid between
Inner swathings of her fold.

When will fire break up her screen?
When will life burst through her mould?
Earth, earth, earth, thy cold is keen.
Earth grown old.

TONE MOOD AND ATMOSPHERE

I Say

Pattern of stressed and unstressed syllables

Leaving behind her still, on either side,
Small circles glittering idly in the moon,
Until they melted all into one track
Of sparkling light.

Objectives

- To identify ways in which you can approach the reading of poetry
- To explore ways of writing about poetry
- To consider some of the features to look for in analysing poems
- To prepare for studying set poetry texts
- To prepare for encountering 'unseen' poetry texts

The nature of poetry

Like prose, poetry cannot be neatly categorized, and the question of what exactly poetry is – what it is that marks it out as being different from prose – is a question that has tested writers, critics, philosophers, and all concerned with literature for centuries. Certainly poets can choose from a whole range of different forms, structures, techniques, and styles when writing their poetry. They can play with language and manipulate it, even invent a 'new' language to express their feelings, ideas, and themselves. Because, generally, the ideas in poems are expressed in fewer words than are used in prose, the messages or ideas in a poem are sometimes more difficult to understand than if they were written in prose. Also, the poet may be expressing himself or herself in a unique way – it is more acceptable for the language of poetry to deviate from generally observed rules. This 'poetic licence' allows poets to experiment with language, perhaps playing around with word order, or using dialectal forms, or using lexical or syntactical patterning to create or reinforce meaning.

Of course, prose writers can use these techniques too, but they will be much more frequently found in the language of poetry.

Throughout your life you will probably have encountered various kinds of poetry – at school, college, in reading for pleasure, on the radio, television, etc.

Activity   Based on your experience of poetry, write down all the features you can think of that make poetry different from other kinds of writing. If you are working with a group, discuss your findings with others.

Reading poetry

The study of poetry is an important part of your Diploma programme. Whether you are studying a poetry set text for the detailed study paper or preparing for the commentary examination involving 'unseen' texts, you will need to engage in detailed study of various poems. Even though the outcome of your work might be presented in different forms, the skills, techniques, and approaches that you need to use are essentially the same.

It is true that poetry can present particular challenges. For a number of reasons, some poetry is only fully accessible to us today if we carry out a certain amount of research such as looking up difficult words, phrases, and references. However, 'responding to poetry' cannot be 'taught' (or learned, for that matter) in the same way that some subjects can. It is no good looking for some kind of 'secret formula' that you can apply to any poem. Although most poetry is written to be read by others, and in that sense carries a 'public' voice, it can also be an intensely individual medium of communication and the responses it can evoke can be equally intense and individual. Much poetry works in a very personal way and your response to a particular poem might not be the same as another person's. Words and images carry with them connotations (suggestions or associations) that might trigger different responses in the minds of different people. So while it is often possible to say what a poem 'is about' in general terms, the only really genuine response is that 'personal response' that an individual reader feels.

This does not mean that 'anything goes', of course. For example, comments like 'I haven't a clue about this' or 'This means nothing to me' may be personal responses but they are not much good in terms of a 'literary' response. You need to give your personal analysis, and show your personal engagement with a text. In your Diploma studies you will be required to show what the programme objectives describe as 'an ability to engage in independent literary criticism in a manner which reveals a personal response to literature' (Higher Level) or 'an ability to approach works in an independent manner which reveals a personal response to literature' (Standard Level).

In this unit we will look at some of the things that you can do to find your way into and through a poem. Here are some general strategies for improving your understanding of poetry.

- Read voraciously – become as familiar as possible with as wide a range of poetry as possible.
- Think about how language is used and make a note of any interesting features, lines, images, etc. that you come across in your reading of poetry.
- Think about the ideas contained in the poems you read.
- Read other people's responses to poetry – not as a substitute for forming your own views but as a 'broadening' influence. (These responses could be found in various study guides, articles in literary journals, or reviews in newspapers or critical works.) They might suggest things that had not occurred to you or they might stimulate your own thoughts if you disagree with their view.
- Read poems aloud – either in company or alone. Very often reading a poem aloud helps deepen understanding and it certainly gives you a greater insight into features such as tone and rhythm.
- Adopt a questioning attitude. Whenever you read a poem ask yourself questions about it. The three key questions to ask are: 'What is this poem about?'; 'How is it written?'; 'Why has the poet chosen to write the poem in this particular way?'
- If you are studying the work of an individual poet, reading beyond the set poems will help you to understand the particular poems you are working on.

Although there is no set formula that can be applied to poetry to produce the required response, there are certain features of poetry that you will need to be aware of in order to begin to appreciate how a poem 'works', i.e. what the poet does to achieve the desired effect on the reader. Different critical books may refer to them in slightly different terms but basically these are the key elements that combine to create the overall effect of a poem. You will, no doubt, be familiar with some or all of these already.

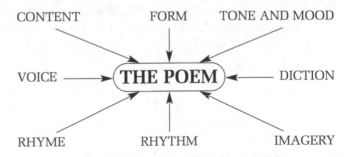

Activity   Consider each of these aspects of poetry. Think about them for yourself or discuss your ideas in a small group and write brief notes explaining what each means.

Features of poetry

Poetry is an extremely varied genre in every respect – in content, structure, style, intention, and every other way. Some poems present narratives that tell stories; some are written to be performed; some explore philosophical, emotional, or spiritual concepts and ideas; some are amusing, some are sad. In fact, it is probably safe to say that in one way or another poetry covers the whole range of human experience, and the features that it possesses can be many and varied. Poems can rhyme or not, they can use figurative language or not, they can be organized in stanzas or not, they can be written in conventional English or they can break all the rules of grammar. In other words every poem is an individual piece of work with a range of features peculiar to itself. When you are reading a poem for the first time, therefore, it is important to establish what the poet is saying to the reader – in other words, what the **purpose** of the poem is. Having identified that, you can then go on to examine *how* the poet says whatever it is that he or she wishes to say.

The purpose of poetry

In poetry, language is used in both poetic and expressive ways to convey meaning to the reader, and the purpose of the poem could be to serve any one of a wide range of functions. For example, a poem could:

- entertain
- describe
- arouse emotions
- tell a story
- provoke thought
- inform
- console
- celebrate
- express grief

or any combination of these things.

Of course the choices of vocabulary, style, form, and other features that a poet makes are closely linked to the purpose of the poem, and all provide useful clues as to what the poet's intentions are.

In order to comprehend fully any message that a poem might carry for us, it is important to look at all the features of the poem. Poets can draw upon many varied features and it is not possible to consider them all in detail here, but we will now look at some of these features.

Tone, mood, and atmosphere

The overall effect that a poem creates in the mind of the reader is very closely linked to the mood and tone that it evokes. Think of the tones and moods created in a piece of music. The 'voice' of the poem can create a **tone** that conveys to the reader certain messages about the poem itself. Obviously there are many different kinds of tone.

Activity   Think of as many words as you can to describe tone.

Tone can be difficult to delineate exactly, but there are many words that can be used to describe it. This is not an exhaustive list – add any more you have on your own list. Looking at these lists may help you when you are uncertain as to how to describe a particular tone. (Make sure you know what all the words mean.)

Playful	Ironic	Assertive	Frivolous	Gloomy
Humorous	Sarcastic	Cynical	Calm	Heavy
Melancholy	Sardonic	Dogmatic	Serious	Personal
Mocking	Light-hearted	Dramatic	Impersonal	Angry
Sad	Philosophical	Flat	Intimate	Wistful
Evaluative	Clinical	Sharp	Solemn	Religious

Just as you might pick up clues as to how a friend feels through the tone of voice that he or she uses, so you can pick up clues from the 'voice' of the poem.

The **mood** of the poem, although closely linked to the tone, is a slightly different thing – it refers to the atmosphere that the poem creates. Very often tone and mood are closely linked and a certain tone produces a certain mood. For example, if a poet uses a lively, humorous tone it is far more likely to produce a light atmosphere than a melancholy one. In your studies for the Diploma you will not only need to recognize the tone, mood, and atmosphere of poems but you will also need to examine the ways in which poets use language to create their tones, moods, and atmosphere.

Activity

Read the following poems carefully and think about the manner in which they are written. What kind of relationship do you think each poet wishes to establish with the reader? Comment on the tone, mood, and atmosphere created in each poem and the ways in which the poets use language to create it.

Hey There Now!

(For Lesley)

Hey there now
my brownwater flower
    my sunchild branching
from my mountain river
    hey there now!
my young stream
    headlong
        rushing
I love to watch you
    when you're
        sleeping
            blushing

Grace Nichols

Advent

Earth grown old, yet still so green,
    Deep beneath her crust of cold
Nurses fire unfelt, unseen;
    Earth grown old.

    We who live are quickly told;
Millions more lie hid between
    Inner swathings of her fold.

When will fire break up her screen?
    When will life burst through her mould?
Earth, earth, earth, thy cold is keen.
    Earth grown old.

Christina Rossetti

I Say I Say I Say

Anyone here had a go at themselves
for a laugh? Anyone opened their wrists
with a blade in the bath? Those in the dark
at the back, listen hard. Those at the front
in the know, those of us who have, hands up,
let's show that inch of lacerated skin
between the forearm and the fist. Let's tell it
like it is: strong drink, a crimson tidemark
round the tub, a yard of lint, white towels
washed a dozen times, still pink. Tough luck.
A passion then for watches, bangles, cuffs.
A likely story: you were lashed by brambles
picking berries from the woods. Come clean, come good,
repeat with me the punch line 'Just like blood'
when those at the back rush forward to say
how a little love goes a long long long way.

Simon Armitage

Activity   One student had clear ideas about what these poems meant to her. Read her responses through carefully. How close are her responses to your own thoughts on these poems? Remember, responses to poetry can be very individual.

Grace Nichols appears to have written the poem 'Hey There Now!', in celebration of someone she loves very dearly. Writing in an informal manner, she appears to invite the reader into sharing in this celebration. The poem has a loving tone which Nichols has created through the sentiments she expresses and which is enhanced by her use of language. For example, Nichols repeats the personal pronoun 'my' when referring to the subject of the poem, emphasizing ownership of the subject. In addition, the subject is described in affectionate terms, 'my sunchild', 'my brownwater flower'. The vitality of her love for the subject is complemented by Nichols's use of natural imagery which also adds to the celebratory mood. 'Flower', 'stream', 'river', and 'mountain' are all natural images included in the poem and they present the idea of a 'forever' love which is natural and pure. The sense of 'forever', as in an unending love, is further enhanced by the use of present continuous verb forms: 'branching', 'rushing', 'sleeping', 'blushing'. These verb endings give the poem movement and add to the lively tone. The repetition of the exclamatory phrase, 'Hey there now!' also adds to the lively tone, enhancing the celebratory mood of the poem as a whole.

Although natural imagery is contained in Christina Rossetti's poem, 'Advent', the mood of the poem is somewhat sorrowful. Writing in a formal manner, the poet adopts a melancholy tone in her presentation of 'Earth grown old'. The language that Rossetti uses helps to create a mood of sadness. For instance, the earth is described as 'cold', 'earth, earth, thy cold is keen', which suggests that it is an unwelcoming, uncomfortable place to be. The formal manner in which the poem is written further enhances the detachment from her surroundings that the poet feels. Rather than seeing Advent as a time which precedes the warmth of Spring, Rossetti presents the near-end of the year as a time of unfulfilment and decay and this is evident in the poem's vocabulary: 'unseen', 'unfelt', 'mould'. The hope of Spring, a 'better' time, is questionable and uncertain in this poem: 'when will fire break up her screen?' adding to the melancholy tone by creating a sense of despair. The unyielding nature of the earth, as seen by the poet, is expressed and enhanced by the apparent rigidity and restrictiveness of the rhyme sequence.

The disturbing content of the poem 'I Say I Say I Say' is made more so as it places us in a context in which we would expect to be in a 'happy' environment. As readers, we are placed in the audience of the poet as a stand-up comedian. The poem uses informal words and phrases such as we would expect to hear in light-hearted humour from the comedian on stage: 'Anyone here had a go at themselves for a laugh?', 'Those in the dark at the back', 'Those at the front'. However, the poet shocks the audience with his subject of attempted suicide. An uncomfortable atmosphere is therefore created as a sad, solitary act, an attempted suicide, is given centre stage, the poem acting as an exposé: 'Let's tell it like it is'. However, the poet expresses the difficulty of 'telling it like it is' through various means and use of language in the poem. For instance, he describes how one would cover up the marks on the wrists left after a suicide attempt by developing a 'passion then for watches, bangles, cuffs'. In addition, he includes a 'cover story', a 'likely story' in which 'you were lashed by brambles picking berries from the woods'. Indeed, the whole poem avoids 'telling it like it is' as it fronts the disturbing act of attempted suicide with a light-hearted, comical approach: 'I Say I Say I Say'. Individual phrases in the poem are also seen to avoid directness. For instance, by writing, 'between the forearm and the fist', which almost sounds like a comical attempt at Cockney rhyming slang, the poet avoids using the word 'wrist'. When people are faced with uncomfortable situations, it is often difficult to know what to say and they often resort to using clichés. Consequently,

Armitage concludes the poem with a clichéd response from 'those at the back', those who are not 'in the know'. This clichéd response confirms and enhances the uncomfortable, disturbing mood of the poem, 'A little loving goes a long long long way'. The unsuitability of this expected response is further stressed as an extra 'long' has been inserted into this well-known cliché.

Vocabulary and word order

The choice of vocabulary (sometimes called diction) refers to the decisions about language that a poet has made when writing his or her poem. The choices that are made will depend on the poet's intentions and the effect that the piece is intended to have on the reader.

Of the various aspects to consider in looking at vocabulary, probably the most important is thinking about the connotations of words (the particular ideas, feelings or associations suggested by a word). This can be something quite separate from its denotation, or dictionary definition. Words can carry with them many connotations that might bring suggested meanings quite different from the dictionary definition of the word. Connotations can be acquired by words depending on the tone they create, the ideas or images they bring to the reader's mind, and how they have been used in the past.

Activity

> Look at the following list of words. Although they share a common basic meaning, they have very different connotations. Use each of the words in a sentence, to show the difference in connotation between them.
>
> cunning; sly; devious; crafty; wily; artful; shifty; subtle; guileful.

There are occasions when writers choose words which have the clearest meaning or denotation, without complicating connotations. It all depends on the effects that the writer wishes to achieve – words are chosen to suit the audience and purpose. Sometimes a writer or poet might choose words that are particularly colloquial or particularly formal, according to context. Sometimes archaisms are used to give a sense of the past or add a sense of dignity and solemnity to the language. Some poetry from different cultures, rather than using Standard English, uses the non-standard English and/or dialect forms of the particular cultural background it comes from. Read the opening of *The Song of the Banana Man* by Evan Jones, a poem set in Jamaica:

The Song of the Banana Man

Touris, white man, wipin his face,
Met me in Golden Grove market place.
He looked at m'ol' clothes brown wid stain,
And soaked right through wid de Portlan rain,
He cas his eye, turn up his nose,
He says, 'You're a beggar man, I suppose?'
He says, 'Boy, get some occupation,

Be of some value to your nation.'
> I said, 'By God and dis big right han
> You mus recognize a banana man.

'Up in de hills, where de streams are cool,
An mullet an janga swim in de pool,
I have ten acres of mountain side,
An a dainty-foot donkey dat I ride,
Four Gros Mitchel, and four Lacatan,
Some coconut trees, and some hills of yam,
An I pasture on dat very same lan
Five she-goats an a big black ram,
> Dat, by God an dis big right han
> Is de property of a banana man.'

Evan Jones

Activity

Read Jones's poem carefully.
1 Try writing a Standard English version of it.
2 What are the differences between the two versions?
3 Why do you think Jones chose to write this in dialect form?

Poets can make their vocabulary very modern by using **neologisms** (invented words), which can add a sense of individuality to the poem. Sometimes a word may be chosen because it is incongruous and doesn't fit in with the rest of the vocabulary. It may jar or shock the reader, or defy the reader's expectations.

Activity

Look at the following extracts from various poems.

Fill each blank with one word from the selection given beneath, and explain why you have made your choice.

1 ___**a**___ the spring onions,
  She made this mental note:
  You can tell it's love, the real thing,
  When you ___**b**___ of slitting his throat.

Wendy Cope

a slicing, decapitating, washing
b think, talk, dream

2 On shallow straw, in ___a___ glass,
  Huddled by empty bowls, they sleep:
  No dark, no dam, no ___b___ , no grass –
  Mam, get us one of them to keep.

Philip Larkin

a transparent, glaring, shadeless
b water, earth, food

3 Wild, wild the storm, and the sea ___a___ running,
  Steady the ___b___ of the gale, with incessant undertone ___c___ ,
  Shouts of demoniac ___d___ fitfully piercing and pealing,
  Waves, air, midnight, their savagest trinity lashing

Walt Whitman

a fast, high, violently
b wail, crash, roar
c muttering, flowing, moaning
d screams, laughter, cackling

Now we will have a look at the vocabulary in a complete poem. Read the following poem by Sylvia Plath through carefully.

Crossing the Water

Black lake, black boat, two black, cut-paper people.
Where do the black trees go that drink here?
Their shadows must cover Canada.

A little light is filtering from the water flowers.
Their leaves do not wish us to hurry:
They are round and flat and full of dark advice.

Cold worlds shake from the oar.
The spirit of blackness is in us, it is in the fishes.
A snag is lifting a valedictory, pale hand;
Stars open among the lilies.
Are you not blinded by such expressionless sirens?
This is the silence of astounded souls.

Sylvia Plath

Activity

1 Why do you think Plath has decided to begin her poem with the word 'black' and repeat it twice in the first line? What effect does this have on the poem?
2 What unusual words have you noted in the poem? What effect do these have on the poem?
3 What overall effect is produced by Plath's choices of words in this poem?

Sometimes poets use vocabulary in non-standard or ungrammatical ways in order to achieve the effects they want.

Some poets might deliberately disrupt our expectations to create their effects, and sometimes they go further still in breaking the conventions of grammar. For example, E. E. Cummings is well known for the unconventional ways in which he uses language in his poems. Here is the first stanza from one of his poems. Some of the words have been removed.

> _____**a**_____ lived in a pretty _____**b**_____ town
> (with _____**c**_____ so floating many bells _____**d**_____)
> spring summer autumn winter
> he sang his _____**e**_____ he danced his _____**f**_____ .

Activity

Fill in the blanks in this stanza choosing words from the appropriate lists below.

a	b	c	d	e	f
someone	small	light	din	song	jig
Bill	quiet	gleaming	down	didn't	round
she	how	up	bright	turn	dance
they	hot	down	clamour	notes	did
anyone	slow	chimes	clash	solo	favourite

Now check your version against the original. Here are Cummings's words:

a anyone   **b** how   **c** up   **d** down   **e** didn't   **f** did

You probably found some or all of these choices rather surprising – not least because they apparently produce lines that seem nonsensical. This is because Cummings breaks the grammatical rules for combining the parts of speech or units of structure together.

Now have a look at the whole poem:

anyone lived in a pretty how town

anyone lived in a pretty how town
(with up so floating many bells down)
spring summer autumn winter
he sang his didn't he danced his did.

Women and men(both little and small)
cared for anyone not at all
they sowed their isn't they reaped their same
sun moon stars rain

children guessed(but only a few
and down they forgot as up they grew
autumn winter spring summer)
that noone loved him more by more

when by now and tree and leaf
she laughed his joy she cried his grief
bird by snow and stir by still
anyone's any was all to her

someones married their everyones
laughed their cryings and did their dance
(sleep wake hope and then)they
said their nevers they slept their dream

stars rain sun moon
(and only the snow can begin to explain
how children are apt to forget to remember
with up so floating many bells down)

one day anyone died i guess
(and noone stooped to kiss his face)
busy folk buried them side by side
little by little and was by was

all by all and deep by deep
and more by more they dream their sleep
noone and anyone earth by april
wish by spirit and if by yes.

Women and men(both dong and ding)
summer autumn winter spring
reaped their sowing and went their came
sun moon stars rain

E. E. Cummings

Activity

> Now you have read the whole poem, answer the following questions:
> 1 Does the poet's use of the word 'anyone' mean more to you now in the context of the whole poem? How do you think we are meant to interpret 'anyone' and 'someone'?
> 2 How does Cummings use pairings of words such as, 'up/down', 'did/didn't'? Have you found any more such pairings of opposites?
> 3 How does Cummings make use of repetition in the poem?
> 4 Now write a brief summary of what the poem is about.
> 5 The key question is why Cummings chooses to break the conventions of grammar and write his poem in this way. What effects do you think he achieves by this?

When dealing with poems such as this one where the meaning is not necessarily immediately apparent, your initial responses may well be quite tentative. Don't worry about this, and don't worry about putting things down on paper that you feel unsure about. It is all part of the process of unravelling meaning from the text.

Here are the initial, tentative responses of two students as they work towards finding their meaning of *Anyone lived in a pretty how town*.

Student A

1 The word 'Anyone' is used to describe the people in the town. It also indicates that it is informal and impersonal, making the poem a story open to interpretation. A trivial tale about two or three people, yet the words indicate he's talking about mankind. 'Anyone' and 'Someone' are opposite words and the poet contrasts these types of words throughout the poem. They are meant to be interpreted as words which create a larger scale to the environment it is set in. The word 'Anyone' throws the poem open to a wider scale of people and 'Someone' is specific to one person. Anyone – male, Someone – female – gives it a universal theme.

2 He uses pairs of words such as 'did' and 'didn't', and 'up' and 'down', to describe how objects did things (in place of a adjective). Examples of pairing of words are:
did/didn't, down/up, joy/grief, sun/moon, rain/snow – gives a pattern to the words.

3 He uses repetition to emphasize his points, for example about sleep he says 'all by all' and 'more by more'. The repetition of the seasons indicates people moving on, living and then dying.

4 The poem describes what happens to anyone in a certain town. Through the seasons and through the weather how the men and women dance, sleep, and live.

Student B

1 The poet uses the words 'Anyone' and 'Someone' throughout the poem. This could be to give the poem a more universal and wider meaning than would have been achieved if the characters had been named. 'Anyone' and 'Someone' could mean that the poem would be meant to apply to the reader. It stops stereotyping. Anyone is male + Someone is female.

2 Cummings uses pairings of words and opposites throughout the poem such as 'up/down', 'did/didn't', 'joy/grief' 'little/small', 'dong/ding'. This gives some degree of logic to often illogical sentences. It also means there is some rhyme in the verses. It leaves quite a lot open to interpretation.

3 Some words and lines are repeated throughout the poem. Although in a different order, 'spring, summer, autumn, winter' and 'reaped' and 'sowed' are repeated to show a sense of passing of time. There is also the sense of people moving on and a cyclical element – closely tied in with environment.

4 This poem seems to tell a life story of a person. The fact that there are no names or characters generalizes the story, so it could apply to anyone. The repetition of 'spring, summer, autumn, winter' suggests that life is the same every year. The inclusion of 'sun, moon, stars' and 'rain', especially at the end, shows that things go on and everybody is the same, as the sun, moon, stars, and rain are a constant for everyone. It seems to trivialize life as everyone is there, they do their thing ('reaped their sowing and went their came') and then die, and it is no big deal.

Although these comments are initial and tentative, they are also exploratory. Both students have begun the process of coming to terms with a tricky brief. There are quite a number of points here that could be picked up and examined in more detail – some ideas are very perceptive, and already the students are beginning to identify the effects of such features as word pairings and repetition.

Imagery

Very often the language of poetry is made more intense through the use of images, which can add layers of meaning to a poem beyond the literal sense of the words on the page. Images can be created in various ways and language used in this way is sometime called 'figurative language'.

Old English poets used a device of figurative language called the 'kenning' which consisted of a word or phrase made up to identify a particular object or thing without naming it directly. They had a large selection of kennings for their most frequently used nouns. For example, instead of 'ocean' they could say 'swan's road' or 'foaming field' or 'realm of monsters'; for 'ship' they might say 'sea goer' or 'sea wood'; for a 'lord' a 'dispenser of rings' or 'treasure giver'; for 'the sun', 'candle of the world'.

Look at this poem by John Updike.

Winter Ocean

Many-maned scud-thumper, tub
of male whales, maker of worn wood, shrub-
ruster, sky-mocker, rave!
portly pusher of waves, wind slave.

John Updike

Activity

> **1** How many kennings can you identify here?
> **2** What is the effect of the use of kennings in this poem?
> **3** Make up three or four kennings of your own.

In this use of kennings, the Old English poets were using a kind of imagery to describe their particular subject. Images can work in several ways in the mind of the reader. For example, an image can be used literally to describe something, as in Wordsworth's description of taking a boat out on to the lake at night. The boat moves forward:

Leaving behind her still, on either side,
Small circles glittering idly in the moon,
Until they melted all into one track
Of sparkling light . . .

William Wordsworth

This creates a **literal image** as we can picture the scene in our minds from the way in which Wordsworth describes it. Non-literal, figurative or representational images can be created when the thing being described is compared to something else. You will probably already be familiar with the **simile**, in which the comparison is made very clear by the poet using the words 'like' or 'as'. Often the elements being compared are essentially different in nature, but they come together in the poet's perception and ultimately in the reader's perception. For example, here Nichols uses a simile to describe a lizard she saw as a child:

Saw an iguana once
when I was very small
in our backdam backyard
came rustling across my path

green like moving newleaf sunlight

big like big big lizard
with more legs than centipede
so it seemed to me.

Grace Nichols

Activity

Now look at the following poem by Sylvia Plath.
1 Identify the similes that Plath uses here.
2 Describe the effect created by each simile.

Blackberrying

Nobody in the lane, and nothing, nothing but blackberries,
Blackberries on either side, though on the right mainly,
A blackberry alley, going down in hooks, and a sea
Somewhere at the end of it, heaving. Blackberries
Big as the ball of my thumb, and dumb as eyes
Ebon in the hedges, fat
With blue-red juices. These they squander on my fingers.
I had not asked for such a blood sisterhood; they must love me.
They accommodate themselves to my milkbottle, flattening their sides.

Overhead go the choughs in black, cacophonous flocks –
Bits of burnt paper wheeling in a blown sky.
Theirs is the only voice, protesting, protesting.
I do not think the sea will appear at all.
The high, green meadows are glowing, as if lit from within.
I come to one bush of berries so ripe it is a bush of flies,
Hanging their bluegreen bellies and their wing panes in a Chinese screen.
The honey-feast of the berries has stunned them; they believe in heaven.
One more hook and the berries and bushes end.

The only thing to come now is the sea.
From between two hills a sudden wind funnels at me,
Slapping its phantom laundry in my face.
These hills are too green and sweet to have tasted salt.
I follow the sheep path between them. A last hook brings me
To the hills' northern face, and the face is orange rock
That looks out on nothing, nothing but a great space
Of white and pewter lights, and a din like silversmiths
Beating and beating at an intractable metal.

Sylvia Plath

The **metaphor** is another feature that poets often use, and with which you will probably be familiar. In some ways a metaphor is like a simile in that it too creates a comparison. However, the comparison is less direct than the simile in that it does not include the terms 'like' or 'as', but often describes the subject as *being* the thing to which it is compared. For example, in the poem you have just examined, Plath describes the choughs (large black birds rather like crows) in this way:

Overhead go the choughs in black, cacophonous flocks –
Bits of burnt paper wheeling in a blown sky.

Of course, Plath does not literally mean that the choughs are bits of burnt paper – it is meant metaphorically. The look of the black birds wheeling in the sky reminds her of the way bits of burnt paper can float around in the air.

Another kind of feature frequently used by poets is **personification**. This is really a kind of metaphor in which the attributes of a person are given to either abstract or non-human things. Plath makes use of personification in *Blackberrying*. For example, she describes the juices which the blackberries

. . . squander on my fingers.
I had not asked for such a blood sisterhood; they must love me.
They accommodate themselves to my milkbottle, flattening their sides.

Here the blackberries are described as having human feelings and doing what they can to help her collect them.

Poets often use **symbolism**, too, to help to create the effects they want, sometimes drawing on commonly recognized symbols and sometimes inventing their own. In basic terms a symbol is simply a feature whereby a word or phrase represents something else – for example, the colour white could be used to represent peace. Symbolism in poetry can be very complex, with some poems operating on two levels, the literal and the symbolic. Sometimes in order to fully understand the significance of a poem it is necessary to understand the symbolic importance of some of the ideas or images used.

Activity   Read carefully *The Road Not Taken* by Robert Frost, below. The poem can be taken on a literal level as describing the poet encountering two roads and having to choose which one to take. However, the real meaning of the poem lies in something much deeper. In order to understand the poem fully it is necessary to recognize that Frost is here using the idea of roads diverging, and the traveller having to choose, in a symbolic way.

Think about this idea and write down your thoughts on what the road might symbolize.

The Road Not Taken

Two roads diverged in a yellow wood,
And sorry I could not travel both
And be one traveller, long I stood
And looked down one as far as I could
To where it bent in the undergrowth;

Then took the other, as just as fair,
And having perhaps the better claim,
Because it was grassy and wanted wear;
Though as for that the passing there
Had worn them really about the same,

And both that morning equally lay
In leaves no step had trodden black.
Oh, I kept the first for another day!
Yet knowing how way leads on to way,
I doubted if I should ever come back.

I shall be telling this with a sigh
Somewhere ages and ages hence:
Two roads diverged in a wood, and I –
I took the one less travelled by,
And that has made all the difference.

Robert Frost

Aural imagery

Some kinds of images rely not on the 'pictures' they create in the mind of the reader, but on the effects they have on the ear, or a combination of both.

Alliteration

This involves the repetition of the same consonant sound, usually at the beginning of each word, over two or more words together, as in Shakespeare's lines from *The Tempest*:

Full **f**athom **f**ive thy **f**ather lies,
Of his bones are coral made.

The repeated 'f' sounds create a sense of solemnity and give an incantatory feel to the line.

Assonance

Assonance is a feature similar to alliteration, but instead of consonants it involves the repetition of vowel sounds to achieve a particular effect. An example is the long, drawn-out 'o' sounds in the first line of Sylvia Plath's *Frog Autumn*:

Summer grows old, cold-blooded mother

This creates an impression of lethargy and lack of life as summer passes and winter approaches.

Onomatopoeia

Onomatopoeia refers to words that, by their sound, reflect their meaning — 'bang' or 'ping' are simple examples that sound like the noises they describe. Here is a more sophisticated example, from Coleridge's *The Rime of the Ancient Mariner*.

The ice was here, the ice was there,
The ice was all around;
It **cracked** and **growled**, and **roared** and **howled**,
Like noises in a swound

The words 'cracked', 'growled', 'roared', and 'howled' suggest the sounds of the icebergs grinding around the ship, and therefore make the description more graphic in an aural as well as visual way. It is perhaps worth noting also that Coleridge makes use of repetition here, emphasizing the fact that ice was everywhere.

It is very important to bear in mind when writing about poetry that there is little value in simply identifying the features unless you explain the effects they create in the poem and on the reader.

Now read the following poem by Sylvia Plath.

Mirror

I am silver and exact. I have no preconceptions.
Whatever I see I swallow immediately
Just as it is, unmisted by love or dislike.
I am not cruel, only truthful –
The eye of a little god, four-cornered.
Most of the time I meditate on the opposite wall.
It is pink, with speckles. I have looked at it so long
I think it is part of my heart. But it flickers.
Faces and darkness separate us over and over.

Now I am a lake. A woman bends over me,
Searching my reaches for what she really is.
Then she turns to those liars, the candles or the moon.
I see her back, and reflect it faithfully.
She rewards me with tears and an agitation of hands.
I am important to her. She comes and goes.
Each morning it is her face that replaces the darkness.
In me she has drowned a young girl, and in me an old woman
Rises towards her day after day, like a terrible fish.

Sylvia Plath

Activity   Remind your self of *The Road Not Taken* by Robert Frost (page 115). Write a detailed analysis comparing the ways in which Plath uses imagery in *The Mirror* with the ways in which Frost uses it in *The Road Not Taken*.

Form and structure

Form and **structure** can also tell the reader something about the poet's intentions. The way that the language of the poem is laid out will have been carefully chosen by the poet to enhance or reflect the meaning of the poem. There are many different ways in which poems can be structured, and in looking at the structure of a particular poem we must ask ourselves why the poet has chosen to use a particular form.

Form can refer to the way that the poem is written on the page, or the way that the lines are organized or grouped. Basically, poetry can be divided into general categories. First there is the kind where the lines follow on from each other continuously without breaks. Long narrative poems often take this form, and poems such as Frost's *Out, Out* – or Keats's *Lamia*. The technical term for this kind of poetic form is **stichic** poetry.

The other kind of poetry is that where the lines are arranged in groups, which are sometimes incorrectly called 'verses'. The correct term for these groups of lines is **stanzas**. This kind of poetic form is called **strophic** poetry and examples of its use are in poems such as Margaret Atwood's *Late Night* or Sylvia Plath's *Crossing the Water*.

Stanzas can be organized in many different ways. Here are some examples.

The sonnet

The sonnet is a very popular form in English poetry, and one that poets have used for centuries. Basically a sonnet consists of fourteen lines with a structured rhyme scheme and a definite rhythm pattern (usually iambic pentameter, see pages 124–5). There are two main kinds of sonnet. The petrarchan or Italian sonnet is so called because it is named after the medieval Italian writer, Petrarch. The Petrarchan sonnet divides the fourteen lines into an octave (eight lines) and a sestet (six lines). The rhyme scheme can vary but generally the pattern is *abbaabba cdecde* or *abbaabba cdcdcd*. The octave sets out the theme or key idea of the poem and the sestet provides some kind of response to it.

The other main kind of sonnet is the Shakespearean or English sonnet. In this kind of sonnet the lines are divided into three quatrains (of four lines each) and end with a couplet (two lines). The rhyme scheme in this kind of sonnet generally follows the pattern of *abab cdcd efef gg*. The theme or idea is developed through the quatrains, and summed up or answered in the couplet.

Now read the following two sonnets.

To My Brothers

Small, busy flames play through the fresh laid coals,
> And their faint cracklings o'er our silence creep
> Like whispers of the household gods that keep
A gentle empire o'er fraternal souls.
And while, for rhymes, I search around the poles,
> Your eyes are fix'd, as in poetic sleep,
> Upon the lore so voluble and deep,
That aye at fall of night our care condoles.

This is your birth-day Tom, and I rejoice
> That thus it passes smoothly, quietly.
Many such eves of gently whisp'ring noise
> May we together pass, and calmly try
What are this world's true joys, – ere the great voice,
> From its fair face, shall bid our spirits fly.

John Keats

Sonnet XVIII

Shall I compare thee to a Summers day?
Thou art more lovely and more temperate:
Rough windes do shake the darling buds of Maie,
And Sommers lease hath all too short a date:
Sometime too hot the eye of heaven shines,
And often is his gold complexion dim'd,
And every faire from faire some-time declines,
By chance, or natures changing course untrim'd:
But thy eternall Sommer shall not fade,
Nor loose possession of that faire thou ow'st,
Nor shall death brag thou wandr'st in his shade,
When in eternall lines to time thou grow'st,
> So long as men can breath or eyes can see,
> So long lives this, and this gives life to thee.

William Shakespeare

Activity

> 1 Examine the form each sonnet is written in and the rhyme scheme each poet has employed.
> 2 What are the key ideas each sonnet deals with? Examine the language each poet has used to express his ideas.
> 3 How does the language combine with the structure of each sonnet to fulfil the poets' intentions?

Other forms which you may come across in your studies include the following.

Ballads

Ballads date back to the oral tradition of the late Middle Ages and originally were often set to music. They are poems that tell a story, and therefore the focus tends to be on action and dialogue rather than the contemplative exploration of some kind of theme. The structure of the ballad normally consists of rhyming quatrains, sometimes using dialect forms or repetition to create effects.

Odes

Odes are lyrical poems, often elaborate, addressed to a particular person or thing or an abstract idea. They can present straightforward praise or they can develop complex philosophical ideas, and they can focus on positive or negative feelings with, perhaps, involved arguments. They are complex poems – the language often reflects the complexity of the content and many images may be contained within the poem. Odes are generally organized into fairly long stanzas. In the odes of Keats, for example, the stanzas are usually ten lines long.

Here is Keats's *Ode on a Grecian Urn*. Read it through carefully.

Ode on a Grecian Urn

Thou still unravish'd bride of quietness,
Thou foster-child of silence and slow time,
Sylvan historian, who canst thus express
A flowery tale more sweetly than our rhyme:
What leaf-fring'd legend haunts about thy shape
Of deities or mortals, or of both,
In Tempe or the dales of Arcady?
What men or gods are these? What maidens loth?
What mad pursuit? What struggle to escape?
What pipes and timbrels? What wild ecstasy?

Heard melodies are sweet, but those unheard
Are sweeter; therefore, ye soft pipes, play on;
Not to the sensual ear, but, more endear'd,
Pipe to the spirit ditties of no tone:

Fair youth, beneath the trees, thou canst not leave
Thy song, nor ever can those trees be bare;
Bold Lover, never, never canst thou kiss,
Though winning near the goal – yet, do not grieve;
She cannot fade, though thou hast not thy bliss,
For ever wilt thou love, and she be fair!

Ah, happy, happy boughs! that cannot shed
Your leaves, nor ever bid the Spring adieu;
And, happy melodist, unwearied,
For ever piping songs for ever new;
More happy love! more happy, happy love!
For ever warm and still to be enjoy'd,
For ever panting, and for ever young;
All breathing human passion far above,
That leaves a heart high-sorrowful and cloy'd,
A burning forehead, and a parching tongue.

Who are these coming to the sacrifice?
To what green altar, O mysterious priest,
Lead'st thou that heifer lowing at the skies,
And all her silken flanks with garlands drest?
What little town by river or sea shore,
Or mountain-built with peaceful citadel,
Is emptied of this folk, this pious morn?
And, little town, thy streets for evermore
Will silent be; and not a soul to tell
Why thou art desolate, can e'er return.

O Attic shape! Fair attitude! with brede
Of marble men and maidens overwrought,
With forest branches and the trodden weed;
Thou, silent form, dost tease us out of thought
As doth eternity: Cold Pastoral!
When old age shall this generation waste,
Thou shalt remain, in midst of other woe
Than ours, a friend to man, to whom thou say'st,
'Beauty is truth, truth beauty,' – that is all
Ye know on earth, and all ye need to know.

John Keats

Activity   **1** Examine this ode and draw a diagram to show how Keats develops his
thoughts throughout the poem.
2 How does this development of ideas relate to the form of the poem?
3 What have you noted about Keats's use of language in this poem?

Free verse

Another form of verse that we should mention here is **free verse**. Although modern poets also write in forms which adhere to strict patterns and forms, some of which we have already looked at, it is true that in the twentieth century there was a move towards poetry that does not have constraints of form, structure, rhyme, or rhythm. Sometimes this type of verse does not even have regular lines, and the flexibility of free verse allows poets to use language in whatever ways seem appropriate to their purpose, and to create the effects they desire in their work.

Here is a poem written in free verse. Read it carefully.

To Women, As Far As I'm Concerned

The feelings I don't have I don't have.
The feelings I don't have I won't say I have.
The feelings you say you have, you don't have.
The feelings you would like us both to have, we neither of us have.
The feelings people ought to have, they never have.
If people say they've got feelings, you may be pretty sure
        They haven't got them.
So if you want either of us to feel anything at all
You'd better abandon all ideas of feelings altogether.

D. H. Lawrence

Activity

> **1** From the evidence of the way Lawrence uses language here, what do you think are the main features of free verse?
> **2** How do you think it differs from most other kinds of poetry?

You might have noted some of the following:
- Free verse does not follow any regular syllabic, metrical, or rhyming pattern.
- It tends to follow speech rhythms of language.
- The line is the basic unit of rhythm.
- Spaces on the page can indicate pauses in the movement of the poem.
- Free verse may rely on effects such as alliteration, or repetition, to provide unity.

Other poetic techniques

There are a range of other techniques in using language that poets can draw on in writing their poetry. For the most part these techniques, like the use of imagery for example, are common to all kinds of literary writing. However, some are generally only found in poetry. Here are some of the main ones.

Enjambment

Enjambment is the term used to describe an instance where, because of its grammatical structure, verse runs on from one line to another. This can sometimes take the reader by surprise, as the meaning is not complete at the end of the line. Often, punctuation elsewhere in the line reinforces the need to run on at the end of the line.

End stop

End stop, in contrast, describes an instance where the grammatical break coincides with the end of a line. The break is often marked by a punctuation mark, and the meaning of the line is complete in itself.

Caesura

A caesura is simply a break or a pause in a line of verse, but it can be very important in influencing the rhythm of the poem.

I never had noticed it until
Twas gone, – the narrow copse,

Edward Thomas

Now read *Postcard* by Margaret Atwood.

Postcard

I'm thinking about you. What else can I say?
The palm trees on the reverse
are a delusion; so is the pink sand.
What we have are the usual
fractured coke bottles and the smell
of backed-up drains, too sweet,
like a mango on the verge
of rot, which we have also.
The air clear sweat, mosquitoes
& their tracks; birds, blue & elusive.

Time comes in waves here, a sickness, one
day after the other rolling on;
I move up, it's called
awake, then down into the uneasy
nights but never
forward. The roosters crow
for hours before dawn, and a prodded
child howls & howls
on the pocked road to school.
In the hold with the baggage
there are two prisoners,
their heads shaved by bayonets, & ten crates

of queasy chicks. Each spring
there's a race of cripples, from the store
to the church. This is the sort of junk
I carry with me; and a clipping
About democracy from the local paper.

Outside the window
they're building the damn hotel,
nail by nail, someone's
crumbling dream. A universe that includes you
can't be all bad, but
does it? At this distance
you're a mirage, a glossy image
fixed in the posture
of the last time I saw you.
Turn you over, there's the place
for the address. Wish you were
here. Love comes
in waves like the ocean, a sickness which goes on
& on, a hollow cave
in the head, filling & pounding, a kicked ear.

Margaret Atwood

Activity

> **1** Look at the poem carefully and make a note of where lines are end-stopped and where Atwood uses enjambment. What effect does this have on the poem?
>
> **2** Notice how Atwood's punctuation often forces you to pause in the middle of a line rather than at the end. What effect do you think this has?

Rhythm

Rhythm can be an important element in poetry and some of the poems you remember from your earliest childhood, such as nursery rhymes, have very strong rhythms. It is these strong rhythms, along with the sounds of the words themselves and the rhymes, that give them such appeal to young children.

However, the influence of rhythm is not something exclusively reserved for nursery rhymes – a sense of rhythm can exert a profound influence on the overall effect of any poem. The rhythm can help to create mood and influence the tone and atmosphere of a poem. It is this rhythm that can give a poem its feeling of movement and life, and the poet can use rhythm to create a whole variety of effects within the poem.

Syllable stress

Poets can create rhythms in poetry in various ways. Language has natural rhythms built into it, which we use automatically every time we pronounce words. For example, with the word 'randomly' we naturally stress the first syllable and not the second. Poets use these natural stresses and in-built rhythm patterns to contribute to the overall rhythmic effect.

Emphatic stress

Poets often deliberately place the emphasis on a particular word or part of the word in order to achieve a particular effect. The stress could be shifted to emphasize a particular meaning or reinforce a point, or even change meaning.

Phrasing and punctuation

The rhythm of poetry, along with other kinds of writing, can be influenced by factors such as word order, length of phrases, or the choice of punctuation marks, line and stanza breaks, and use of repetition.

Metre

Poetic metre is the pattern of stressed and unstressed syllables in a line of poetry, and as such is very closely linked to the idea of rhythm. The concept originated from the principles of classical Greek and Latin verse and was adopted by English poets from early times. These principles stated that each line of verse should follow a precise and regular pattern in terms of how many syllables it contained and the stress pattern used. These regular patterns of stressed and unstressed syllables are called **metres**. By analysing the metre, the reader can see how the poet is using the stress patterns within the language as one of the ways by which the meaning of the poem is conveyed. Variations in the pattern could mark changes in mood or tone, or signify a change of direction in the movement of the poem.

In identifying the metre of a poem, the first thing to do is to establish how the rhythm pattern is created. The syllables can be divided into groups of two or three (depending on the particular pattern). Each of these groups is called a **foot**. The number of **feet** in a line can vary.

Here are the main patterns:

One foot	monometer
Two feet	dimeter
Three feet	trimeter
Four feet	tetrameter
Five feet	pentameter
Six feet	hexameter
Seven feet	heptameter
Eight feet	octameter

The process of identifying the metre is called **scansion**. Stressed syllables are marked $^/$ while unstressed syllables are marked $^\smile$ and the feet are divided up using vertical lines $|$. A double vertical line $\|$ indicates a caesura.

There are five basic patterns of stress. These are:

- Iambic: one unstressed syllable followed by a stressed one. (iamb)

When I | have fears | that I | may cease | to be
Before | my pen | hath glean'd | my teem | ing brain,

Keats

- Trochaic: one stressed syllable followed by one unstressed. (trochee)

Tyger! | Tyger! | Burning | bright
In the | forests | of the | night

Blake

- Dactylic: one stressed syllable followed by two unstressed syllables. (dactyl)

Half a league, | half a league,
Half a league | onward

Tennyson

- Anapaestic: two unstressed syllables followed by one stressed syllable. (anapaest)

Will's | at the dance | in the Club | -room below,
Where | the tall liqu | or cups foam;

Hardy

- Spondaic: two stressed syllables. (spondee)

One, two
Buckle my shoe.

Anon

For example, look at these lines from Keats's *When I have fears*.

When I have fears

When I have fears that I may cease to be
    Before my pen hath glean'd my teeming brain,
Before high-piled books, in charact'ry,
    Hold like rich garners the full-ripen'd grain:
When I behold, upon the night's starr'd face,
    Huge cloudy symbols of a high romance,

And think that I may never live to trace
    Their shadows, with the magic hand of chance;
And when I feel, fair creature of an hour!
    That I shall never look upon thee more,
Never have relish in the faery power
    Of unreflecting love! – then on the shore
Of the wide world I stand alone, and think
    Till love and fame to nothingness do sink.

John Keats

The first two lines were scanned for you on page 125. Now scan the remainder of the poem. How many metrical feet are there per line? What is the metrical pattern? Look at the poem again. What effect does the metrical pattern have on the overall effect of the poem?

Rhyme

Rhyme can make an important contribution to the musical quality of a poem and, like rhythm, it affects the sound and the overall effectiveness. The system of rhyme within a poem, or rhyme scheme, can influence this effect in a variety of ways. The rhyme scheme could help to unify the poem and draw it together; it could give it an incantatory quality or add emphasis to particular elements of the vocabulary. There are various kinds of rhymes and rhyme schemes. The most common rhymes work on the basis of a rhyme occurring at the end of a line and are called **complete rhymes**, as in 'free' rhyming with 'tree', or 'feel' with 'seal'.

Sometimes rhymes occur within the line itself. These are called **internal rhymes**. Coleridge makes use of this kind of rhyme in *The Rime of the Ancient Mariner*.

The fair breeze blew, the white foam flew,
The furrow followed free;
We were the first that ever burst
Into that silent sea.

In this case, the rhyming of 'blew' and 'flew' stresses these words and adds emphasis to the image of the ship's speed and movement.

A rhyme may appear incomplete or inaccurate in various ways. The vowels may not be pronounced in the same way, for example 'love' and 'move' or 'plough' and 'rough'. These are called **eye rhymes** or **sight rhymes**. Some poets choose deliberately to weaken the force of the rhyme by making either the consonant or vowel different. Wilfred Owen frequently uses this technique, as here for example:

Like twitching agonies of men among its brambles
Northward, incessantly, the flickering gunnery rumbles

Or:

We only know war lasts, rain soaks, and clouds sag stormy
Dawn massing in the east her melancholy army
Attacks once more in ranks on shivering ranks of gray

This kind of rhyme is called **half rhyme**, **slant rhyme** or **para-rhyme**.

In the same way that the rhythm in a poem often follows a recognized pattern, so can rhyme. The important thing in looking at the rhyme scheme of a poem, however, is not spotting the rhymes or working out the scheme but being able to identify what effect the rhyme scheme has on the poem. In other words you need to be able to explain why the poet has chosen to use language in this particular way, and what the overall effects of those language choices are.

Here are some of the effects that the use of rhyme might have on a poem.

- It can make a poem sound musical and pleasing to the ear.
- It can create a jarring, discordant effect.
- It can add emphasis to certain words and give particular words an added prominence.
- It can act as a unifying influence on the poem, drawing it together through the rhyme patterns.
- It can give the poem a rhythmic, incantatory, or ritualistic feel.
- It can influence the rhythm of the verse.
- It can provide a sense of finality – the rhyming couplet, for example, is often used to give a sense of 'ending'.
- It can exert a subconscious effect on the reader, drawing together certain words or images, affecting the sound, or adding emphasis in some way.

Now read the following two poems carefully:

Mushrooms

Overnight, very
Whitely, discreetly,
Very quietly

Our toes, our noses
Take hold on the loam,
Acquire the air.

Nobody sees us,
Stops us, betrays us;
The small grains make room.

Soft fists insist on
Heaving the needles,
The leafy bedding,

Even the paving.
Our hammers, our rams,
Earless and eyeless,

Perfectly voiceless,
Widen the crannies,
Shoulder through holes. We

Diet on water,
On crumbs of shadow,
Bland-mannered, asking

Little or nothing.
So many of us!
So many of us!

We are shelves, we are
Tables, we are meek,
We are edible,

Nudgers and shovers
In spite of ourselves.
Our kind multiplies:

We shall by morning
Inherit the earth.
Our foot's in the door.

Sylvia Plath

Season

Rust is ripeness, rust,
And the wilted corn-plume.
Pollen is mating-time when swallows
Weave a dance
Of feathered arrows
Thread corn-stalks in winged
Streaks of light. And we loved to hear
Spliced phrases of the wind, to hear
Rasps in the field, where corn-leaves
Pierce like bamboo slivers.

Now, garnerers we,
Awaiting rust on tassles, draw
Long shadows from the dusk, wreathe
The thatch in wood-smoke. Laden stalks
Ride the germ's decay – we await
The promise of the rust.

Wole Soyinka

Activity   Compare the techniques Soyinka and Plath use and the effects that they achieve in these two poems.

Carol Ann Duffy

Carol Ann Duffy was born in Glasgow in 1955. She grew up in Stafford and later moved to Liverpool. She graduated from Liverpool University with a degree in Philosophy and now lives in London where she works as a freelance writer. In 1977, she embarked on a career as a playwright and two of her plays were performed at Liverpool Playhouse. This led her into television where she worked as a freelance scriptwriter. However, it is for her poetry that Carol Ann Duffy is best known and has gained acclaim, winning the Dylan Thomas Award in 1989 and the Whitbread Poetry Award in 1993. She is regarded now as one of Britain's leading contemporary poets, her work dealing with themes that have universal significance touching on the concerns of all people. Although it is easy to see some of her poetry reflecting her own life, in reading her work it is a mistake to see it as autobiographical and to look for clues to its significance in Duffy's own life. The poems should be viewed in a much wider context than this and the voice of the poems should be seen as expressing concerns, experiences and emotions that lie deep within us all.

She has written several anthologies of poetry, perhaps the best known being her fourth, 'Mean Time'. In this Detailed Study we will focus on poems from this collection to illustrate the nature of her poetry and the ideas, themes, and issues that she explores through it. Remember, when you are thinking and writing about her poetry, examiners are not interested in students 'spotting' features of language such as the use of similes or metaphors or alliteration. Just identifying such features really tells us nothing about how a poem works or the effect that it might create in the mind of the reader. What examiners really want you to look at is *how* poets use language and why they make the language choices that they do. In other words you need to be aware of the language choices the poet has made, be sensitive to why the poet has chosen a particular form of words, and explain the effect that is created by the words that have been chosen.

Themes and issues in Duffy's poetry

Carol Ann Duffy has said that the title of her collection, 'Mean Time', can have a variety of interpretations.

Activity   Think about this title and write down the different ideas that can be associated with the phrase 'Mean Time'.

Here are some ideas that you may have thought about:

- the passage of time – 'in the mean time'
- time is 'mean' – hard and unforgiving
- time is 'mean' – we don't get enough of it
- time means something – the 'meaning' of time
- Greenwich Meantime – this sets standard time for the world.

Here is the title poem of the collection:

Mean Time

The clocks slid back an hour
and stole light from my life
as I walked through the wrong part of town,
mourning our love.

And, of course, unmendable rain
fell to the bleak streets
where I felt my heart gnaw
at all our mistakes.

If the darkening sky could lift
more than one hour from this day
there are words I would never have said
nor have heard you say.

But we will be dead, as we know,
beyond all light.
These are the shortened days
and the endless nights.

Activity

Read the poem through carefully several times. What is it about, and why do you think Duffy chose this particular poem to provide the title for the whole anthology?

Here are some ideas you might have thought of:

- The poem opens with the clocks being 'put back' one hour, referring to the adjustment we make to our clocks in the autumn, which in Britain changes them from BST (British Summer Time) to GMT (Greenwich Mean Time.) One obvious result when we do this is that it gets dark an hour earlier in the evenings. Note how she uses this image of 'stealing light' to reveal the poet's emotional state at the breakdown of a relationship. This darkness/loss idea is further reinforced by connotations of death introduced through her use of 'mourning'. The sense of disorientation the poet feels at this loss is emphasized in 'I walked through the wrong part of town'.
- The second stanza continues this sense of despair and darkness with images such as 'unmendable rain', and 'bleak streets/where I felt my

heart gnaw/at all our mistakes'. The word 'gnaw' here is particularly powerful, implying a constant insidious eating away at the mistakes that cannot be changed. This heightens the sense of destructive pain the poet endures.

- In the third stanza we return to the idea of 'time' and again the mood is darkened, this time through the image of the 'darkening sky' which reinforces the sense of hopelessness and resignation. Even the possibility of metaphorically 'turning back the clocks' could provide no solution.
- The finality of the situation is evoked in the last stanza through the bleak image of death. The poet uses this in both a literal sense (one day they will be dead) and a metaphorical sense (they are dead in the sense that they have lost the light in their lives). The poem ends with a return to the image of the taking away of light and the ensuing darkness.
- This poem encapsulates all the central themes that Duffy explores in the poems in this selection and, as such, can be seen as a poem that sounds the 'key note' of the anthology as a whole.

Activity | Write a list of the central themes that you think the poem explores.

Here is our list:

- the breakdown of a relationship
- loss
- time
- change
- emotional darkness
- pain
- love and the loss of it.

Now read *Havisham*.

This will, perhaps, mean more to you if you have read Charles Dickens's *Great Expectations*. In that novel, Miss Havisham is an old woman who, many years previously, had been deserted by her fiancé on her wedding day. This experience leaves her a bitter and lonely woman who spends the rest of her life in solitude, shut off from the world.

Havisham

Beloved sweetheart bastard. Not a day since then
I haven't wished him dead. Prayed for it
so hard I've dark green pebbles for eyes,
ropes on the back of my hands I could strangle with.

Spinster. I stink and remember. Whole days
in bed cawing Nooooo at the wall; the dress
yellowing, trembling if I open the wardrobe;
the slewed mirror, full-length, her, myself, who did this

to me? Puce curses that are sounds not words.
Some nights better, the lost body over me,
my fluent tongue in its mouth in its ear
then down till I suddenly bite awake. Love's

hate behind a white veil; a red balloon bursting
in my face. Bang. I stabbed at a wedding-cake.
Give me a male corpse for a long slow honeymoon.
Don't think it's only the heart that b-b-b-breaks.

Activity   What does this poem have in common with *Mean Time*? What message do you think Duffy wants to convey to her readers?

The language of 'Mean Time'

When we examine Duffy's use of language in her poetry, every poem needs to be looked at individually. However, in talking about what she hopes to achieve through her writing she has drawn attention to several specific features that you might like to keep in mind when looking in detail at her work. These features include:

- her use of rhyme
- her use of 'echoes' and assonance
- the form of her poetry – the ways in which stanzas are organized to give an ordered shape to the poems
- the use of imagery
- the use of a language and vocabulary of her time.

Now read the following poem carefully.

Confession

Come away into this dark cell and tell
your sins to a hidden man your guardian angel
works your conscience like a glove-puppet It
smells in here doesn't it does it smell
like a coffin how would you know C'mon
out with them sins those little maggoty things
that wriggle in the soul . . . *Bless me Father* . . .

Just how bad have you been there's no water
in hell merely to think of a wrong's as evil
as doing it . . . *For I have sinned* . . . Penance
will cleanse you like a bar of good soap so
say the words into the musty gloom aye
on your knees let's hear that wee voice
recite transgression in the manner approved . . . *Forgive me* . . .

You do well to stammer A proper respect
for eternal damnation see the flicker
of your white hands clasping each other like
Hansel and Gretel in the big black wood
cross yourself Remember the vinegar and sponge
there's light on the other side of the door . . . *Mother
of God* . . . if you can only reach it Jesus loves you.

Activity

> Look carefully at the form and structure and the poet's use of imagery
> here. What effect do the poet's choice of imagery and the overall form
> and structure create? (Note particularly the effect on the reader of the
> lack of punctuation.)

Here are some points that you might have noticed:

- The poem opens with a rather threatening image as the poet is invited to
  'Come away into this dark cell and tell/your sins to a hidden man'.
  Normally the religious idea of the confessional is associated with a
  comforting spiritual cleansing, but here the image is sinister and
  threatening. This feeling is increased through the image of the priest
  working 'your conscience like a glove-puppet', which implies that the
  priest has total control, and the poet is helpless in his grip. The lack of
  punctuation here merges the voice of the priest and the voice of the poet
  into one, almost as if they have no separate identity. The image of sins as
  'maggoty things/that wriggle in the soul' creates an unpleasant image of
  them eating away at the individual.
- Stanza 2 opens with what seems to be the voice of the priest again
  drawing the poet into the act of confession by evoking an image of hell
  and damnation. Penance, which is usually seen as an act of spiritual
  cleansing, is compared to being cleansed by a bar of soap. Through this
  imagery, Duffy is criticizing the narrow, limited, and perhaps shallow
  nature of the ritual of the confessional.
- The final stanza begins with the priest's reference to the poet's
  'stammering' through the confessional. Again punctuation marks are
  omitted, although capital letters are used to denote when the priest
  begins a new point. Again the poet's fear is played on, this time through
  the image of Hansel and Gretel alone 'in the big black wood'. This
  creates a sense of insecurity and alienation which is used to reinforce the
  need to 'cross yourself'. The image of the vinegar and the sponge brings
  to mind the crucifixion of Christ and complements the image of there
  being light on the other side of the door. However, the final line – '. . . if
  you can only reach it Jesus loves you' – leaves the unresolved question
  of whether the 'light' is attainable and, if it is, is the confession box the
  way to attain it?

Now read the following two poems.

First Love

Waking, with a dream of first love forming real words,
as close to my lips as lipstick, I speak your name,
after a silence of years, into the pillow, and the power
of your name brings me here to the window, naked,
to say it again to a garden shaking with light.

This was a child's love, and yet I clench my eyes
till the pictures return, unfocused at first, then
almost clear, an old film played at a slow speed.
All day I will glimpse it, in windows of changing sky,
in mirrors, my lover's eyes, wherever you are.

And later a star, long dead, here, seems precisely
the size of a tear. Tonight, a love-letter out of a dream
stammers itself in my heart. Such faithfulness.
You smile in my head on the last evening. Unseen
flowers suddenly pierce and sweeten the air.

Stuffed

I put two yellow peepers in an owl.
Wow. I fix the grin of Crocodile.
Spiv. I sew the slither of an eel.

I jerk, kick-start, the back hooves of a mule.
Wild. I hold a red rag to a bull.
Mad. I spread the feathers of a gull.

I screw a tight snarl to a weasel.
Fierce. I stitch the flippers on a seal.
Splayed. I pierce the heartbeat of a quail.

I like her to be naked and to kneel.
Tame. My motionless, my living doll.
Mute. And afterwards I like her not to tell.

Activity   Compare and contrast these two poems examining the following:
  - the ways in which Duffy uses imagery
  - the form and structure of the poems
  - the themes and issues she examines through these poems.

6 Studying Drama

Objectives
- To prepare yourself for writing and talking about drama
- To consider some of the features to look for in evaluating drama texts
- To prepare for studying drama texts

What is drama?

A dictionary definition will state that:

'drama is something intended specifically for performance on stage in front of an audience'.

This definition points to the fact that drama is written to be seen rather than read and its meaning can only be fully appreciated when seen in performance. This makes it a much more 'public' form than prose or poetry, in that the experience of the play in performance is a shared experience. This essential aspect of drama is easy to lose sight of when sitting in a classroom, or on your own, grappling with the language of a drama text.

Visualizing the script

It is essential, then, that you are aware in approaching a play that you are dealing with a work that is very different from, say, a novel and that you will need to employ quite different strategies to handle it. You must be able to visualize the play in your head – be able to bring the play alive in your mind and see and hear the action as if you were at the theatre. Developing the ability to do this can be difficult simply by reading from the printed page. However, there are things you can do, from the outset, to help.

- Recognize that reading a play is essentially a group activity and so work with others as much as possible.
- Go and see plays performed as often as possible. (Do not restrict yourself to the ones you are studying, or just to professional productions.)
- Keep a notebook or journal of plays that you see, noting your responses – thoughts and feelings about performances and ideas on production.
- Take part in 'acting out' parts of a play – this will help you to appreciate the staging implications of a text in a way that straight reading never can.
- Listen to audio tapes or watch video recordings of plays. (These do not replace seeing the play 'live' but they are better than only reading the scripts.)

With this key point in mind, let us consider some aspects of plays that you will need to examine in the texts that you study.

Opening scenes

The way that a play opens is obviously crucial to engaging the audience's attention and writers can take many options here depending on the effects that they wish to achieve. In looking at an opening scene there are some key questions that are worth asking. The central questions are: 'What effect does the writer want this scene to have on the audience?' and 'What purpose does the scene serve in the play as a whole?'. Here are some possible answers to these questions.

- The scene provides an explanation of the situation, background information, and details the audience needs in order to understand what is going on. This is sometimes called **exposition** (see page 151). An example is Sheridan's *The Rivals*.
- The scene creates a setting or background against which the play is set, as in Williams's *A Streetcar Named Desire*.
- The scene creates a mood or creates tension which captures the audience's attention immediately (the opening scene of *Hamlet* is a good example of this).
- The scene introduces characters, situations, and relationships, as in Shakespeare's *King Lear*.
- The scene provokes a sense of intrigue which captures the audience's attention and makes them want to know more, as in Shakespeare's *Macbeth*.

Activity

1 Read carefully the opening to Brian Friel's *Making History*. Think about what Friel hopes to achieve here and what effect it would have on the audience.

> **2** Discuss this opening with a partner or think about it on your own, focusing on these aspects:
> - your impression of the two characters and their concerns
> - the information conveyed to the audience here and the techniques that Friel uses to put it across
> - the kind of atmosphere created and how Friel creates it.

Making History

Act I Scene 1

(A large living room in **O'Neill's** *home in Dungannon, County Tyrone, Ireland. Late August in 1591. The room is spacious and scantily furnished: a large, refectory-type table; some chairs and stools; a sideboard. No attempt at decoration.*

O'Neill *moves around this comfortless room quickly and energetically, inexpertly cutting the stems off flowers, thrusting the flowers into various vases and then adding water. He is not listening to* **Harry Hoveden** *who consults and reads from various papers on the table.*

O'Neill *is forty-one. A private, sharp-minded man at this moment uncharacteristically outgoing and talkative. He always speaks in an upper-class English accent except on those occasions specifically scripted.* **Harry Hoveden**, *his personal secretary, is about the same age as* **O'Neill**. **O'Neill** *describes him as a man 'who has a comforting and a soothing effect'.)*

Harry:	That takes care of Friday. Saturday you're free all day – so far. Then on Sunday – that'll be the fourteenth – O'Hagan's place at Tullyogue. A big christening party. The invitation came the day you left. I've said you'll be there. All right? *(Pause)* It's young Brian's first child – you were at his wedding last year. It'll be a good day. *(Pause)* Hugh?
O'Neill:	Yes?
Harry:	O'Hagan's – where you were fostered.
O'Neill:	Tell me the name of these again.
Harry:	Broom.
O'Neill:	Broom. That's it.
Harry:	The Latin name is genista. Virgil mentions it somewhere.
O'Neill:	Does he really?
Harry:	Actually that *genista* comes from Spain. *(***O'Neill** *looks at the flowers in amazement.)*
O'Neill:	Good Lord – does it? Spanish broom – magnificent name, isn't it?
Harry:	Give them plenty of water.
O'Neill:	Magnificent colour, isn't it?
Harry:	A letter from the Lord Deputy –
O'Neill:	They really transform the room. Splendid idea of yours, Harry. Thank you. *(***O'Neill** *silently mouths the word* Genista *again and then continues distributing the flowers.)*

Harry: A letter from the Lord Deputy 'vigorously urging you to have your eldest son attend the newly established College of the Holy and Undivided Trinity in Dublin founded by the Most Serene Queen Elizabeth'. That 'vigorously urging' sounds ominous, doesn't it?

O'Neill: Sorry?

Harry: Sir William Fitzwilliam wants you to send young Hugh to the new Trinity College. I'm told he's trying to get all the big Gaelic families to send their children there. He would like an early response.

O'Neill: This jacket – what do you think, Harry? It's not a bit . . . excessive, is it?

Harry: Excessive?

O'Neill: You know . . . a little too – too strident?

Harry: Strident?

O'Neill: All right, damn it, too bloody young?

Harry: (*Looking at his papers*) It's very becoming, Hugh.

O'Neill: Do you think so? Maybe I should have got it in maroon.
(*He goes off to get more flowers.*)

Harry: A reminder that the Annual Festival of Harpers takes place next month in Roscommon. They've changed the venue to Roosky. You're Patron of the Festival and they would be very honoured if you would open the event with a short –
(*He now sees that he is alone. He looks through his papers.
Pause.* **O'Neill** *enters again with an armful of flowers.*)

Brian Friel

This opening scene starts the play off in quite a private and intimate setting. The stage directions at the beginning describe the setting and what is going on and this will help you to visualize the scene in your mind. Although the audience will not be so fully aware of what is happening here the activity taking place will capture their attention. The two characters, O'Neill and Harry, seem to have very different concerns at the opening of the play. O'Neill is immersed in the domestic – arranging the flowers in the room and seeking Harry's opinion about his attire. Harry, on the other hand, is concerned with imparting business and political news to O'Neill. Within this apparently low-key opening Friel makes it clear that O'Neill is a prominent public figure from the details that are mentioned – his presence being requested at important domestic and public occasions and the letter from the Lord Deputy trying to persuade him to send his son to Trinity College confirm this.

Notice how Friel's economical technique allows him to give the audience a good deal of information and establishes the central character of O'Neill right at the outset. If you were to study the whole of this play you would find that Friel also establishes one of the central themes of the play here – that of the conflict between O'Neill the private man and O'Neill the public figure. He is also able to give a clear indication of O'Neill's stature and importance, both as a political figure and as a man with pastoral responsibilities towards his people.

Activity **1** Read the following extract, which is the opening scene from Shakespeare's tragedy *Hamlet*.

2 Think about the scene for yourself or discuss it with a partner and consider these points:
- the effect of the opening on the audience
- the intention of the playwright
- the techniques used
- the purpose of any stage directions.

Hamlet

Act I Scene 1

*(Enter **Barnardo** and **Francisco**, two sentinels)*

Barnardo:	Who's there?
Francisco:	Nay, answer me. Stand and unfold yourself.
Barnardo:	Long live the King.
Francisco:	Barnardo?
Barnardo:	He.
Francisco:	You come most carefully upon your hour.
Barnardo:	'Tis now struck twelve. Get thee to bed, Francisco.
Francisco:	For this relief much thanks. 'Tis bitter cold,
	And I am sick at heart.
Barnardo:	Have you had quiet guard?
Francisco:	Not a mouse stirring.
Barnardo:	Well, good night.
	If you do meet Horatio and Marcellus,
	The rivals of my watch, bid them make haste.

*(Enter **Horatio** and **Marcellus**)*

Francisco:	I think I hear them. Stand, ho! Who is there?
Horatio:	Friends to this ground.
Marcellus:	And liegemen to the Dane.
Francisco:	Give you good night.
Marcellus:	O, farewell honest soldier,
	Who hath relieved you?
Francisco:	Barnardo hath my place.
	Give you good night.

(Exit)

Marcellus:	Holla, Barnardo!
Barnardo:	Say,
	What, is Horatio there?
Horatio:	A piece of him.
Barnardo:	Welcome, Horatio. Welcome, good Marcellus.
Marcellus:	What, has this thing appeared again tonight?
Barnardo:	I have seen nothing.
Marcellus:	Horatio says 'tis but our fantasy,
	And will not let belief take hold of him
	Touching this dreaded sight, twice seen of us.
	Therefore I have intreated him along

With us to watch the minutes of this night,
That, if again this apparition come,
He may approve our eyes and speak to it.

Horatio: Tush, tush, 'twill not appear.

Barnardo: Sit down awhile,
And let us once again assail your ears,
That are so fortified against our story,
What we have two nights seen.

Horatio: Well, sit we down,
And let us hear Barnardo speak of this.

Barnardo: Last night of all,
When yon same star that's westward from the pole,
Had made his course t'illume that part of heaven
Where now it burns, Marcellus and myself,
The bell then beating one –

(Enter **Ghost***)*

Marcellus: Peace, break thee off. Look where it comes again!

Barnardo: In the same figure like the King that's dead.

Marcellus: Thou art a scholar, speak to it, Horatio.

Barnardo: Looks 'a not like the King? Mark it, Horatio.

Horatio: Most like. It harrows me with fear and wonder.

Barnardo: It would be spoke to.

Marcellus: Question it Horatio.

Horatio: What art thou that usurp'st this time of night,
Together with that fair and warlike form
In which the majesty of buried Denmark
Did sometimes march? By heaven I charge thee speak.

Marcellus: It is offended.

Barnardo: See, it stalks away.

Horatio: Stay, speak, speak, I charge thee speak.

(Exit **Ghost***)*

Presenting character

A key element in the impact of a dramatic production is the extent to which the playwright achieves a convincing sense of character. However, the nature of drama is such that the playwright employs very different methods of characterization from those employed by a novelist. Novelists can provide the reader with as much background information as they wish. They can enter the minds of the characters, let their readers know what characters think, feel, and are planning to do. A playwright does not have all these options.

Activity

Focusing on a play that you are studying, think carefully about the ways the characters are presented to the audience to give a full and rounded impression of them. Make a list of these methods and devices.

Perhaps the most straightforward way in which a playwright can define exactly how he or she intends a character to appear to the audience is through detailed and explicit stage directions. So it is important that when you begin to study a play you pay close attention to this information. When watching the play on the stage, of course, you will not be reading stage directions but you will be seeing them in performance.

Some playwrights give a great deal of information through their descriptions of how characters are meant to appear. Look carefully at the following two examples from Tennessee Williams's *A Streetcar Named Desire*: the first one describes Blanche as she appears in the play for the first time. She has come to New Orleans to visit her younger sister, Stella, who lives in a rather 'down-market' part of the city. The second one describes the entrance of Stanley, Stella's husband.

1 **Blanche** *comes round the corner, carrying a valise. She looks at the slip of paper, then at the building, then again at the slip and again at the building. Her expression is one of shocked disbelief. Her appearance is incongruous to this setting. She is daintily dressed in a white suit with a fluffy bodice, necklace and earrings of pearl, white gloves and hat, looking as if she were arriving at a summer tea or cocktail party in the garden district. She is above five years older than* **Stella**. *Her delicate beauty must avoid strong light. There is something about her uncertain manner, as well as her white clothes, that suggests a moth.*

2 **Stanley** *throws the screen door of the kitchen open and comes in. He is of medium height, about five feet eight or nine, and strongly, compactly built. Animal joy in his being is implicit in all his movements and attitudes. Since earliest manhood the centre of his life has been pleasure with women, the giving and the taking of it, not with weak indulgence, dependently, but with the power and pride of a richly feathered male bird among hens. Branching out from this complete and satisfying centre are all the auxiliary channels of his life, such as his heartiness with men, his appreciation of rough humour, his love of good drink and food and games, his car, his radio, everything that is his, that bears his emblem of the gaudy seed-bearer. He sizes women up at a glance, with sexual classifications, crude images flashing into his mind and determining the way he smiles at them.*

Activity   On your own or in a small group, read these stage directions carefully. Imagine you are a producer and a team of actors discussing preliminary views of these characters. Think about their appearances and personalities.

Tennessee Williams here presents anyone reading the text with a good deal of guidance not only on how to visualize the characters but on their deeper aspects. Some playwrights provide little or no such direct guidance on how to interpret their characters, but rely on other methods to convey a sense of character. These include:

- how characters speak (also sometimes embedded in stage directions)
- how characters are described by other characters
- what the characters say and do
- how other characters respond to or interact with them.

Most playwrights (including Williams) use a combination of all these methods in order to give a sense of fully developed characters, although in some cases playwrights deliberately create stereotypical characters in order to achieve their particular effect. Some of the 'stock' characters to be found in Restoration comedy, such as *The Way of the World*, or a comedy of manners, such as *The Rivals*, are examples of this.

Activity

Look at the following extract from *A Streetcar Named Desire*. The annotations are on the opening stage directions of the scene followed by an excerpt from a little later in the scene.

Blanche Dubois, a complex woman with much to hide, is staying with her sister Stella and Stella's husband Stanley in New Orleans. Their life is very different from the unrealistic expectations she carries from her girlhood as a 'Southern Belle'. Here, she and Stella return from an evening out to find Stanley playing poker with his friends.

Make a note of the impression you form of the characters and how Williams conveys that impression.

Then write as fully as you can about Scene 3 of *A Streetcar Named Desire*, focusing on the way the male and female characters are presented.

A Streetcar Named Desire

Scene 3
The Poker Night

(There is a picture of Van Gogh's of a billiard-parlour at night. The kitchen now suggests that sort of lurid nocturnal brilliance, the raw colours of childhood's spectrum. Over the yellow linoleum of the kitchen table hangs an electric bulb with a vivid green glass shade. The poker players – **Stanley**, **Steve**, **Mitch**, *and* **Pablo** *– wear coloured shirts, solid blues, a purple, a red-and-white check, a light green, and they are men at the peak of their physical manhood, as coarse and direct and powerful as the primary colours. There are vivid slices of watermelon on the table, whisky bottles, and glasses. The bedroom is relatively dim with only the light that spills between the portières and through the wide window on the street. The sisters appear around the corner of the building.) ...*

Annotations (handwritten):
- Colours bold, bright, simple, modern
- 'Raw' suggests uncultivated
- (Brilliant light where the men are)
- Colour of watermelon could suggest raw flesh
- (Where the women will be is 'dim': only light from outside)

Stella:	The game is still going on.	
Blanche:	How do I look?	*Blanche concerned with her appearance.*
Stella:	Lovely, Blanche. ←	*Stella gives the answers she needs to hear*
Blanche:	I feel so hot and frazzled. Wait till I powder before you open the door. Do I look done in?	
Stella:	Why no. You are as fresh as a daisy.	

(**Stella** *opens the door and they enter.*)

Stella:	Well, well, well. I see you boys are still at it!
Stanley:	Where you been?
Stella:	Blanche and I took in a show. Blanche, this is Mr Gonzales and Mr Hubbel.

Blanche: Please don't get up. *Old-fashioned – she expects courtesy*

Stanley: Nobody's going to get up, so don't be worried. *She doesn't get it!*

Stella: How much longer is this game going to continue? *Stan takes no account of Stella's wishes. His responses to both women are abrupt, rude.*

Trying to get 'in' with the men → **Blanche:** Poker is so fascinating. Could I kibitz? = *Look over someone's shoulder and sit in on their hand of cards*

Stanley: You could not. Why don't you women go up and sit with Eunice?

Stan will have none of it → **Stella:** Because it is nearly two-thirty. *Derogatory tone* *He wants them out of the way – poker is a man's world. Women excluded*

(**Blanche** *crosses into the bedroom and partially closes the portières.*)

Stella: Couldn't you call it quits after one more hand? *'loud whack' – Stanley is solid, boisterousness*

Stella trying to be reasonable → (*A chair scrapes.* **Stanley** *gives a loud whack of his hand on* **Stella's** thigh.) *Chauvinistic reaction – treats Stella roughly, disrespectfully, as his possession*

Stella: (*Sharply*) That's not fun, Stanley.

(*The men laugh.* **Stella** *goes into the bedroom.*)

Tennessee Williams — *She dislikes this; at least she expresses her anger – but she gets no support – the men think her annoyance is funny. All she can do is walk out*

Here are some brief ideas;
Men: dominant, forceful, violent
Poker: a man's world – women excluded
Women: feminine – much less powerful
Blanche: nervous, flirtatious
Setting: men – 'lurid' kitchen; women – 'dim' bedroom
Colours: men – bold; women – white, delicate

We know that the central theme for discussion is the contrast between the male characters – presented as dominant, hard, and forceful – and the female characters – portrayed as gentler and less powerful. Yet, in the course of the essay, we are likely to explore several side issues, some of which will contribute to the main argument, while others offer exceptions to it or alternative views. It is important to find ways of incorporating these while maintaining a strong sense of direction and flow in the writing. Using connecting devices like the ones shown in the following examples can help achieve this successfully.

A

One aspect of Williams's presentation in the scene, which contributes to our sense that the men are more powerful than the women, is the way in which he uses colours . . .
[. . . discussion of the use of colour and its effect . . .]
Having examined the use of colours in the scene, we can see that it reinforces the impression that the men are dominant here.

B

The relative powerlessness of the female characters is demonstrated by the fact that neither Blanche nor Stella commands any respect from the poker players. However, the two women are different in the ways in which they respond to the men . . .
[. . . comparison of the behaviour of Blanche and Stella . . .]
Although the female characters differ in the ways they react to the situation, they are presented in general as less forceful than the male characters.

C

Although we have seen that for the most part the men are harder and more forceful than the women, there are some exceptions . . .
[First . . . discussion of Mitch's character . . .
Second . . . examine how Stanley becomes like a pathetic small boy in his need for Stella once she has left . . .
Third . . . example of Eunice shouting roughly and angrily . . .]
There are, therefore, some occasions when male characters seem weaker. On the whole, however, they are presented as powerful.

In each of these examples the writer moves temporarily away from the central line of argument to discuss a side issue, but each time returns to the central question, pointing out how the side issue relates to it. This leaves the writer back on track, ready either to continue the main argument or to explore another 'by way'.

Activity

With a partner, look at how one student answers the question on Scene 3, *The Poker Night*. The student (Ian) has written on the whole scene and not just the extract printed here. As you read, take note of the annotations written by an examiner and discuss how Ian has structured his work.

A fair introductory paragraph which refers to the question and leads into his discussion of the characters

It has been said that Scene 3, which is the poker scene, actually represents the whole play and acts as a miniature version of the play. *The Poker Night* is an important scene because it shows how the male and female characters are presented by Tennessee Williams.

An interesting point in this opening sentence which could do with more explanation

The male characters as a group are presented as dominant and forceful because they have ordered the women out for the night so they can play poker and enjoy themselves. The group of men, Stanley, Steve, Mitch, and Pablo are presented as strong, powerful, and coarse. This is said in the stage directions:

'They are men at the peak of their physical manhood, as coarse and direct as the primary colours.'

'The primary colours' are the colours of the shirts the men are wearing. The colours are 'solid blues, a purple, a red-and-white check, a light green'. Also from these colours and the shirts being worn these are modern men unlike the type Stella and Blanche would have been used to in their past.

The group of men are seen as brutes of men as they sit around the poker table. Here the men start to 'argue hotly':

'I didn't hear you name it.'

'Didn't I name it, Mitch?'

Several good points about the men as a group, including some discussion of the significance of the colours they wear. Next Ian focuses on individual male characters, which makes good sense

The group of men argue over a simple game of cards. This is almost like a children's squabble.

Stanley is the prime example of a forceful modern man in a world where Stella and Blanche must do as he says. He is the most dominating male character in the group of four. Here, Stella comes in and complains to Stanley about the time they are still playing poker at. Stanley shows he isn't respectful of Stella's wishes.

'A chair scrapes. Stanley gives a loud whack of his hand on her thigh.'

Structure works quite well here. Ian conveys a sense of how the men behave as a group and also draws a contrast between them

Stanley shows his masculinity and authority over Stella by slapping her thigh in a manly way. Stanley is showing off around his friends, proving how much of a man he is. Stanley again shows his dominance over the females when he demands Blanche turns the radio off and when she doesn't do so on his word he becomes fierce.

'Stanley stalks fiercely through the portières into the bedroom. He crosses to the small white radio and snatches it off the table. With a shouted oath, he tosses the instrument out of the window.'

He uses appropriate quotations and attempts more detailed analysis in places (for example, where he comments on the significance of individual words such as 'stalks')

Even the way Stanley approaches the radio before he acts presents him in a fierce and forceful light. The words 'stalks', as if he was a primitive caveman stalking his prey, and 'fiercely', which is his anger, show how Stanley is going to act before he acts. Stanley acts more like a modern barbarian around women than a modern gentleman. Mitch is the only exception to the group. Mitch is sympathetic and much more considerate to what Blanche and Stella want than Stanley. Mitch shows he is more gentle in these stage directions:

'..coughing a little shyly. He realizes he still has the towel in his hands and with an embarrassed laugh hands it to Stella.'

Quotations usually introduced quite neatly, providing enough information to place them in context but Ian fails to do this when he quotes Mitch's moment of embarrassment. To make the situation fully clear to the reader, he needs to say: '...in these stage directions when he comes out of the bathroom and has to pass the women, who are in the bedroom...'

This is the first time we see Mitch around females and he shows he is different to the other men around him by the way he embarrassedly laughs at his little mistake. This shows a kinder and gentler side to the male populace and is a contrast to Stanley's hard, rough and ready nature. Mitch is presented as a fine character who is more suitable to Blanche and Stella and is more like the men they once knew. Here Blanche waltzes to the music with romantic gestures to Mitch.

Ian also slightly misreads Mitch's character here, not picking up that, although he is relatively gentle, he is also rather naïve and undignified in the way he responds to Blanche's flirtation

'Mitch is delighted and moves in awkward imitation like a dancing bear.'

The point here is although Mitch didn't know how to waltz he gladly made a fool of himself dancing strangely just to please Blanche. Stanley, from what we know of him, would have laughed and walked away.

This section is less successful: the first sentence is ambiguous. Does he mean that the women are similar to each other, or to the men? He needs to round off his discussion of the men and then lead into his discussion of the women, like this: 'Although Mitch seems different from Stanley and the others, on the whole the men are strong and rough and form a powerful group. On the other hand, the women, although different from each other, seem much less forceful...'

The female characters are quite similar in the way they are presented. Stella is presented as strong by the way she stands up to Stanley over the card game:

'Drunk – drunk – animal thing you! All of you – please go home! If any of you have one spark of decency in you ...'

Stella confronts the group of males playing poker and challenges them. Also, Stella is shown as wanting to be treated with respect.

Stanley slaps Stella's thigh and she reacts sharply and then tells Blanche:

'It makes me so mad when he does that in front of people.'

Stella is showing how she wants to look as if she is respected in front of people.

Stella may be presented as strong and brave and trying to gain respect, but she is also weak when it comes down to what Stanley wants. After Stanley hits her and she and Blanche go up to Eunice's, when Stanley stands downstairs crying, she gives in and goes to Stanley, showing she needs him no matter what he's done.

Blanche shows or presents another image of the female which is provocative, flirty and deceitful ...

Ian's essay continues with a discussion of Blanche's character and actions and concludes like this...

This is rather disappointing. The essay just stops, without a conclusion to draw the ideas together. The mention of the previous scene is a red herring – not relevant to the question here

...Blanche is easily older than Stella and has blatantly lied about her age so that Mitch will become more interested in her. Blanche always tries to present herself in a better light:

'I can't stand a naked light bulb, any more than I can a rude remark or a vulgar action.'

Blanche is trying to sound much more refined than she actually is. She is being provocative and flirtatious, exactly as she was in the previous scene when she was alone with Stanley.

Ian   *Ian has not really made use of opportunities to analyse details in his later paragraphs. For example, Blanche's statement that she 'can't stand a naked light bulb' deserves much more attention. As Ian has pointed out, she is deceitful. The naked light bulb would reveal too much literally – she lies about her age – and metaphorically – it also represents the fact that she has a lot more to hide*

Activity

1 Swap answers to a recent essay on drama with a partner. Assess the structure of your partner's essay. Annotate it to show where the structure is clear and informative and where it could be improved. (Use the notes around Ian's essay as models for your own.)
2 Hand back the annotated essay and discuss your comments on it with your partner.

Asides and soliloquies

To succeed in creating a convincing character, the dramatist needs to give the audience some sense of deeper, inner thoughts and feelings. Unlike the novelist, however, who can describe these as fully as desired to the reader, the dramatist has much more limited means at his or her disposal.

Two methods that are often used to provide some insight into characters' minds are the aside and the soliloquy. The **aside** is a kind of 'stage whisper', a behind-the-hand comment. Sometimes it is directed to another character but often it is aimed at the audience, or characters 'speak to themselves'. Asides tend to be short, often a single sentence, sometimes a single word. They are used by the playwright to convey small pieces of information concerning the plot or character to the audience.

In Shakespeare's *Othello*, for example, there is substantial use of both long and short asides. They reveal to the audience what is going on in the mind of the speaker. Below is a particularly long aside from *Othello*. Iago watches his enemy, Cassio, take the hand of Othello's wife, Desdemona. Read it through carefully.

Othello

Act II Scene 1

Iago: *(Aside)* He takes her by the palm. Ay, well said, whisper. With as little web as this will I ensnare as great a fly as Cassio. Ay, smile upon her, do. I will gyve thee in thine own courtship. You say true, 'tis so indeed. If such tricks as these strip you out of your lieutenantry, it had been better you had not kissed your three fingers so oft, which now again you are most apt to play the sir in. Very good: well kissed, an excellent courtesy! 'Tis so indeed. Yet again your fingers to your lips? Would they were clyster-pipes for your sake!

The repeated use of asides also give us an insight into Othello's growing torment. For example, in this extract Iago urges him to secretly observe his conversation with Cassio, to convince Othello (quite wrongly) that Cassio and Desdemona are having an affair. In fact, he and Cassio are talking about Bianca.

Act IV Scene 1

Othello: *(Aside)* Look, how he laughs already!
Iago: I never knew a woman love man so.
Cassio: Alas, poor rogue! I think i'faith she loves me.
Othello: *(Aside)* Now he denies it faintly, and laughs it out.
Iago: Do you hear, Cassio?
Othello: *(Aside)* Now he importunes him to tell it o'er. Go to, well said, well said!
Iago: She gives it out that you shall marry her. Do you intend it?
Cassio: Ha, ha, ha!
Othello: *(Aside)* Do you triumph, Roman? Do you triumph?
Cassio: I marry her! What! A customer! Prithee bear some charity to my wit: do not think it so unwholesome. Ha, ha, ha!
Othello: *(Aside)* So, so, so, so: they laugh that win.

Activity

> Look carefully at these asides. Why do you think Shakespeare used them in this way and what effects does he achieve through their use?

Soliloquies, too, are also often used by playwrights to convey both information and inward emotion to the audience. The soliloquy is one key way in which Shakespeare lets us, the audience, know what a character is really like. Through a soliloquy characters tell us directly about themselves and can inform us about a whole range of issues, such as what is in their minds, why they are acting as they are, and what they intend to do in the future.

Activity

> This soliloquy is taken from *Othello*, and in it Iago reveals a good deal about his own attitudes. Read it carefully and make a list of the key points that Iago reveals about himself here.

Othello

Act I Scene 3

Iago: Thus do I ever make my fool my purse:
For I mine own gained knowledge should profane
If I would time expend with such a snipe
But for my sport and profit. I hate the Moor,
And it is thought a broad that 'twixt my sheets
He's done my office. I know not if't be true
But I, for mere suspicion in that kind,
Will do as if for surety. He holds me well:
The better shall my purpose work on him.
Cassio's a proper man: let me see now;
To get his place and to plume up my will
In double knavery. How? How? Let's see.
After some time, to abuse Othello's ear
That he is too familiar with his wife;
He hath a person and a smooth dispose
To be suspected, framed to make women false.
The Moor is of a free and open nature,
That thinks men honest that but seem to be so,
And will as tenderly be led by th'nose
As asses are.
I have't. It is engendered. Hell and night
Must bring this monstrous birth to the world's light.

(Exit)

Activity

> Now look at the play you are studying. Make a list of the soliloquies in it and what those soliloquies tell you about the characters who speak them. Make a note of the following details:
> • who is speaking

> - the context of the soliloquy
> - what is being said
> - why the playwright uses a soliloquy at that point in the drama.

Soliloquies are frequently used at some special moment in the play or when a character is undergoing some kind of emotionally or psychologically heightened experience – for example, when a character is distressed or suffering some kind of confusion of mind or alternatively when a character is feeling exultant or wants to work through his or her own thoughts and feelings.

It has often been noted that both the aside and the soliloquy are artificial devices and that in 'real life' people do not go around delivering speeches to themselves. In fact, they are just two of many conventions that we accept when watching a play which can be termed 'dramatic licence'. In the context of the theatre we forget their artificiality and accept them quite naturally.

Issues and themes

Complex though the formation and development of characters may be, they are themselves part of a more complex web that makes up the play as a whole. Within this web the playwright will have interwoven certain themes and issues. In studying a play, you will need to be able to identify these and to look at how the playwright explores them through the drama. Such ideas can be presented to the audience in two key ways. First, we can detect ideas, issues, thoughts, etc. expressed by the characters in a play. Secondly, we can detect themes, issues, or ideas that the playwright wants the play as a whole to project.

Sometimes a playwright will have major characters hold views or follow a philosophy that ultimately is shown to be counter to the message that the play as a whole conveys. This is often done to show the problems caused by or shortcomings of certain courses of action or philosophies. The issues that a play might raise can be many and varied but they are almost always presented via action centring on human relationships and conflicts.

Activity List the major characters in a play that you are studying. Draw up a chart which shows briefly the ideas, philosophies, values etc. held by each character, as shown through the action of the play. Then think about these ideas and against each jot down the dramatist's view.

Plot and structure

Obviously plot is central to most plays, although there are certain kinds of play (some of Samuel Beckett's, for example) where the very lack of a plot, or at least something that we would ordinarily recognize as a plot, is essential for the effect. At its simplest the **plot** is the story of the play – what actually happens. Having said that, there is much more to plot than a simple 'story-line'. The whole notion of plot and its development is bound up with the way that the play is put together, with its structure. The creation of an order or pattern needs careful planning and the playwright needs to consider a number of factors. Generally speaking an effective plot should:

- maintain the interest of the audience from beginning to end
- move the action on from one episode to the next
- arouse the interest of the audience in character and situation
- create high points or moments of crisis at intervals
- create expectation and surprise.

Usually, the structure of a play follows a basic pattern which consists of a number of identifiable elements.

1 **Exposition:** this opens the play and often introduces the main characters and provides background information.
2 **Dramatic incitement:** the incident which provides the starting point for the main action of the play, and causes some type of conflict to arise.
3 **Complication:** this usually forms the main action of the play – the characters respond to the dramatic incitement and other developments that stem from it.
4 **Crisis:** the climax of the play.
5 **Resolution:** this is the final section of the play where things are worked out, conflicts are resolved, and some kind of conclusion is arrived at.

Let us look at this structure as applied to Arthur Miller's *The Crucible* to see how it works out.

1 **Exposition:** The opening of the first act is an example of an exposition, as we see the Reverend Parris, minister of religion in Salem, praying beside the bed of his ten-year-old daughter Betty. We learn that rumours of witchcraft are widespread in Salem and that some believe that his daughter's illness is the result of such unnatural causes. The previous night Parris had found his daughter, niece Abigail, and their friends dancing in the woods and the black slave, Tituba, was swaying and making strange noises.
2 **Dramatic incitement:** Another clergyman, the Reverend Hale, a specialist in witchcraft and its detection, is brought to Salem. He secures from Tituba a 'confession' that she has conjured up the devil. A local farmer, John Proctor, is outspokenly sceptical of the claims of witchcraft.
3 **Complication:** The girls are credited with the power to identify all those who are witches and they denounce many people. The ringleader is Parris's niece, Abigail. She has had sexual relations with Proctor and when Abigail denounces his wife, Elizabeth Proctor suspects that has been denounced because if she is hanged he will marry Abigail.
4 **Crisis:** Proctor himself is arrested but Hale, who now begins to suspect the truth and regret his involvement in the proceedings, tries to persuade Proctor to 'confess' and so be pardoned. Although tempted, in the end Proctor goes to his death rather than 'confess' and therefore lie.
5 **Resolution:** Although the play ends with the death of Proctor there is a kind of resolution because the authorities now realize how Abigail has misled

them and there is a suggestion that Proctor's death strengthens others to stand up for the truth and once again restore peace and sanity to Salem.

Activity

> Examine carefully the structure of a play that you are studying. Draw a diagram to represent the way that the play develops, making brief notes of key moments.

Approaching your script

There are a number of things you can do to deepen your understanding of your drama text. Here are some suggestions.

Summary

Plays in performance
- Read your drama text thoroughly prior to seeing it performed.
- See a live performance of the play.
- If you cannot see a live performance, watch a video recording or a film of it.
- Make notes on performances in a play log book to help you to remember those important initial impressions.
- Listen to the play on audio tape.
- See as many other plays as you can to broaden your experience of drama and the theatre.

Directing the text
- Work with others, dramatizing for yourselves scenes from the text.
- Talk to others about staging implications.
- Imagine you are a director – plan carefully how you would stage a production of the play, the kind of actors you would cast, how you would bring your own interpretation out on the stage, etc.
- Use diagrams, drawings, and models to work out sets, stage layout, and props for selected scenes.

Studying the text
- Think about the characters – look at key speeches, look for shifts in focus, different ways of interpreting what they do and say.
- Look for various possible 'meanings' and 'patterns' in the play.
- Consider how/if the theatrical effects are signalled.
- Think about the pace and variety of the action.
- Think about the overall shape and structure of the play and the impact that this could have on an audience.
- Consider the particular characteristics and qualities of the play you are studying.
- Think about relationships between these various elements of the play and how together they present a whole.
- Apply the broader knowledge you have about the nature of plays and drama.

All these activities will help you to formulate and develop your own informed critical response to the play and therefore fulfil the objectives which lie at the heart of your study of drama.

Shakespeare and dramatic study

Since Shakespeare is a dramatist, it follows that his plays have a great deal in common with those of other dramatists. They follow the clear structural pattern that we discussed in some detail earlier:

EXPOSITION ➡ DRAMATIC INCITEMENT ➡ COMPLICATION ➡ CRISIS ➡ RESOLUTION

Approaching a Shakespeare text

In approaching the text you are studying, make use of the knowledge you already possess as to the nature of drama generally. This can help you understand the plot of your Shakespeare text when reading it for the first time. For example, it will help if you know that Shakespeare's plays follow this pattern:

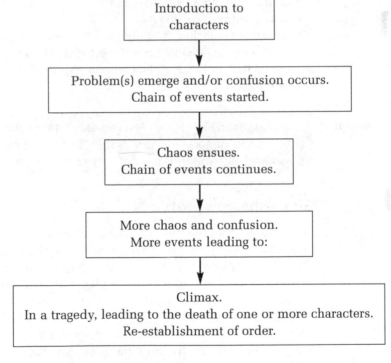

Knowledge of this general structure can help you to follow the storyline of any play, but more than this, it can provide you with a framework for your analysis of the play as a whole. One of the problems that students frequently encounter when studying a Shakespeare text is that they focus so closely on detailed summaries of scene, character, and theme that they sometimes lose sight of the fact that the play is an integrated whole. Being able to see the play in terms of its overall framework can help you to appreciate the broad pattern of the text, thus helping you to make sense of the detail when it emerges through close study.

The tragedies

The idea of disorder lies at the heart of Shakespeare's tragedies. The Roman history plays are often included in the list of tragedies. The four plays that are regarded as 'the great' tragedies are *Hamlet*, *King Lear*, *Othello*, and *Macbeth*. At the heart of each of these plays is the central character after whom the play is named – the **eponymous hero**, to give the technical term – and the action focuses very much on this character. However, other characters are important too, and often several innocent victims are claimed before the play reaches its end.

Overall, Shakespeare's tragedies have many of the key features we associate with the concept of dramatic tragedy in general.

- At the beginning of the play something occurs that disrupts the normal order of things.
- Chaos or disorder in society results.
- Extreme emotions are involved.
- Social restraint disintegrates.
- A climax is reached, usually with the death of the main character (and several others), before order is restored. The purging of emotions that affects the audience at the end of a tragedy is sometimes referred to as **catharsis**.

Activity

> If you are studying one of Shakespeare's tragedies think about how the play fits this general pattern. Note down one thing that happens in the play which corresponds to each of the above features.

Shakespeare's plots

As we have seen, the plots of Shakespeare's plays adhere to a general pattern common to many plays. However, when studying your text one of the first things you will need to do is to get to grips with the details of the plot. Very often your first encounter with the play will be through a reading, perhaps in class, with students taking the various parts. When reading the play either to yourself or as part of a group, however, it is easy to lose sight of the fact that you are studying a drama. The text you are reading was written to be performed and therefore brought to life on the stage. Although we now read Shakespeare's plays as 'literary texts', we must not forget this central fact, and you should view the 'text' as a 'script'. A 'script' suggests something that in itself is incomplete because it needs a dramatic enactment to achieve its purpose. This opens up the whole question of how the play is to be enacted, and touches on the fact that the play has many meanings rather than a single meaning.

In coming to terms with the plot of a Shakespeare play, therefore, you first need to understand generally what is happening, and then think about ways in which this could be enacted on the stage. To help you appreciate the variety of ways that a play can be interpreted, you should try to see as many performances of it (live in the theatre, on film, or video, etc.) as you can.

Activity

> In **ten** sentences, summarize the plot of the Shakespeare play you are studying. Then take the opening scene of that play and describe two possible, but contrasting, ways in which that scene could be enacted on the stage.

Structure

The structure of each play is integral to the way in which Shakespeare develops its central issues. The structure of his plays (or any play) can be viewed in two ways. What is sometimes called the **dynamic structure** of the play consists of the sequence of events which builds up in a 'cause and effect' fashion to create the plot of the play, and so drives the play forward.

Underlying this obvious structure, however, it is often possible to detect another that is less prominent but just as important. This second structure consists of various parallels and cross-references, or repeated images, symbols, and language that create a network of threads running through the play. This kind of structure is sometimes called the **symmetric structure**, and it can exert a powerful influence on the overall effect of a play.

In *Hamlet*, for example, the repeated parallels between Hamlet and Laertes as avenging sons, and Hamlet's repeated contemplation of death with its associated imagery, are just two elements that help to form a web of patterning developed throughout the play. Similarly, in *King Lear*, the theme of 'blindness' to the truth as well as physical blindness, presented through Gloucester and Lear, create parallels that give another kind of structure to the play.

Activity

> Draw two diagrams, one to represent the dynamic structure of the Shakespeare play you are studying, the other to represent the symmetric structure.

Shakespeare's themes and ideas

Each of Shakespeare's plays is concerned with certain ideas or issues that recur and develop as the play progresses. These topics with which the play is preoccupied are the play's 'themes'. They are the subject that Shakespeare explores through the events, characters, and language of the play. It is the themes that give a shape and pattern to the play and give it a significance beyond the events it describes.

The themes are developed through the language of the play, and often Shakespeare creates powerful images. For example, in *Othello* one of the themes of the play is 'honesty' and Iago's 'dishonesty'. The language itself draws attention to this theme in a variety of ways, one of which is the repetition of the word 'honest' to emphasize Othello's complete belief in Iago's 'honesty' and Desdemona's 'dishonesty'.

It has often been said that one of the reasons that Shakespeare's plays have remained so popular for so long is that they deal with great and universal themes that were of concern to people in Shakespeare's time, and are of no less significance to us today. His plays often deal with themes such as love, hate, envy, jealousy, death, revenge, guilt, corruption, destiny.

Certain themes seem to have particularly interested Shakespeare and can be seen in one form or another in all of his plays. These themes are:

- conflict
- appearance and reality
- order and disorder
- change
- love.

Conflict

Conflict, of one type or another, is the starting point for many dramas, and it can take many forms. In *Othello*, for example, we have the conflict between Iago and Othello (a conflict that Othello is unaware of until it is too late), and the inner conflict that Othello experiences as he battles to control his growing jealousy. In *Macbeth*, conflict exists externally at the beginning of the play, as Duncan faces rebellion and invasion.

Appearance and reality

In all of Shakespeare's plays there is a mis-match between how things seem to be and how they actually are. In *Othello*, for example, everyone thinks Iago is 'honest' but in fact he is completely the opposite. In *Twelfth Night*, Viola disguises herself as a boy, while in *Hamlet* the apparently popular and effective King, Claudius, is in reality guilty of the murder of his brother and seduction of his brother's wife. *Measure for Measure* is closely concerned with 'seeming', as the Duke leaves his apparently incorruptible deputy, Angelo, in charge of the state, to see 'If power change purpose, what our seemers be'. He certainly finds out, when it is revealed that Angelo attempted to seduce the innocent Isabella.

Order and disorder

In all of Shakespeare's plays there is some kind of breakdown in order, and some form of confusion temporarily gains the upper hand. Sometimes the breakdown is in the order of the state, as in *Macbeth*, where the murder of Duncan plunges the state into turmoil and war. In *Henry IV* (Parts 1 and 2), King Henry faces rebellion and civil war, while *Twelfth Night* begins with Olivia's rejection of Orsino's suit and Viola shipwrecked on the coast of Illyria. The causes of the disruption vary from play to play, but they tend to include key causes such as jealousy, love, hate, and ambition. Very often the protagonist undergoes some kind of learning process during the course of the play before order is re-established.

Change

In all Shakespeare plays the characters undergo some kind of change. Sometimes the ultimate result of this change is death, as in *Othello*, where Othello changes from a respected military leader to a man eaten away by jealousy who murders his wife and then, realizing the terrible mistake he has made, takes his own life. In *Twelfth Night,* Malvolio changes from a puritan figure into a foolish lover.

Love

For Shakespeare, one of the instruments of change is love, which has a transforming power and is often at the heart of his plays. *Twelfth Night* begins with the words 'If music be the food of love, play on.' It goes on to present a world of romantic love. In *A Midsummer Night's Dream* we see young men and women who love each other but who also have to endure crosses and frustrations in love. In *Othello* we see a quite different portrayal of love, as Othello's love for Desdemona is corrupted into jealousy and hate by the scheming Iago.

Development of themes

Of course, there are many specific themes that can be traced in individual plays, but in one way or another they will relate to the five key areas discussed above.

The themes in Shakespeare's plays often develop in one of three ways:

- An individual character or characters experience some personal difficulties or inner turmoil, perhaps moral or spiritual, that causes some mental conflict. For example, Hamlet struggles to come to terms with events and revenge his father.
- The family, society, or the country is affected by turmoil. For example, the feuding Capulets and Montagues disrupt Verona in *Romeo and Juliet*, and Rome is at war with Egypt in *Antony and Cleopatra*.
- Nature or the universe may be disordered, or supernatural events may be involved. Examples are the appearance of the witches and Banquo's ghost in *Macbeth*, or the storm imagery in *King Lear*.

At the heart of the development of the themes of a play is Shakespeare's rich and complex use of language.

Shakespeare's language

Often students encounter difficulties when first studying a Shakespeare play because they find the language of Shakespeare different in a number of ways from the kind of English they are used to. This difficulty is particularly evident when reading the text rather than watching the play being performed, when actions are brought to life and give the words much more meaning.

At first, concentrate on arriving at a broad understanding of what is happening, in terms of the plot of the play. Once this basic knowledge has been established, you will very soon progress to a more detailed study of the language of the play and the effects that it creates to bring the drama to life.

Below are some of the uses to which Shakespeare puts language.

Creating atmosphere

You should remember that in Shakespeare's time theatres did not have the elaborate scenery, backdrops, and the sophisticated technology that is used to create effects in modern theatres. If you have ever visited Shakespeare's Globe in London or seen drawings of the Elizabethan theatre, you will know that they had little more than a bare stage, and in that sense theatregoers went to 'hear' a play rather than to 'see' a play as we would say today. The plays would also usually take place in daylight, without the elaborate lighting effects we are used to today.

Apart from all its other important functions, language was therefore essential to the creation of setting and atmosphere. In a Shakespeare play the atmosphere and setting are created through words.

Shakespeare's imagery

The use of imagery, designed to conjure up vivid images in the mind, is a very important aspect of the way in which Shakespeare works with language. Such imagery plays a key part in every Shakespeare play and very often it is closely linked to central themes of the play. For example, as Othello becomes convinced of Desdemona's infidelity, his jealousy is expressed in increasingly unpleasant animal imagery.

In *King Lear*, certain images recur time and again. Here, too, there is an abundance of animal imagery, often used to stress the inhuman behaviour of Lear's daughters. Here, Lear complains to Regan about the treatment he has received from Goneril.

King Lear

Act II Scene 4

Regan: Good sir, no more; these are unsightly tricks.
Return you to my sister.
Lear: *(Rising)* Never, Regan.
She hath abated me of half my train;
Looked black upon me; struck me with her tongue,
Most serpent-like, upon the very heart.
All the stored vengeances of Heaven fall
On her ungrateful top! Strike her young bones,
You taking airs, with lameness!
Cornwall: Fie, sir, fie!
Lear: You nimble lightnings, dart your blinding flames
Into her scornful eyes! Infect her beauty,
You fen-sucked fogs, drawn by the pow'rful sun,
To fall and blister her!

Regan: O the blest Gods! so will you wish on me,
When the rash mood is on.

Lear: No, Regan, thou shalt never have my curse:
Thy tender-hefted nature shall not give
Thee o'er to harshness: her eyes are fierce, but thine
Do comfort and not burn. 'Tis not in thee
To grudge my pleasures, to cut off my train,
To bandy hasty words, to scant my sizes,
And, in conclusion to oppose the bolt
Against my coming in:

Storm imagery also plays an important part in the language of the play, reflecting the chaos and breakdown caused to society and the mental chaos created within Lear's mind.

King Lear

Act III Scene 2

Another part of the heath. Storm still
Enter **Lear** *and* **Fool**.

Lear: Blow, winds, and crack your cheeks! rage! blow!
You cataracts and hurricanoes, spout
Till you have drenched our steeples, drowned the cocks!
You sulph'rous and thought-executing fires,
Vaunt-couriers of oak-cleaving thunderbolts,
Singe my white head! And thou, all-shaking thunder,
Strike flat the thick rotundity o'th'world!
Crack Nature's moulds, all germens spill at once
That makes ungrateful man!

Fool: O Nuncle, court holy-water in a dry house is better than this rain-water out
o'door. Good Nuncle, in, ask thy daughters blessing; here's a night pities neither
wise men nor Fools.

Lear: Rumble thy bellyful! Spit, fire! spout, rain!
Nor rain, wind, thunder, fire, are my daughters:
I tax you not, you elements, with unkindness;
I never gave you kingdom, called you children,
You owe me no subscription: then let fall
Your horrible pleasure; here I stand, your slave,
A poor, infirm, weak, and despised old man.
But yet I call you servile ministers,
That will with two pernicious daughters join
Your high-engendered battles 'gainst a head
So old and white as this. O, ho! 'tis foul.

Activity   1 Find examples of vivid imagery in the play you are studying.
            2 Are there any links between the kind of imagery the play contains and
              the themes of the play?

3 Pick **two** examples of imagery and analyse the ways in which Shakespeare uses language to achieve his effects.

4 Now write an essay in which you analyse the imagery patterns in the play you are studying.

Verse and prose

It has often been said that Shakespeare's greatness is rooted in his ability to use language to suit all moods, occasions, and characters. Much of his work is written in **blank verse** (without rhymes and in iambic pentameter, see pages 124–5) – a flexible form which he adapts to suit many purposes, from moments of intense passion to bawdy bantering. However, we must not lose sight of the fact that Shakespeare makes substantial use of prose, too, which prompts the question 'Why does he switch between verse and prose in his plays?'

A common answer to this question is that the 'high' characters use poetry, in keeping with their elevated natures and the substance of their dialogue, while the 'low' or comic characters use the more plebeian prose. An alternative answer is that Shakespeare uses prose for sub-plots, or to indicate madness or a highly wrought emotional state in a character. It is easy to find examples to support these ideas, but it is also easy to find examples to disprove them. The truth is that all these explanations are too general and simplistic to help us much, and the real explanation is rather more complex.

For example, *Hamlet* begins with the guards, Francisco and Barnardo, who are 'ordinary' and minor characters, speaking in verse (see page 139). This helps to create a solemn and dignified tone with which to open the play, in keeping with the serious events that are about to unfold with the appearance of the Ghost. When Ophelia becomes mad she speaks prose but she also speaks prose in the 'play-within-the-play' scene where she is perfectly sane. Hamlet himself speaks both prose and verse depending on the situation and who he is speaking to. The Players speak prose when they are not performing and verse when they are in role.

In looking at Shakespeare's use of verse and prose, therefore, you need to look at the context of the specific episode to determine why Shakespeare has chosen to use language in the form he has. In every instance there will be a good dramatic reason on which his decision is based. Remember also that Shakespeare's prose is not an unplanned, casual form of writing. It is as much an art-form as his verse, and is just as carefully structured and organized.

Activity Make a note of where switches between verse and prose occur in the text you are studying. Choose four of these points. Give reasons why you think the switch is made in each case.

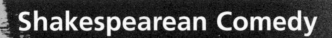

Shakespearean Comedy

There are three categories that we might use to describe Shakespearean comedy:

- the romantic comedies, which include *The Taming of the Shrew*, *Love's Labour's Lost*, *A Midsummer Night's Dream*, *Much Ado About Nothing*, *The Merchant of Venice*, *As You Like It*, and *Twelfth Night*
- the romances – *Cymbeline*, *The Winter's Tale*, *The Tempest*
- the problem comedies – *Troilus and Cressida*, *All's Well that Ends Well*, *Measure for Measure*.

In this Detailed Study we will focus on romantic comedy, illustrated through extracts from *Twelfth Night*.

Very often the romantic comedies are looked on as the 'lightweights' of Shakespearean drama, and it is true that they do not deal with serious issues in the way that the tragedies focus on them. However, it is important to realize that despite their apparently light nature and their comic characters and situations, they are 'serious' plays with real substance.

Thinking about the nature of Shakespeare's comedies will help you to understand what he is doing with this kind of drama. In many ways the structure follows the general structure of drama, which we discussed earlier:

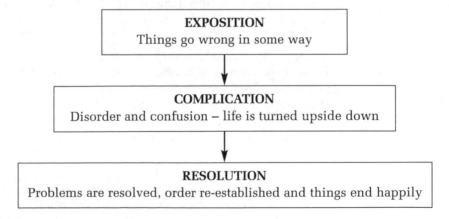

EXPOSITION
Things go wrong in some way

↓

COMPLICATION
Disorder and confusion – life is turned upside down

↓

RESOLUTION
Problems are resolved, order re-established and things end happily

The pattern of the comedies, then, follows the pattern of other Shakespearean drama, but there are key differences to do with how things work out within the general pattern.

- The actions of the characters create chaos and confusion, but whereas in a tragedy this chaos disturbs the audience, in romantic comedy the audience laughs at it.

- The perspective on events is one that focuses on comic rather than tragic views. A tragedy could very easily be changed into a comedy, and vice versa, by changing this perspective.

Activity

> Think about the last statement carefully. Choose one tragedy and one comedy that you know. Now write a brief synopsis showing how you would convert the tragedy into a comedy and the comedy into a tragedy.

The following brief plot summary will show you how the plot structure works out in *Twelfth Night*.

The play opens with Orsino, the Duke of Illyria, in love with Olivia but she does not return his love. Twins Viola and Sebastian are shipwrecked off the Coast of Illyria. Viola believes Sebastian drowned.	The exposition
Viola disguises herself as a boy (Cesario) and is welcomed at Orsino's court. Orsino sends Cesario to woo Olivia on his behalf. Olivia is not moved by Orsino's declaration of love sent via Cesario, but she does feel attracted to Cesario.	Complications
Sebastian has been saved from the shipwreck by Antonio and is on his way to Orsino's court. Antonio, though, is an enemy of Orsino's. Orsino is very unhappy at Olivia's rejection and it is clear that she is in love with Cesario. However, her love is rejected by Cesario.	Complications
There then follows a variety of incidents involving the mistaking of Viola (Cesario) for Sebastian and vice versa. Olivia mistakes Sebastian for Cesario – Sebastian in turn is amazed to be invited home by a beautiful woman. She gives him a jewel and proposes marriage to him and he agrees.	Complications
Orsino confronts Antonio, who tells him he has only come to Illyria to be with his friend. Olivia enters and thinks she has just married Cesario. Viola is amazed as she knows nothing of this. The comic confusion reaches its height when Sebastian enters. Slowly the confusion begins to unravel.	Complications
All is resolved at last as Orsino realizes he is in love with Viola and he declares a double celebration when he will marry Viola, and celebrate Olivia's marriage to Sebastian.	Resolution

The sub-plot involving Sir Toby Belch, Malvolio, and various other characters also forms an integral part of the main action, and is central to the thematic development of the play.

Activity

> If you are studying a different Shakespeare comedy, work out a brief synopsis of the plot to see in what ways it follows this pattern.

Shakespeare and the fantasy world

One of the features often found in Shakespeare's comedies is that the action takes place in an imaginary world. This is certainly true in *Twelfth Night*, which is set in the fictional land of Illyria. The fantasy setting allows the audience more readily to suspend their disbelief and enter a world where characters act in curious ways, and where events are not governed by the normal rules that regulate our society. There are, of course, points in the play where the characters experience sadness and pain, and they have to deal with realistic emotions. But the play is very much a fantasy in a number of ways:

- adults behave like unruly children
- the behaviour of the lovers as they fall in and out of love is not rational
- the storyline of the play is basically absurd – there are many unlikely events and coincidences that do not bear close scrutiny
- Malvolio, the one apparently serious person, is made a complete fool of.

It is worth noting that Feste's song at the end of the play recognizes that while the audience has temporarily escaped from reality into a fantasy world, they will have to emerge from the theatre into a less happy world.

Act V Scene 1

Feste: *(Sings)* When that I was and a little tiny boy
    With hey, ho, the wind and the rain,
A foolish thing was but a toy,
    For the rain it raineth every day.

But when I came to man's estate,
    With hey, ho, the wind and the rain,
'Gainst knaves and thieves men shut their gate,
    For the rain it raineth every day.

But when I came, alas, to wive,
    With hey, ho, the wind and the rain,
By swaggering could I never thrive,
    For the rain it raineth every day.

But when I came unto my beds,
    With hey, ho, the wind and the rain,
With toss-pots still had drunken heads,
    For the rain it raineth every day.

A great while ago the world begun,
> With hey, ho, the wind and the rain,

But that's all one, our play is done,
> And we'll strive to please you every day.

(Exit)

Openings

In the tragedies the opening scenes prepare us for what to expect. For example, in *Romeo and Juliet* the servants of the Capulet and Montague families come into conflict, which foreshadows the deeper conflict that is to come. Similarly, the openings of *Macbeth* and *Hamlet* prepare us for the troubling events that are to be portrayed.

The openings of comedies work in much the same way, in that they prepare the audience for what is to come. The opening of *Twelfth Night* prepares us, but in this case the things that are about to happen come about through coincidence, mistaken identity, disguise, and strange adventures.

Now look at the opening of the play.

Act I Scene 1

(The Duke's Palace
*Music. Enter **Orsino**, Duke of Illyria, **Curio**, and other Lords)*

Duke:	If music be the food of love, play on,
	Give me excess of it; that, surfeiting,
	The appetite may sicken, and so die.
	That strain again – it had a dying fall.
	O, it came o'er my ear like the sweet sound
	That breathes upon a bank of violets,
	Stealing and giving odour. Enough, no more,
	'Tis not so sweet now as it was before.
	O spirit of love, how quick and fresh art thou,
	That, notwithstanding thy capacity
	Receiveth as the sea, nought enters there,
	Of what validity and pitch soe'er,
	But falls into abatement and low price,
	Even in a minute! So full of shapes is fancy,
	That it alone is high fantastical.
Curio:	Will you go hunt, my lord?
Duke:	What, Curio?
Curio:	The hart.
Duke:	Why so I do, the noblest that I have.
	O when mine eyes did see Olivia first,
	Methought she purged the air of pestilence.
	That instant was I turned into a hart,
	And my desires, like fell and cruel hounds,
	E'er since pursue me.

*(Enter **Valentine**)*

How now, what news from her?

Valentine: So please my lord, I might not be admitted,
But from her handmaid do return this answer:
The element itself, till seven years' heat,
Shall not behold her face at ample view;
But like a cloistress she will veiled walk,
And water once a day her chamber round
With eye-offending brine; all this to season
A brother's dead love, which she would keep fresh
And lasting, in her sad remembrance.

Duke: O she that hath a heart of that fine frame
To pay this debt of love but to a brother,
How will she love, when the rich golden shaft
Hath killed the flock of all affections else
That live in her; when liver, brain, and heart,
These sovereign thrones, are all supplied and filled,
Her sweet perfections, with one self king.
Away before me to sweet beds of flowers:
Love-thoughts lie rich when canopied with bowers.

Activity

Look at this opening to *Twelfth Night*.
1 What do you make of Orsino's profession of love here?
2 What sort of mood does the play open with?
3 What power does music have?
4 Olivia, the woman Orsino is love-sick for, has said that she will not stop mourning for her brother for seven years. What effect does this have on the opening of the play?
5 What comfort does Orsino draw from this?

Now look at the opening of the second scene.

Act I Scene 2

(A Sea Coast
*Enter **Viola**, a **Captain**, and Sailors)*

Viola: What country, friends, is this?
Captain: This is Illyria, lady.
Viola: And what should I do in Illyria?
My brother he is in Elysium.
Perchance he is not drowned – what think you, sailors?
Captain: It is perchance that you yourself were saved.
Viola: O my poor brother, and so perchance may he be.
Captain: True, madam, and to comfort you with chance,
Assure yourself, after our ship did split,
When you and those poor number saved with you

Hung on our driving boat, I saw your brother,
Most provident in peril, bind himself –
Courage and hope both teaching him the practice –
To a strong mast that lived upon the sea;
Where, like Arion on the dolphin's back,
I saw him hold acquaintance with the waves
So long as I could see.

Viola: For saying so, there's gold.
Mine own escape unfoldeth to my hope,
Whereto thy speech serves for authority,
The like of him. Know'st thou this country?

Captain: Ay, madam, well, for I was bred and born
Not three hours' travel from this very place.

Viola: Who governs here?

Captain: A noble duke, in nature as in name.

Viola: What is his name?

Captain: Orsino.

Viola: Orsino – I have heard my father name him.
He was a bachelor then.

Captain: And so is now, or was so very late;
For but a month ago I went from hence,
And then 'twas fresh in murmur – as, you know,
What great ones do the less will prattle of –
That he did seek the love of fair Olivia.

Viola: What's she?

Captain: A virtuous maid, the daughter of a count
That died some twelvemonth since, then leaving her
In the protection of his son, her brother,
Who shortly also died; for whose dear love,
They say, she hath abjured the company
And sight of men.

Viola: O that I served that lady
And might not be delivered to the world,
Till I had made mine own occasion mellow
What my estate is.

Captain: That were hard to compass,
Because she will admit no kind of suit,
No, not the Duke's.

Viola: There is a fair behaviour in thee, captain,
And though that nature with a beauteous wall
Doth oft close in pollution, yet of thee
I will believe thou hast a mind that suits
With this thy fair and outward character.
I prithee – and I'll pay thee bounteously –
Conceal me what I am, and be my aid
For such disguise as haply shall become
The form of my intent. I'll serve this duke;
Thou shalt present me as an eunuch to him

It may be worth thy pains, for I can sing
And speak to him in many sorts of music
That will allow me very worth his service.
What else may hap to time I will commit,
Only shape thou thy silence to my wit.

Captain: Be you his eunuch, and your mute I'll be.
When my tongue blabs, then let mine eyes not see.

Viola: I thank thee. Lead me on.

(Exeunt)

Activity

What information do you draw from this scene? What clues do you get from these opening two scenes as to what might happen later? Use the information you gain about the characters, as well as the clues from the dialogue.

Thematic development

As the plot of *Twelfth Night* develops, various themes begin to emerge. These echo some of Shakespeare's central concerns in many of his plays:

- love
- appearance and reality
- order and disorder.

In *Twelfth Night* Viola is disguised as a boy in the service of Orsino. He sends her to try to woo Olivia for him. Viola has by this time fallen in love with Orsino. However, Viola now begins to realize that Olivia has fallen in love with her, believing her to be a man. Look carefully at this extract.

Act II Scene 2

Viola: Poor lady, she were better love a dream.
Disguise, I see thou art a wickedness
Wherein the pregnant enemy does much.
How easy is it for the proper false
In women's waxen hearts to set their forms.
Alas, our frailty is the cause, not we.
For such as we are made of, such we be.
How will this fadge? My master loves her dearly.
And I, poor monster, fond as much of him;
And she, mistaken, seems to dote on me.
What will become of this? As I am man,
My state is desperate for my master's love;
As I am woman, – now alas the day –
What thriftless sighs shall poor Olivia breathe.
O time, thou must untangle this, not I;
It is too hard a knot for me t'untie.

(Exit)

Activity

1 What does Viola have to say in this soliloquy?
2 How does what she says relate to the theme of appearance and reality?

As noted earlier, another thematic strand that is commonly found in the plays of Shakespeare is that of order and disorder. In *King Lear* or *Macbeth* this disruption of order has far-reaching and ultimately tragic consequences. In a comedy such as *Twelfth Night* the disruption of order ultimately adds to the comedy.

Sir Toby Belch is a key character associated with disorder. However, the sense of disorder within the play is much more deeply embedded in the play than merely in the superficial disruption of Sir Toby. The whole essence of *Twelfth Night* implies a relaxation of order and a liberal, 'festive' attitude. This is reinforced by the play's subtitle – 'What You Will'. In more subtle ways Feste, the clown, subverts order and even Viola and Sebastian play roles that contribute to disorder, in that through them conventional distinctions are broken down.

Activity

Think about the play that you are studying and write about the ways in which the theme of order/disorder is relevant to it.

Endings

At the end of a Shakespearean comedy there is always some kind of resolution, a sorting out of the confusions and misunderstandings that have developed through the action. In *Twelfth Night* the long, single closing scene of Act V resolves all the problems of the play. In this lengthy concluding scene all the various plot entanglements are disentangled and the confusions of identity are sorted out.

Even in a comedy there may be some bitter moments to be endured during this period of resolution. For example, read this extract from the closing of *Twelfth Night*.

Act V Scene 1

Duke: Is this the madman?
Olivia: Ay, my lord, this same.
         How now, Malvolio?
Malvolio: Madam, you have done me wrong,
         Notorious wrong.
Olivia: Have I, Malvolio? No.
Malvolio: Lady, you have. Pray you peruse that letter.
         You must not now deny it is your hand;
         Write from it if you can, in hand or phrase;
         Or say 'tis not your seal, not your invention;
         You can say none of this. Well, grant it then,

	And tell me, in the modesty of honour,
	Why you have given me such clear lights of favour,
	Bade me come smiling and cross-gartered to you,
	To put on yellow stockings and to frown
	Upon Sir Toby and the lighter people;
	And, acting this in an obedient hope,
	Why have you suffered me to be imprisoned,
	Kept in a dark house, visited by the priest,
	And made the most notorious geck and gull
	That e'er invention played on? Tell me why.
Olivia:	Alas, Malvolio, this is not my writing,
	Though, I confess, much like the character;
	But out of question 'tis Maria's hand.
	And now I do bethink me, it was she
	First told me thou wast mad; then cam'st in smiling,
	And in such forms which here were presupposed
	Upon thee in the letter. Prithee be content,
	This practice hath most shrewdly passed upon thee.
	But when we know the grounds and authors of it,
	Thou shalt be both the plaintiff and the judge
	Of thine own cause.
Fabian:	Good madam, hear me speak,
	And let no quarrel nor no brawl to come
	Taint the condition of this present hour,
	Which I have wondered at. In hope it shall not,
	Most freely I confess myself and Toby
	Set this device against Malvolio here,
	Upon some stubborn and uncourteous parts
	We had conceived against him. Maria writ
	The letter at Sir Toby's great importance,
	In recompense whereof he hath married her.
	How with a sportful malice it was followed
	May rather pluck on laughter than revenge,
	If that the injuries be justly weighed
	That have on both sides passed.
Olivia:	Alas, poor fool, how have they baffled thee!
Feste:	Why, 'Some are born great, some achieve greatness, and some have greatness thrown upon them.' I was one, sir, in this interlude, one Sir Topas, sir; but that's all one. 'By the Lord, fool, I am not mad.' But do you remember? – 'Madam, why laugh you at such a barren rascal? An you smile not he's gagged.' And thus the whirligig of time brings in his revenges.
Malvolio:	I'll be revenged on the whole pack of you.
	(Exit)
Olivia:	He hath been most notoriously abused.
Duke:	Pursue him, and entreat him to a peace;
	He hath not told us of the captain yet.
	*(Exit **Fabian** or some other)*

Activity   Think about the comedy that you are studying or one that you have studied in the past. How does it end? Make notes on the ways in which it fits in with the patterns we have seen with *Twelfth Night*.

Now write an essay on the nature of Shakespearean comedy, based on two plays that you have read or seen.

Part 3
World Literature

7 Comparative Study

Objectives	• To establish a strategy of approaching World Literature assignments • To practise comparing texts • To understand the requirements of the Comparative Study

If you are studying at Higher Level you will complete **two** World Literature Assignments for your Language A1 English course. If you are studying at Standard Level you will complete **one**.

All students, Standard and Higher Level, must complete Assignment 1, which involves a comparative study of at least two of the three World Literature works studied in Part 1 of the programme. Although you can, if you wish, base your assignment on three works studied in Part 1, most students write better assignments using two works. Having said that, some very good assignments have been written based on three works.

Here are some general points to bear in mind:
• You are required to study independently, under the supervision of a teacher, and to submit your written work for external assessment.

- You should choose the type and title of the assignment, although you should discuss this work with the teacher.
- You should select any aspect of the World Literature works studied in your programme for the assignment.
- Where another student has chosen to write about the same topic or aspect, you must work independently of one another and the content of your assignments must be different.
- Your assignment must be written in English.
- Your assignment must be 1000–1500 words in length and the number of words used must be stated at the end of each assignment. Quotations from works must be included in the word count, but footnotes and bibliographies are not to be included.

Assignment 1: Comparative Study

Assignment 1 must be a comparative study, based on at **least two** of the three World Literature works studied in Part 1 of the programme. It must be between 1000 and 1500 words in length.

Aspects

You must select an aspect of the Part 1 World Literature works for your assignment. The aspect selected must focus on some relevant link between the two or three works used for the assignment, and may reflect your own interests.

You may choose, for your assignment, a topic which focus on aspects such as:
- narrative technique
- characterization
- portrayal of society in the literature studied
- international perspectives on common human problems
- cross-cultural perspectives on the artist's role in society.

Approach

In writing your assignment, you should adopt the following approach:
- The assignment must be a cogent piece of writing and should include some introductory and concluding remarks, within the conventions of writing in English.
- Although the main body need not consist of a formal exposition and development of ideas, it should constitute a reasoned argument.

Structure

- The **introduction** should tell the reader the nature of the topic and how it is to be approached. It could be, for example, a brief statement of the aims of the assignment.
- The **main body** should reveal your insight into the works and your appreciation of the chosen link between the works. A variety of methods

is acceptable including, for example, Socratic Dialogue, interview, or a formal development of ideas as in an essay.
- The **conclusion** could be, for example, a brief summary and personal evaluation of the discussion or the particular achievement of the writing.

Approaching the comparison

Before you can really get to grips with the comparison, of course, you must study each of the texts carefully, looking at all the relevant features that we have discussed in earlier units. However, when you have developed a sound knowledge of the two texts you are studying, you will need to begin to think carefully about them as a pair. Of course, as you have been reading and studying them it is likely that you will have been noting links, similarities, or differences between them, but in order to fully compare them it is useful to have some kind of framework to help structure your thoughts and your work.

The following model is one way in which you could approach your comparative study.

Plan

- Identify and think about comparative areas and issues in the texts.

Analysis and explanation

- Identify, with examples, the context and structure of the texts.
- Describe and compare the features of the texts, e.g. exploration of ideas, themes, character, and linguistic issues.
- Consider and compare meanings and effects created in each text.
- Consider different ways of analysing the texts.

Evaluation

- Consider and compare the chosen aspects of the texts.

The main focus of interest will depend on the nature of the texts under discussion.

Developing your plan

Begin by establishing the framework which will provide the structure for your comparison work. In order to do this you need to identify the areas and issues within the two or three texts that you are going to compare.

Here are some of the areas you might look at:
- characters
- themes
- linguistic features

- dramatic techniques
- historical context
- social context.

We will now look at some approaches to the comparison of two texts, *The Outsider* by Albert Camus and *Metamorphosis* by Franz Kafka. To help you contextualize the passages, we will look at a brief outline of the plot of each novel.

The Outsider

In *The Outsider* Meursault, the protagonist and also narrator of the novel, is a young shipping clerk living in Algiers. The book opens as Meursault recalls his mother's death. The day after his mother's funeral Meursault meets a beautiful young woman, Marie Cardona, and the two spend the day together. They later return to Meursault's apartment where they make love. Meursault returns to his mundane life and becomes friendly with a neighbour, Raymond Sintès. One day Raymond takes Meursault and Marie to the beach to visit his friend, Masson. During this excursion they fight with a group of Arabs who then run off. After the three men return to Masson's cottage Meursault goes back to the beach with Raymond's gun. Here he meets one of the Arabs they had fought with earlier. The Arab draws a knife and Meursault shoots him once, and then fires four more bullets into his body.

He is arrested and put in jail to await trial. Several months later when his trial begins, the prosecution makes much of his apparent indifference to the death of his mother. Marie also tells the court that they began their relationship immediately after his mother's funeral. The jury and the judges are convinced that Meursault is a callous, unfeeling monster. He is convicted of premeditated murder and sentenced to be executed in public by guillotine. While awaiting his execution he thinks over his life and what he has done, but his indifference does not change. The chaplain tries to offer him comfort but Meursault does not believe in God and rejects his offers of help. Finally, as he approaches his own death he realizes how his mother must have felt when at the point of death herself – a kind of liberation and readiness to live her life again.

Metamorphosis

In *Metamorphosis*, Gregor Samsa is a young travelling salesman who lives with and selflessly supports his parents and younger sister. One morning he awakes to discover that he has turned into an insect during the night. To begin with he is concerned with the practical everyday problems of how to move about with his newly acquired multiple legs, and how he will get to the office on time.

As he has not arrived at the office the chief clerk arrives at Gregor's house to find him still shut in his bedroom unable to show himself to his family. His family think that he is unwell and they try to persuade him to open the door.

The chief clerk suggests that Gregor's strange behaviour has something to do with some cash payments which had recently been entrusted to him. Gregor is obviously dismayed at this slur on his previously unblemished reputation and tries even harder to get up and move about. And eventually, after great efforts, he manages to unlock the door and reveals himself to the others. Understandably his family is terrified and the chief clerk runs away. Finally Gregor's father pushes him back into the room and locks the door.

In Chapter 2 the family has calmed down to some extent and Gregor stays hidden away in his room. His sister takes him food and cleans up after him. His parents ignore him and try to pretend he is not there. Gregor can hear them talking about their money worries now that Gregor is not working to support them. His parents do not enter his room or see him for the first two weeks, and he is looked after entirely by his sister. However, his mother does eventually enter his room and accidentally catches sight of him and faints. When Gregor's father comes in he blames Gregor for everything and in his disgust throws apples at Gregor. One of them lodges in his back, wounding him and driving him back into his room.

In the third chapter the family's resentment of Gregor grows and even his sister stops caring for him very well. The wound on his back caused by the apple begins to fester and slowly he becomes weaker and weaker. In the end Gregor, thinking how much he loves his sister, finds that he is rejected by her and retreats into his room for a third time, where he dies. His body is cleared away by the maid. In the end the family prepare to start a new life, forgetting all about Gregor.

Activity

Now read the following passage taken from the opening of *Metamorphosis*. Think about these questions and write down your responses:

1 What is the impact of Kafka's opening sentence?
2 How is this impact reinforced in the remainder of the opening paragraph?
3 What effect is created by the details that you are given in the second paragraph?
4 What is your response to the rest of the extract? Think about the ideas it contains, the ways in which Kafka uses language, and the effects he achieves.

Metamorphosis

As Gregor Samsa awoke one morning from uneasy dreams he found himself transformed in his bed into a gigantic insect. He was lying on his hard, as if it were armour-plated, back and when he lifted his head a little he could see his dome-like brown belly divided into stiff, arched segments on top of which the bed-quilt could hardly keep in position and was about to slide off completely. His numerous legs, which were pitifully thin compared to the rest of his bulk, waved helplessly before his eyes.

What has happened to me? he thought. It was no dream. His room, a regular human bedroom, only rather too small, lay quiet between the four familiar walls. Above the table on which a collection of cloth samples was unpacked and spread out – Samsa was a commercial traveller – hung the picture which he had recently cut out of an illustrated magazine and put into a pretty gilt frame. It showed a lady, with a fur cap on and a fur stole, sitting upright and holding out to the spectator a huge fur muff into which the whole of her forearm had vanished.

Gregor's eyes turned next to the window, and the overcast sky – one could hear the raindrops beating on the window gutter – made him quite melancholy. What about sleeping a little longer and forgetting all this nonsense, he thought, but it could not be done, for he was accustomed to sleep on his right side and in his present condition he could not turn himself over. However violently he forced himself towards his right side he always rolled onto his back again. He tried it at least a hundred times, shutting his eyes to keep from seeing his struggling legs, and only desisted when he began to feel in his side a faint dull ache he had never experienced before.

Oh God, he thought, what an exhausting job I've picked on! Travelling about day in, day out. It's much more irritating work than doing the actual business in the warehouse, and on top of that there's the trouble of constant travelling, of worrying about train connexions, the bed and the irregular meals, casual acquaintances that are always new and never become intimate friends. The devil take it all! He felt a slight itching up on his belly; slowly pushed himself on his back nearer to the top of the bed so that he could lift his head more easily; identified the itching place which was surrounded by many small white spots the nature of which he could not understand, and made to touch it with a leg, but drew the leg back immediately, for the contact made a cold shiver run through him.

Franz Kafka

Here are some notes made by a student on these activities. Read them through and compare her ideas with your own.

1 • The contrast between the 'normal' and the 'absurd' in the opening sentence is very striking.
  • The image of the 'gigantic insect' is somewhat disturbing.
  • The inclusion of the words 'uneasy dreams' suggests an air of foreboding.

2 • Detailed descriptions such as: 'his hard . . . armour-plated back', 'his dome-like brown belly', 'His numerous legs . . . waved helplessly before his eyes', reinforce the disturbing opening.
  • The image of a gigantic insect lying underneath a 'bed-quilt' reinforces the absurd nature of the opening.
  • The matter-of-fact way in which Gregor is described makes the images appear all the more startling.

3 • Realization that 'It was no dream'.
  • Inclusion of materialistic elements which portray images of extravagance: 'gilt frame', 'fur cap', 'fur stole', and 'a huge fur muff into which the whole of her forearm had vanished'.

- These extravagant images contrast with the comparatively meagre 'regular . . . bedroom' which is 'rather too small'.

4 • The 'overcast sky' reasserts the sense of foreboding.
  - A sense of his helplessness and despair is created through the line 'What about sleeping a little longer and forgetting all this nonsense, he thought, but it could not be done'. This is also true of Gregor's exclamation: 'The devil take it all!' Although, it is unclear whether he is thinking about his physical condition or his job.
  - The twist in the phrase 'Oh God, he thought, what an exhausting job I've picked on!' One assumes he is referring to the effort he is putting into turning over – 'He tried it at least a hundred times' – but here he is actually referring to his job as a commercial traveller.
  - His dissatisfaction with his job is shown through descriptions of it as 'irritating work', with 'constant travelling' and 'irregular meals'.
  - A sense of his solitary existence is achieved through 'casual acquaintances that are always new and never become intimate friends'.
  - A suggestion of how, in his job, time is an added pressure is given in 'worrying about train connexions'.
  - Additional details describe his transformation. He now has 'small white spots'.
  - 'He felt a slight itching up on his belly' because of the spots; this suggests that the transformation will not be a positive change or a pleasant experience.

Activity

> Now read the second part of this opening section of the story.
> 1 What do you learn about the nature of Gregor's life and daily routine prior to his change into an insect?
> 2 How does Kafka present this picture of his life?
> 3 Look back over the whole of this opening section of the story and make notes on the following aspects of it:
>   - the ideas it contains
>   - the ways in which the characters are presented
>   - the tone of the writing
>   - the language that Kafka uses and the effects he creates.

Metamorphosis

He slid down again into his former position. This getting up early, he thought, makes one quite stupid. A man needs his sleep. Other commercials live like harem women. For instance, when I come back to the hotel of a morning to write up the orders I've got, these others are only sitting down to breakfast. Let me just try that on with my chief; I'd be sacked on the spot. Anyhow, that might be quite a good thing for me, who can tell? If I didn't have to hold my hand because of my parents I'd have given notice long ago, I'd have gone to the chief and told him exactly what I think of him. That would knock him endways from his desk! It's a queer way of acting, too, this sitting on high at a desk and talking down to employees, especially when they have to come quite near because the chief is hard of hearing. Well, there's still hope; once I've saved enough money to pay back my parents' debts to him – that should take another five or six years – I'll do it without fail. I'll cut myself completely loose then. For the moment, though, I'd better get up, since my train goes at five.

He looked at the alarm-clock ticking on the chest. Heavenly Father! he thought. It was half past six o'clock and the hands were quietly moving on, it was even past the half hour, it was getting on for a quarter to seven. Had the alarm-clock not gone off? From the bed one could see that it had been properly set for four o'clock; of course it must have gone off. Yes, but was it possible to sleep quietly through that ear-splitting noise? Well, he had not slept quietly, yet apparently all the more soundly for that. But what was he to do now? The next train went at seven o'clock; to catch that he would need to hurry like mad and his samples weren't even packed up, and he himself wasn't feeling particularly fresh and active. And even if he did catch the train he wouldn't avoid a row with the chief, since the warehouse porter would have been waiting for the five o'clock train and would have long since reported his failure to turn up. The porter was a creature of the chief's, spineless and stupid. Well, supposing he were to say he was sick? But that would be most unpleasant and would look suspicious, since during his five years' employment he had not been ill once. The chief himself would be sure to come with the sick-insurance doctor, would reproach his parents with their son's laziness, and would cut all excuses short by referring to the insurance doctor, who of course regarded all mankind as perfectly healthy malingerers. And would he be so far wrong on this occasion? Gregor really felt quite well, apart from a drowsiness that was utterly superfluous after such a long sleep, and he was even unusually hungry.

As all this was running through his mind at top speed without his being able to decide to leave his bed – the alarm-clock had just struck a quarter to seven – there came a cautious tap at the door behind the head of his bed. 'Gregor,' said a voice – it was his mother's – 'it's a quarter to seven. Hadn't you a train to catch?' That gentle voice! Gregor had a shock as he heard his own voice answering hers, unmistakably his own voice, it was true, but with a persistent horrible twittering squeak behind it like an undertone, that left the words in their clear shape only for the first moment and then rose up reverberating round them to destroy their sense, so that one could not be sure one had heard them rightly. Gregor wanted to answer at length and explain everything, but in the circumstances he confined himself to saying: 'Yes, yes, thank you, mother, I'm getting up now.' The wooden door between them must have kept the change in his voice from being noticeable outside, for his mother contented herself with this statement and shuffled away. Yet this brief exchange of words had made the other members of the family aware that Gregor was still in the house, as they had not expected, and at one of the side-doors his father was already knocking, gently, yet with his fist. 'Gregor, Gregor,' he called, 'what's the matter with you?' And after a little while he called again in a deeper voice: 'Gregor! Gregor!' At the other side-door his sister was saying in a low, plaintive tone: 'Gregor? Aren't you well? Are you needing anything?' He answered them both at once: 'I'm just ready,' and did his best to make his voice sound as normal as possible by enunciating the words very clearly and leaving long pauses between them. So his father went back to his breakfast, but his sister whispered: 'Gregor, open the door, do.' However, he was not thinking of opening the door, and felt thankful for the prudent habit he had acquired in travelling of locking all doors during the night, even at home.

Franz Kafka

Activity

Now look at the following extract. It is taken from the opening of *The Outsider* by Albert Camus.
1 What effect does Camus create in his opening paragraph?
2 What attitude does Meursault show towards the death of his mother?
3 Summarize Meursault's relationship with his mother before she died.
4 What techniques does Camus use to give us a sense of this relationship?
5 What is your response to this opening of the novel? Make notes on the following aspects of it:
  • the ideas it contains
  • the ways in which the central character is presented
  • the tone of the writing
  • the language that Camus uses and the effects he creates.

The Outsider

Mother died today. Or maybe yesterday, I don't know. I had a telegram from the home: 'Mother passed away. Funeral tomorrow. Yours sincerely.' That doesn't mean anything. It may have been yesterday.

The old people's home is at Marengo, fifty miles from Algiers. I'll catch the two o'clock bus and get there in the afternoon. Then I can keep the vigil and I'll come back tomorrow night. I asked my boss for two days off and he couldn't refuse under the circumstances. But he didn't seem pleased. I even said, 'It's not my fault.' He didn't answer. Then I thought maybe I shouldn't have said that. After all, it wasn't for me to apologize. It was more up to him to offer me his condolences. But he probably will do the day after tomorrow, when he sees me in mourning. For the moment it's almost as if mother were still alive. After the funeral though, the death will be a classified fact and the whole thing will have assumed a more official aura.

I caught the two o'clock bus. It was very hot. I ate at Céleste's restaurant, as usual. They all felt very sorry for me and Céleste told me, 'There's no one like a mother.' When I left, they came to the door with me. I was in a bit of a daze because I had to go up to Emmanuel's place to borrow a black tie and armband. He lost his uncle, a few months ago.

I had to run for the bus. It was probably all this dashing about and then the jolting and the smell of petrol and the glare of the sky reflecting off the road that made me doze off. I slept almost all the way. And when I woke up, I found myself cramped up against a soldier who smiled at me and asked me if I'd come far. I said, 'Yes' so as not to have to talk any more.

The home is just over a mile from the village. I walked it. I wanted to see mother straight away. But the caretaker told me I had to meet the warden. He was busy, so I waited a bit. The caretaker talked the whole time and then he showed me into the warden's office. He was a small, elderly man with the Legion of Honour. He looked at me with bright eyes. Then he shook my hand and held it for so long that I didn't quite know how to take it back again. He consulted a file and told me, 'Mrs Meursault came here three years ago. You were her only means of support.' I felt as if he was reproaching me for something and I started to explain. But he interrupted me, 'You've no need to justify yourself, my dear boy. I've read your mother's file. You weren't able to look after her properly. She needed a nurse. You only have a modest income. And all things considered, she was happier here.' I said, 'Yes, sir.' He added, 'You see, she had friends here, people of her own age. She could share her interests with them. You're a young man, a different generation, and she must have been bored living with you.'

It was true. When she was at home, mother used to spend all her time just watching me in silence. She cried a lot the first few days at the old people's home. But that was only because she wasn't used to it. That's partly why during this last year I hardly ever went to see her any more. And also because it meant giving up my Sunday – let alone making the effort of going to the bus stop, buying tickets and spending two hours travelling.

The warden spoke to me again. But I wasn't really listening any more. Then he said, 'I expect you'd like to see your mother.' I stood up without saying anything and he led the way to the door. On our way downstairs he explained, 'We've transferred her to our little mortuary. So as not to upset the others. Every time one of the inmates dies the others feel uneasy for two or three days. And that makes it difficult for the staff.' We crossed a courtyard where there were lots of old people, chatting in little groups. They'd stop talking as we went by, then behind us the conversations would start up again. It was like the muted chatter of budgerigars. At the door of a small building the warden stopped. 'I'll leave you now, Mr Meursault. If you need me for anything, I'll be in my office. We've arranged the funeral as usual for ten o'clock in the morning. We thought that that would enable you to watch over the departed tonight. One other thing: your mother apparently often mentioned to her friends that she wished to have a religious funeral. I've taken it upon myself to make the necessary arrangements. But I thought I should let you know.' I thanked him. Though she wasn't an atheist, mother had never given a thought to religion in her life.

I went in. It was a very bright room, with whitewashed walls and a glass roof. The furniture consisted of some chairs and some cross-shaped trestles. Two of these, in the centre of the room, were supporting a coffin. The lid was on, but a row of shiny screws, which hadn't yet been tightened down, stood out against the walnut-stained wood. Near the coffin there was an Arab nurse in a white overall, with a brightly coloured scarf on her head.

At that point the caretaker came in behind me. He must have been running. He stuttered a bit. 'We covered her up. But I was to unscrew the coffin to let you see her.' He was just going up to the coffin when I stopped him. He said, 'Don't you want to?' I answered, 'No.' He didn't say anything and I was embarrassed because I felt I shouldn't have said that. After a moment he looked at me and asked, 'Why not?' but not reproachfully, just as if he wanted to know. I said, 'I don't know.' He began twiddling his white moustache and then, without looking at me, he announced, 'I understand.' He had beautiful bright blue eyes and a reddish complexion. He offered me a chair and then he sat down just behind me. The nurse stood up and went towards the door. At that point the caretaker said to me, 'It's a chancre she's got.' I didn't understand, so I looked at the nurse and saw that she had a bandage round her head just below the eyes. Where her nose should have been, the bandage was flat. Her face seemed to be nothing but a white bandage.

Albert Camus

Here are the notes a student made in response to the questions. Read them through carefully and compare them to your own ideas. Remember, however, that very often a text can be interpreted in more than one way. There is often no 'right' answer. What matters is that you can support your ideas with reference to the text.

1 • Emotionless statement opens the novel: 'Mother died today'.
  • Confusion is created through the telegram 'Funeral tomorrow'.
  • Camus's short sentences mirror the emotionless, uncaring wording in the telegram.

2 • Meursault appears to exhibit a degree of indifference: 'Mother died today'.
  • He appears to lack any emotional attachment to his mother and this can be seen through the calm, calculated manner in which he plans his attendance at her funeral: 'I'll catch the two o'clock bus . . . get there in the afternoon . . . keep the vigil and I'll come back tomorrow night.'
  • The phrase Meursault uses to describe his mother's death as a 'classified fact' emphasizes the suggestion that he is unaffected by it and is somewhat cold in his manner.
  • He is somewhat cold and detached as he appears to concentrate more on the coffin than his mother inside: 'The lid was on, but a row of shiny screws, which hadn't yet been tightened down, stood out against the walnut-stained wood.'
  • His refuses to see his mother in the coffin.

3 • Suggestion that their relationship was a distant one through the line 'That doesn't mean anything'. This could relate to the confusion in the telegram or Meursault's feelings towards his mother's death.
  • He appears to lack compassion in his explanation of why his mother cried when she was first placed in the home '. . . that was only because she wasn't used to it'.
  • This idea is developed further as he states that visiting his mother in the home meant 'giving up my Sunday'.
  • His lack of interest in his mother, and lack of knowledge about her, is suggested in his response to being told that she had asked for a religious funeral: 'Though she wasn't an atheist, mother had never given a thought to religion in her life'.

4 • Camus's use of first-person narrative emphasizes the fact that Meursault's indifferent reaction to his mother's death is an honest one and not merely the assessment of an observer.
  • Camus also includes minor characters through which Meursault's detachment from his mother can be recognized. This can be seen quite clearly through his interactions with the caretaker when asked if he wishes to see his mother's body.
  • Through the line 'But the caretaker told me I had to meet the warden' Camus gives another indication that Meursault's relationship with his mother was not close, as one might expect that he himself would request to see the warden.

5 Ideas:
  • attitude towards death
  • mother/son relationship
  • the guilt associated with putting a relative in a nursing home
  • the attitude towards other cultures through the distinction of race: 'an Arab nurse'
  • the lack of concern by employers for their employees.

Central character:
  • Meursault is presented as cold and unfeeling with regard to his relationship with, and the death of, his mother.
  • His concentration on the physical environment and physical attributes of people rather than emotional involvement reasserts the idea that he is cold and indifferent.
  • He displays a characteristic attention to detail both through his observations of other characters and the environment, and through the attentive planning of his journey.
  • He is in a subordinate position in his place of work.
  • He is unsure how to react in social situations: 'I said, "yes" so as not to have to talk any more'; 'he shook my hand and held it for so long that I didn't quite know how to take it back again'.

Tone of the writing:
  • An uneasy tone is created through Meursault's indifference at the death of his mother.
  • A sense of foreboding is created through the somewhat misplaced comment directed towards his boss when Meursault is asking for time off work: 'It's not my fault'.
  • A degree of sadness is created through the presentation of an old lady weeping while in the nursing home.

Language:
  • The inclusion of the comment that the nursing home is 'fifty miles from Algiers' emphasizes the distance evident in the relationship between the mother and son.
  • The piece is largely constructed of short sentences, which inhibits reader engagement. This mirrors the lack of engagement between mother and son.
  • His omission of emotional references gives the piece a somewhat 'clinical' feel – this also supports the idea of their relationship being unfeeling and distant.

- The description of the residents as 'inmates' connotes a prison-like environment.
- The line '. . . there were lots of old people, chatting in little groups' is somewhat patronizing and disrespectful.
- The contrast between the way Meursault describes his mother as being 'dead' and the warden's euphemistic 'departed' emphasizes the different reactions towards her death by the two.

Activity   Read over these two openings again and write an essay of approximately 500 words comparing the two extracts. You should consider the following:

- the ways in which the characters are presented
- ideas or themes that might be suggested
- the ways in which the writers use language and the effects they achieve
- any other ideas or features that you have found interesting.

Activity   Here is how one student began her essay on these openings. Read it through and make a note of any points you think important.

A comparison of the openings of *Metamorphosis* by Franz Kafka and *The Outsider* by Albert Camus

The openings to the novels *The Outsider* and *Metamorphosis* both concentrate on the reactions of individuals to a change in circumstances. In *Metamorphosis* we see how Gregor awakes to find himself changed into 'a gigantic insect' and in *The Outsider* how Meursault reacts to the death of his mother. Although these are very different circumstances, their reactions in some ways are quite similar. For instance, both display a degree of indifference to the changes that have taken place and both are related in a matter-of-fact manner.

In both openings the theme of isolation appears to be explored. For instance, both Gregor and Meursault appear to be solitary characters, though for very different reasons. Meursault appears to lack the ability to engage socially, as can be seen in his reluctance to engage with the soldier on the bus: 'I said, "Yes" so as not to have to talk any more.' However, Gregor's solitary lifestyle seems to be caused by his job as a commercial traveller: 'casual acquaintances that are always new and never become intimate friends'. Indeed Gregor appears to be extremely dissatisfied with his job due to the restrictions it places on his life, as it involves 'irritating work', with 'constant travelling' and 'irregular meals', etc.

It is interesting to see how both writers include elaborate descriptions in their novels. For instance, Kafka's description of the changes to Gregor's body are very detailed: 'his dome-like brown belly divided into stiff, arched segments . . . His numerous legs . . . waved helplessly before his eyes.' The attention to the details of the coffin in which Meursault's mother lies is similar to this: 'The lid was on, but a row of shiny screws, which hadn't yet been tightened down, stood out against the walnut-stained wood.' However, this level of description is reserved for physical aspects in both works, thus emphasizing the lack of emotional engagement and reasserting the idea of emotional detachment and isolation.

You might have noted some of the following features in this student's handling of the opening of this essay.

- The opening paragraph focuses on both texts and makes it clear that a comparison is being made between them.
- This paragraph indicates that there are differences but also similarities between the two, and an example is given.
- There is also a reference to the significance of the 'tone' of the two texts.
- The second paragraph begins to explore a thematic link between the two, together with some detailed supporting evidence from the texts.
- A comparison is made of the writers' styles, again well-supported through reference to the text.

Although these works are very different in nature they do have some features in common. One of the key points of similarity is the themes they deal with. If you read the whole texts for yourself, you might see the following ideas emerging.

Metamorphosis

- Isolation is a key theme. After Gregor has changed into an insect he becomes increasingly isolated from his family and is ultimately rejected by them. The chief clerk runs away from him and his father throws apples at him (indirectly, therefore, being responsible for his death). Gregor's isolation is increased by the fact that physical movement and speech are difficult for him.
- Questions are raised about the purpose of existence. Before his transformation, Gregor is unhappy and dissatisfied with his work but is trapped in it because he needs to support his family. He accepts his miserable existence.
- The purpose of human lives in the modern world is questioned. Kafka symbolically portrays how far human beings can be reduced and how life's struggle can become futile.
- The absurdity of life is symbolically reflected in the absurdity of the idea that a person could change into an insect. What is Kafka trying to do with this story? It poses questions about the difference between the significant and the insignificant.

The Outsider

- Isolation is also a key theme of *The Outsider*. As the title suggests, Meursault feels himself to be alienated from the 'ordinary' human life that surrounds him.
- He embodies the absurdity of life, working at a mundane job he does not enjoy and trying to fill his spare time with activity, but he often finds himself purposeless and without motivation.
- Love as an emotion has no meaning for him, and he finds no fulfilment in relationships.
- *The Outsider* is a difficult work to interpret. Is it about the meaningless of life? In the end, is Meursault's death as meaningless as his life? In a sense he welcomes death.

Activity   The following two passages are taken from near the end of the texts. In the first one Meursault is found guilty of murder and sentenced to be executed by decapitation. The second extract describes the final rejection and death of Gregor.

Read them carefully and write an essay of 500–750 words in which you explore the two texts. You should consider the following aspects:

- the ways in which the characters are presented
- ideas or themes that might be suggested
- the ways in which the writers use language and the effects they achieve
- any other ideas or features that you have found interesting.

The Outsider

That afternoon the huge fans were still churning up the dense atmosphere in the courtroom and the jurymen were all waving their little coloured fans in the same direction. I thought my lawyer's speech was never going to end. At one point though I listened because he said, 'It's true that I killed a man.' Then he went on like that, saying 'I' every time he meant me. I was very surprised. I leant over to one of the policemen and asked him why this was. He told me to be quiet and a moment later added, 'Lawyers always do that.' It seemed to me that it was just another way of excluding me from the proceedings, reducing me to insignificance and, in a sense, substituting himself for me. But I think I was already a very long way from that courtroom. Besides, I thought my lawyer was ridiculous. He made a quick plea of provocation and then he too started talking about my soul. But he didn't seem to have nearly as much talent as the prosecutor. 'I too,' he said, 'have peered into this man's soul, but unlike my eminent colleague from the State Prosecutor's office, I did find something there and in fact I read it like an open book.' He'd read that I was an honest chap, a regular and tireless worker who was faithful to the company that employed him, popular with everyone and sympathetic to the misfortunes of others. To him I was a model son who had supported his mother for as long as he could. In the end I'd hoped that an old people's home would give the old lady the comforts which my limited means prevented me from providing for her. 'I am amazed, gentlemen,' he added, 'that such a fuss has been made of this home. For after all, if proof were needed of the importance and usefulness of these institutions, one need only say that it is the state itself which subsidizes them.' The only thing was that he didn't talk about the funeral and I felt that this was an important omission in his speech. But what with all these long sentences and the endless days and hours that people had been talking about my soul, I just had the impression that I was drowning in some sort of colourless liquid.

In the end all I remember is that, echoing towards me from out in the street and crossing the vast expanse of chambers and courtrooms as my lawyer went on talking, came the sound of an ice-seller's trumpet. I was assailed by memories of a life which was no longer mine, but in which I'd found my simplest and most lasting pleasures: the smells of summer, the part of town that I loved, the sky on certain evenings, Marie's dresses and the way she laughed. And the utter pointlessness of what I was doing here took me by the throat and all I wanted was to get it over with and to go back to my cell and sleep. I hardly even heard my lawyer exclaim finally that the jury would surely not send an honest worker to his death just because he forgot himself for a moment, and then appeal for extenuating circumstances since my surest punishment for this crime was the eternal remorse with which I was already stricken. The court was adjourned and the lawyer sat down, looking exhausted. But his colleagues came over to shake hands with him. I heard a 'magnificent, old chap'. One of them even called me to witness. 'Eh?' he said. I agreed, but it was hardly a sincere compliment, because I was too tired.

However, the sun was getting low outside and it wasn't so hot any more. From the few street noises that I could hear, I sensed the calm of evening. There we all were, waiting. And what we were all waiting for concerned no one but me. I looked round the room again. Everything was just as it had been on the first day. I met the eye of the journalist in the grey jacket and of the little robot-woman. That reminded me that I hadn't looked for Marie once during the whole trial. I hadn't forgotten her, only I'd been too busy. I saw her sitting between Céleste and Raymond. She gave me a little wave as if to say, 'At last,' and I saw a rather anxious smile on her face. But my heart felt locked and I couldn't even smile back.

The judges returned. The jury was very rapidly read a series of questions. I heard 'guilty of murder . . .', 'premeditation . . .', 'extenuating circumstances'. The jury went out and I was taken into the little room where I'd waited once already. My lawyer came to join me: he was very talkative and spoke to me in a more confident and friendly way than he'd ever done before. He thought that everything would be all right and that I'd get off with a few years of prison or hard labour. I asked him whether there was any chance of getting the sentence quashed if it was unfavourable. He said no. His tactics had been not to lodge any objections so as not to antagonize the jury. He explained that they didn't quash sentences just like that, for no reason. It seemed obvious and I accepted his argument. Looking at it coldly, it was completely natural. If the opposite were the case, there'd be far too much pointless paperwork. 'Anyway,' my lawyer told me, 'you can always appeal. But I'm convinced the outcome will be favourable.'

We waited a very long time, almost three quarters of an hour, I think. At the end of that time a bell rang. My lawyer left me, saying, 'The foreman of the jury is going to read out the verdict. You'll only be brought in for the passing of the sentence.' Some doors banged. People were running up and down stairs, but I couldn't tell how far away they were. Then I heard a muffled voice reading something out in the courtroom. When the bell rang again and the door to the dock opened, what greeted me was the silence that filled the room, the silence and that strange sensation I had when I discovered that the young journalist had looked away. I didn't look over at Marie. I didn't have time to because the judge told me in a peculiar way that I would be decapitated in a public square in the name of the French people. And I think I recognized the expression that I could see on every face. I'm quite sure it was one of respect. The policemen were very gentle with me. The lawyer placed his hand on my wrist. I'd stopped thinking altogether. But the judge asked me if I had anything to add. I thought it over. I said, 'No.' That was when they took me away.

Albert Camus

Metamorphosis

'We must try to get rid of it,' his sister now said explicitly to her father, since her mother was coughing too much to hear a word, 'it will be the death of both of you, I can see that coming. When one has to work as hard as we do, all of us, one can't stand this continual torment at home on top of it. At least I can't stand it any longer.' And she burst into such a passion of sobbing that her tears dropped on her mother's face, where she wiped them off mechanically.

'My dear,' said the old man sympathetically, and with evident understanding, 'but what can we do?'

Gregor's sister merely shrugged her shoulders to indicate the feeling of helplessness that had now over-mastered her during her weeping fit, in contrast to her former confidence.

'If he could understand us,' said her father, half questioningly; Grete, still sobbing, vehemently waved a hand to show how unthinkable that was.

'If he could understand us,' repeated the old man, shutting his eyes to consider his daughter's conviction that understanding was impossible, 'then perhaps we might come to some agreement with him. But as it is – '

'He must go,' cried Gregor's sister, 'that's the only solution, Father. You must just try to get rid of the idea that this is Gregor. The fact that we've believed it for so long is the root of all our trouble. But how can it be Gregor? If this were Gregor, he would have realized long ago that human beings can't live with such a creature, and he'd have gone away of his own accord. Then we wouldn't have any brother, but we'd be able to go on living and keep his memory in honour. As it is, this creature persecutes us, drives away our lodgers, obviously wants the whole apartment to himself and would have us all sleep in the gutter. Just look, Father,' she shrieked all at once, 'he's at it again!' And in an access of panic that was quite incomprehensible to Gregor she even quitted her mother, literally thrusting the chair from her as if she would rather sacrifice her mother than stay so near to Gregor, and rushed behind her father, who also rose up, being simply upset by her agitation, and half spread his arms out as if to protect her.

Yet Gregor had not the slightest intention of frightening anyone, far less his sister. He had only begun to turn round in order to crawl back to his room, but it was certainly a startling operation to watch, since because of his disabled condition he could not execute the difficult turning movements, except by lifting his head and then bracing it against the floor over and over again. He paused and looked round. His good intentions seemed to have been recognized; the alarm had only been momentary. Now they were all watching him in melancholy silence. His mother lay in her chair, her legs stiffly outstretched and pressed together, her eyes almost closing for sheer weariness; his father and his sister were sitting beside each other, his sister's arm around the old man's neck.

Perhaps I can go on turning round now, thought Gregor, and began his labours again. He could not stop himself from panting with the effort, and had to pause now and then to take breath. Nor did anyone harass him, he was left entirely to himself. When he had completed the turn-round he began at once to crawl straight back. He was amazed at the distance separating him from his room and could not understand how in his weak state he had managed to accomplish the same journey so recently, almost without remarking it. Intent on crawling as fast as possible, he barely noticed that not a single word, not an ejaculation from his family, interfered with his progress. Only when he was already in the doorway did he turn his head round, not completely, for his neck muscles were getting stiff, but enough to see that nothing had changed behind him except that his sister had risen to her feet. His last glance fell on his mother, who was now quite overcome by sleep.

Hardly was he well inside his room when the door was hastily pushed shut, bolted and locked. The sudden noise in his rear startled him so much that his little legs gave beneath him. It was his sister who had shown such haste. She had been standing ready waiting and had made a light spring forward, Gregor had not even heard her coming, and she cried 'At last!' to her parents as she turned the key in the lock.

'And what now?' said Gregor to himself, looking round in the darkness. Soon he made the discovery that he was now unable to stir a limb. This did not surprise him, rather it seemed unnatural that he should ever actually have been able to move on these feeble little legs. Otherwise he felt relatively comfortable. True, his whole body was aching, but it seemed that the pain was gradually growing less and would finally pass away. The rotting apple in his back and the inflamed path around it, all covered with soft dust, already hardly troubled him. He thought of his family with tenderness and love. The decision that he must disappear was one that he held to even more strongly than his sister – if that were possible. In this state of vacant and peaceful meditation he remained until the tower clock struck three in the morning. The first broadening of light in the world outside the window entered his consciousness once more. Then his head sank to the floor of its own accord and from his nostrils came the last faint flicker of his breath.

When the charwoman arrived early in the morning – what between her strength and her impatience she slammed all the doors so loudly, never mind how often she had been begged not to do so, that no one in the whole apartment could enjoy any quiet sleep after her arrival – she noticed nothing unusual as she took her customary peep into Gregor's room. She thought he was lying motionless on purpose, pretending to be in the sulks; she credited him with every kind of intelligence. Since she happened to have a long-handled broom in her hand she tried to tickle him up with it from the doorway. When that too produced no reaction she felt provoked and poked at him a little harder, and only when she had pushed him along the floor without meeting any resistance was her attention aroused. It did not take her long to establish the truth of the matter, and her eyes widened, she let out a whistle, yet did not waste much time over it but tore open the door of the Samsas' bedroom and yelled into the darkness at the top of her voice: 'Just look at this, it's dead; it's lying here dead and done for!'

Mr and Mrs Samsa started up in their double bed and before they realized the nature of the charwoman's announcement had some difficulty in overcoming the shock of it. But then they got out of bed quickly, one on either side, Mr Samsa throwing a blanket over his shoulders, Mrs Samsa in nothing but her nightgown; in this array they entered Gregor's room. Meanwhile the door of the living-room opened, too, where Grete had been sleeping since the advent of the lodgers; she was completely dressed as if she had not been to bed, which seemed to be confirmed also by the paleness of her face. 'Dead?' said Mrs Samsa, looking questioningly at the charwoman, although she could have investigated for herself, and the fact was obvious enough without investigation. 'I should say so,' said the charwoman, proving her words by pushing Gregor's corpse a long way to one side with her broomstick. Mrs Samsa made a movement as if to stop her, but checked it. 'Well,' said Mr Samsa, 'now thanks be to God.' He crossed himself, and the three women followed his example. Grete, whose eyes never left the corpse, said: 'Just see how thin he was. It's such a long time since he's eaten anything. The food came out again just as it went in.' Indeed, Gregor's body was completely flat and dry, as could only now be seen when it was no longer supported by the legs and nothing prevented one from looking closely at it.

'Come in beside us, Grete, for a little while,' said Mrs Samsa with a tremulous smile, and Grete, not without looking back at the corpse, followed her parents into their bedroom. The charwoman shut the door and opened the window wide. Although it was so early in the morning a certain softness was perceptible in the fresh air. After all, it was already the end of March.

Franz Kafka

Activity Now think about the assignment that you are going to do work on for your World Literature assessment. Make a note of all the texts that you might consider basing the assignment on and think about possible pairings for a comparative assignment.

The topic

When you have decided on the texts you are going to compare in your assignment, you need to think of a suitable topic. You can discuss your ideas with your teacher and he or she can help to make sure that your topic is appropriate and well-focused, but your teacher is not allowed to set the topic for you. You must have some ideas of your own.

The title

When you have chosen your topic you will need to think of a suitable assignment title. Remember that your title should allow you to show the key things that you will be assessed on. Your assignment should allow you to:

- show that you can produce an effective piece of comparative literary analysis
- compare the literary aspects common to the Part 1 works studied in the course
- explore possible links or relationships between the works
- show insight into the works and a personal engagement and appreciation of relevant similarities and differences through your analysis.

Your title should be closely focused on specific ideas, issues, or features of the works, rather than indicating broad topic areas. For example, thinking again about *Metamorphosis* and *The Outsider*, a title such as 'The presentation of the theme of the futility of life in *Metamorphosis* and *The Outsider*' is better than 'The themes of *Metamorphosis* and *The Outsider*.'

Similarly, a title like 'The relationship between plot structure and character development in *Metamorphosis* and *The Outsider*' is better than 'Characterization in *Metamorphosis* and *The Outsider*'.

The outline

When you have decided on your title you then need to prepare an outline of your assignment in which you plan how you will approach it and structure your ideas. Again you should discuss your ideas with your teacher before you begin to write your first draft.

The first draft

You are now ready to write the first draft of your assignment. When you have completed this you can give it to your teacher, who can read it and make general comments on it. Your teacher is not allowed to mark it or write any comments on it, however.

Further drafts

After you have completed your first draft and have had some general feedback from your teacher on it, you can go on to write further drafts or, if you feel ready, to complete a final draft. After the first draft stage your teacher cannot give any further feedback to you. You now need to work on the assignment on your own.

Summary   Here is a summary of the stages you need to go through in producing your assignment:

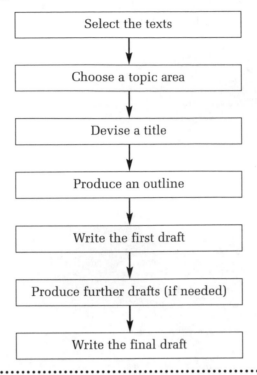

Assessment of your work

Your work will be assessed under four separate criteria. These are:

- Selection of the aspect and its treatment
- Knowledge and understanding of works
- Presentation
- Language.

In order to achieve a good mark you will need to:

- choose an aspect appropriate to the assignment
- ensure that your chosen aspect has a relevant focus
- make sure that your ideas show independence of thought and your treatment is relevant to the aspect chosen
- show detailed knowledge of, and good insight into, the aspects of the works most relevant to the assignment
- show clear and meaningful linking of works
- show good appreciation of the cultural setting relevant to the assignment, where appropriate
- show a clear and logical structure to the assignment
- show precise and pertinent references to the works

- remain within the prescribed word limit
- use an effective register appropriate for the assignment selected
- follow closely the conventions of written work
- write fluently and clearly.

8 Comparative, Imaginative, and Detailed Study

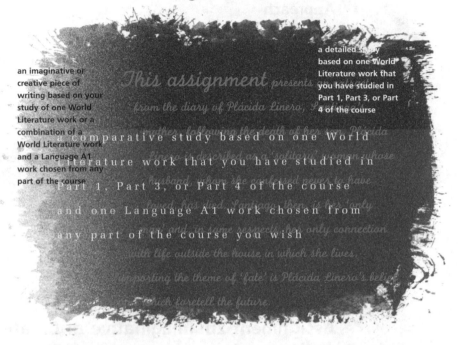

Objectives

- To establish a strategy of approaching World Literature assignments
- To understand the requirements of Comparative, Imaginative, and Detailed Study assignments

If you are studying at Higher Level you will need to complete a second World Literature assignment. For this assignment you must choose one of three alternatives. Here is an outline of what is involved in each of the choices. Remember – you choose only **one** option.

Assignment 2a: Comparative Study

If you choose this option you must undertake a comparative study based on one World Literature work that you have studied in Part 1, Part 3, or Part 4 of the course and one Language A1 work chosen from any part of the course you wish. Note that the World Literature work that you study must not be one that you have used for Assignment 1.

To meet the requirements of this option you must:

- focus on some pertinent link between the two works
- compare the literary aspects of the works

- explore possible links and relationships between the works
- show insight and appreciation of any cultural similarities and differences between the works
- show personal engagement with the works.

Approach

In writing your assignment you should adopt the following approach:

- The assignment must be based on convincing ideas and interpretations.
- It should include an introduction and conclusion.
- The main body of your assignment should present a reasoned argument.

Structure

- The **introduction** could be, for example, a brief statement of the aims of the assignment.
- The **main body** should reveal your insight into the works and your appreciation of the chosen link between the works. There are various ways in which you could approach this such as an interview, or a formal essay in which you develop your ideas.
- The **conclusion** could consist of a brief summary together with your own evaluation of the discussion.

Assignment 2b: Imaginative or Creative Assignment

If you choose this option you will need to produce an imaginative or creative piece of writing based on your study of one World Literature work or a combination of a World Literature work and a Language A1 work chosen from any part of the course. The World Literature work that you choose can be a work studied in Part 1, Part 3, or Part 4 of the course, but it must not be one that you have used for Assignment 1.

This assignment **must** be preceded by a Statement of Intent. This is an essential part of the assignment, which allows you to explain your understanding and interpretation of an author's imagination, values, and techniques.

Your Statement of Intent must immediately precede the body of the assignment and must include a brief explanation of all of the following:

- the work(s) on which the assignment will be based
- the nature of the task you are undertaking, including considerations such as audience, register, and form
- the aspects or elements of the work(s) on which you intend to focus
- how you intend to explore these aspects or elements.

The Statement of Intent must be included in the word count. The length of the statement will depend on the kind of the piece you are writing for the assignment, but normally it should not be longer than 500 words. However, where the assignment takes the form of a single piece of writing, such as a short poem, the statement may be longer than the body of the assignment and longer than 500 words. Whatever the length of the assignment itself, the total number of words must be between 1000 and 1500.

Suggested approaches

There are many possibilities for creative approaches to World Literature assignments, which give you the opportunity to exercise your imagination and ingenuity while at the same time bringing you to a deeper understanding of the work(s) being explored and to an increased appreciation of the writer. The IBO provide the following list of suggestions for assignments:

- The diary of a character, accompanied by critical comment by the candidate.
- A director's letter to the actor playing a particular role or scene.
- An exercise in which the candidate turns the 'story' or a portion of it into another form, such as dramatic monologue, biblical parable, folk tale, or myth.
- A critic's review of a dramatic interpretation/performance.
- An editorial objecting to censorship or exclusion of a work from a school syllabus.
- A letter to a publisher outlining the merits of a work to be published and reasons for publication.
- The creation of dramatic monologues that play the self-perception of the characters against the views of other characters or the author.
- A transcription either of an imaginary interview with the author about the work in question or of a conversation between two authors about their respective works.
- A postscript to a novel, or an extra chapter.
- An additional scene for a play.
- A pastiche (an imitation or re-creation of an already published work). In this type of assignment, you should demonstrate sensitivity to, and understanding of, a work by producing an original composition after the manner of that work.

The assignment should allow you to:
- show the skills of imaginative or creative writing
- focus on and explore a particular literary aspect of the work that interests you
- show an appreciation of relevant cultural aspects of the work
- show both an explicit (through the Statement of Intent) and implicit (through the creative assignment itself) awareness of the ways in which the writer uses language and imagination and presents values and attitudes through the work.

Assignment 2c: Detailed Study

If you choose this option you will need to write a detailed study based on **one** World Literature work that you have studied in Part 1, Part 3, or Part 4 of the course. However, you must not use a work that you have already used for Assignment 1. Your assignment could take the form of a formal essay, or a commentary, or an analysis of one or two key passages.

If extracts are chosen for analysis or commentary, they should **not** be included in the word count, but copies must be attached to the assignment when submitted for assessment.

Approaches

There are a number of possible approaches to this type of assignment. The IBO makes the following suggestions:

- **A formal essay** A formal piece of writing which follows a logical sequence.

- **Analysis of a key passage** The most important word here is 'key'. The passage for study, whether a paragraph, a page, a chapter, or an extract from a poem, should have major significance for any of a variety of explorations that you might choose to make, for example prose or poetic style, character study, plot development, or theme. The reason why you have chosen the passage should be briefly explained and the body of the assignment should explain the significance of the passage in the larger work from which it has been taken.

- **Analysis of two key passages** Two significant passages from the same work could be selected in order to explore, for example, contrasting prose styles, descriptive method, character presentation, and a range of other aspects. You need to justify briefly why the passages you have chosen are of key importance within the works and to demonstrate the particular similarities and differences which you consider interesting.

- **Commentary on an extract** In this exercise an extract, of approximately 30 lines of prose or the equivalent in drama or verse, is taken from a work for in-depth analysis. You should justify briefly your selection of the particular extract, and the body of your assignment should explore how language, imagery, organization of ideas, and stylistic and thematic aspects work in the passage.

We will now look in a little more detail at each of these options.

2a Comparative Study

If you choose this option for your assignment the first thing you will need to think carefully about is which texts to base your assignment on, making sure that you have plenty of scope to undertake your comparative analysis. Having decided on your texts, you will need to think of a title for your assignment. This needs very careful thought. Your title should indicate specific, focused topics, rather than general broad ones. For example, 'A comparison of the presentation and significance of the characters of Winston Smith and Ivan Denisovich in *1984* and *One Day in the Life of Ivan Denisovich*' is better than 'A comparison of Winston Smith and Ivan Denisovich in *1984* and *One Day in the Life of Ivan Denisovich*'.

Activity

Read the following two extracts carefully. The first is from the opening of George Orwell's novel *1984* and the second is from Alexander Solzhenitsyn's novel *One Day in the Life of Ivan Denisovich*.

1 How does each writer capture the reader's attention in the opening paragraphs?
2 What techniques do the writers use to create a vivid picture of the scenes they describe?
3 How would you describe the tone of each piece?
4 What impression do you get of the central character in each extract? How do the writers convey these impressions?
5 What is your overall response to each extract? Give reasons for your comments.
6 Which extract do you find most effective as the opening to a novel? Why?

When you have finished your work, compare your answers with another student's and discuss your ideas.

Nineteen Eighty-Four

It was a bright cold day in April, and the clocks were striking thirteen. Winston Smith, his chin nuzzled into his breast in an effort to escape the vile wind, slipped quickly through the glass doors of Victory Mansions, though not quickly enough to prevent a swirl of gritty dust from entering along with him.

The hallway smelt of boiled cabbage and old rag mats. At one end of it a coloured poster, too large for indoor display, had been tacked to the wall. It depicted simply an enormous face, more than a metre wide: the face of a man of about forty-five, with a heavy black moustache and ruggedly handsome features. Winston made for the stairs. It was no use trying the lift. Even at the best of times it was seldom working, and at present the electric current was cut off during daylight hours. It was part of the economy drive in preparation for Hate Week. The flat was seven flights up, and Winston, who was thirty-nine and had a varicose ulcer above his right ankle, went slowly, resting several times on the way. On each landing, opposite the lift-shaft, the poster with the enormous face gazed from the wall. It was one of those pictures which are so contrived that the eyes follow you about when you move. BIG BROTHER IS WATCHING YOU, the caption beneath it ran.

Inside the flat a fruity voice was reading out a list of figures which had something to do with the production of pig-iron. The voice came from an oblong metal plaque like a dulled mirror which formed part of the surface of the right-hand wall. Winston turned a switch and the voice sank somewhat, though the words were still distinguishable. The instrument (the telescreen, it was called) could be dimmed, but there was no way of shutting it off completely. He moved over to the window: a smallish, frail figure, the meagreness of his body merely emphasized by the blue overalls which were the uniform of the Party. His hair was very fair, his face naturally sanguine, his skin roughened by coarse soap and blunt razor blades and the cold of the winter that had just ended.

Outside, even through the shut window-pane, the world looked cold. Down in the street little eddies of wind were whirling dust and torn paper into spirals, and though the sun was shining and the sky a harsh blue, there seemed to be no colour in anything, except the posters that were plastered everywhere. The black-moustachio'd face gazed down from every commanding corner. There was one on the house-front immediately opposite. BIG BROTHER IS WATCHING YOU, the caption said, while the dark eyes looked deep into Winston's own. Down at street level another poster, torn at one corner, flapped fitfully in the wind, alternately covering and uncovering the single word INGSOC. In the far distance a helicopter skimmed down between the roofs, hovered for an instant like a bluebottle, and darted away again with a curving flight. It was the police patrol, snooping into people's windows. The patrols did not matter, however. Only the Thought Police mattered.

Behind Winston's back the voice from the telescreen was still babbling away about pig-iron and the overfulfilment of the Ninth Three-Year Plan. The telescreen received and transmitted simultaneously. Any sound that Winston made, above the level of a very low whisper, would be picked up by it; moreover, so long as he remained within the field of vision which the metal plaque commanded, he could be seen as well as heard. There was of course no way of knowing whether you were being watched at any given moment. How often, or on what system, the Thought Police plugged in on any individual wire was guesswork. It was even conceivable that they watched everybody all the time. But at any rate they could plug in your wire whenever they wanted to. You had to live – did live, from habit that became instinct – in the assumption that every sound you made was overheard, and, except in darkness, every movement scrutinized.

Winston kept his back turned to the telescreen. It was safer; though, as he well knew, even a back can be revealing. A kilometre away the Ministry of Truth, his place of work, towered vast and white above the grimy landscape. This, he thought with a sort of vague distaste – this was London, chief city of Airstrip One, itself the third most populous of the provinces of Oceania. He tried to squeeze out some childhood memory that should tell him whether London had always been quite like this. Were there always these vistas of rotting nineteenth-century houses, their sides shored up with baulks of timber, their windows patched with cardboard and their roofs with corrugated iron, their crazy garden walls sagging in all directions? And the bombed sites where the plaster dust swirled in the air and the willow-herb straggled over the heaps of rubble; and the places where the bombs had cleared a larger patch and there had sprung up sordid colonies of wooden dwellings like chicken-houses? But it was no use, he could not remember; nothing remained of his childhood except a series of bright-lit tableaux occurring against no background and mostly unintelligible.

The Ministry of Truth – Minitrue, in Newspeak – was startlingly different from any other object in sight. It was an enormous pyramidal structure of glittering white concrete, soaring up, terrace after terrace, 300 metres into the air. From where Winston stood it was just possible to read, picked out on its white face in elegant lettering, the three slogans of the party:

WAR IS PEACE

FREEDOM IS SLAVERY

IGNORANCE IS STRENGTH

George Orwell

One Day in the Life of Ivan Denisovich

As usual, at five o'clock that morning reveille was sounded by the blows of a hammer on a length of rail hanging up near the staff quarters. The intermittent sound barely penetrated the window-panes on which the frost lay two fingers thick, and they ended almost as soon as they'd begun. It was cold outside, and the camp-guard was reluctant to go on beating out the reveille for long.

The clanging ceased, but everything outside still looked like the middle of the night when Ivan Denisovich Shukhov got up to go to the bucket. It was pitch dark except for the yellow light cast on the window by three lamps – two in the outer zone, one inside the camp itself.

And no one came to unbolt the barrack-hut door; there was no sound of the barrack-orderlies pushing a pole into place to lift the barrel of nightsoil and carry it out.

Shukhov never overslept reveille. He always got up at once, for the next ninety minutes, until they assembled for work, belonged to him, not to the authorities, and any old-timer could always earn a bit – by sewing a pair of over-mittens for someone out of old sleeve lining; or bringing some rich lag in the team his dry valenki* – right up to his bunk, so that he wouldn't have to stumble barefoot round the heaps of boots looking for his own pair; or going the rounds of the store-huts, offering to be of service, sweeping up this or fetching that; or going to the mess-hall to collect bowls from the tables and bring them stacked to the dishwashers – you're sure to be given something to eat there, though there were plenty of others at that game, more than plenty – and, what's worse, if you found a bowl with something left in it you could hardly resist licking it out. But Shukhov had never forgotten the words of his first team-leader, Kuziomin – a hard-bitten prisoner who had already been in for twelve years by 1943 – who told the newcomers, just in from the front, as they sat beside a fire in a desolate cutting in the forest:

'Here, lads, we live by the law of the taiga. But even here people manage to live. D'you know who are the ones the camps finish off? Those who lick other men's left-overs, those who set store by the doctors, and those who peach on their mates.'

---

* Knee-length felt boots for winter wear

As for the peachers, he was wrong there. Those people were sure to get through the camp all right. Only, they were saving their own skin at the expense of other people's blood.

Shukhov always arose at reveille. But this day he didn't. He had felt queer the evening before, feverish, with pains all over his body. He hadn't been able to get warm all through the night. Even in his sleep he had felt at one moment that he was getting seriously ill, at another that he was getting better. He had longed for the morning not to come.

But the morning came as usual.

Anyway, it wasn't surprising that he'd felt cold in the night. That ice on the window-pane! And the white cobwebs of hoar-frost all along the huge hut where the walls joined the ceiling!

He didn't get up. He lay there in his bunk on the top tier, his head buried in a blanket and a coat, his two feet stuffed into one sleeve, with the end tucked under, of his wadded jacket. He couldn't see, but his ears told him everything going on in the barrack-room and especially in the corner his team occupied. He heard the heavy tread of the orderlies carrying one of the big barrels of nightsoil along the passage outside. A light job, that was considered, a job for the infirm, but just you try and carry out the muck without spilling any. He heard some of the 75th slamming bunches of boots on to the floor from the drying-shed. Now their own lads were doing it (it was their own team's turn, too, to dry valenki). Tiurin, the team-leader, and his deputy Pavlo put on their valenki without a word but he heard their bunks creaking. Now Pavlo would be going off to the bread-stores and Tiurin to the staff quarters to see the P.P.D.†

Ah, but not simply to report as usual to the authorities who distributed the daily assignments. Shukhov remembered that this morning his fate hung in the balance: they wanted to shift the 104th from the building-shops to a new site, the 'Socialist Way of Life' settlement. It lay in open country covered with snow-drifts, and before anything else could be done there they would have to dig pits and put up posts and attach barbed wire to them. Wire themselves in, so that they wouldn't run away. Only then would they start building.

There wouldn't be a warm corner for a whole month. Not a dog-kennel. And fires were out of the question. Where was the firewood to come from? Warm up with the work, that was your only salvation.

No wonder the team-leader looked so worried, that was his responsibility – to elbow some other team, some bunch of clod-hoppers, into the assignment instead of the 104th. Of course he wouldn't get the authorities to agree if he turned up empty-handed. He'd have to take a pound of pork-fat to the senior official there, if not a couple of pounds.

There's never any harm in trying, so why not have a go at the sick-bay and get a few days off if you can? After all, he did feel as though every limb was out of joint.

Alexander Solzhenitsyn

† Production Planning Department

Activity Now write a comparative literary analysis of these two openings. Your response should be about 500 words in length.

2b Imaginative or Creative Assignment

It has been pointed out that when students have problems with this option they are not so much to do with the topic they select as with the approaches they use to carry out their intended assignment. It is important, therefore, that when you have decided on a topic you think very carefully about how you are going to carry it out.

Here are some general ideas that have been suggested:

- the diary of a character accompanied by critical comment
- transcript of an imaginary interview
- an extra chapter
- a pastiche.

The key thing about any of these options is that your response must allow you to show your knowledge of and insight into the literature in such a way as to meet the demands of the assessment criteria.

You must avoid such approaches as:

- an extra chapter that is purely imaginative and has no real relationship to what happens in the text
- simple summary or paraphrase of the text or parts of it
- a response that is so far from the original that it shows little evidence of knowledge, understanding, and appreciation of the original
- tasks aimed at 'improving' the original.

Activity Read the following example of a student's Statement of Intent and make a note of the key points she makes in it. What do you think are the strengths and weaknesses of this as a Statement of Intent?

Chronicle of a Death Foretold by Gabriel Garcia Marquez
Statement of Intent

Gabriel Garcia Marquez's *Chronicle of a Death Foretold* relates the murder of a young man, Santiago Nasar, by twins who believe they are 'defending the honour of their sister', Angela Vicario. The horrific image of Santiago being butchered 'like a pig' is revealed early in the novel, so too is the identity of his killers. However, the incident becomes even more horrific as we learn later that he was, in fact, an innocent man.

Santiago Nasar is presented as a proud, accomplished man who stands out in his own village not only because of his physical stature and grace but also because he is of another race, he is a 'Turk'. Perhaps that is why Angela Vicario names him as the man to whom she has lost her virginity and, through this, her new husband, Bayado San Román. However, this can only be speculation as Angela's motives for this are never revealed.

The crime is presented as a series of accounts attained by an unknown narrator who states that he comes from the village, is well acquainted with its residents and has returned to question them about the events of 'that fateful day' in an effort to fully comprehend them. The novel is somewhat unconventional in structure as we are told early on who is murdered and who the murderers are. Indeed, we learn that most of the people in the village knew that the twins were going to murder Santiago, hence the title 'Chronicle of a Death Foretold'. However, this promotes and supports one of the major themes in the novel – that of 'fate'.

This assignment presents an extract from the diary of Plácida Linero, Santiago's mother, following the death of her son. Plácida Linero is described as a 'solitary' woman whose husband, whom she confessed never to have loved, has died. Santiago, then, is her 'only man' and, in some respects, her only connection with life outside the house in which she lives. Supporting the theme of 'fate' is Plácida Linero's belief in dreams which foretell the future. Indeed, the guilt that she carries following his death is born out of her mistake in interpreting the bird in Santiago's last dream to be a 'good' rather than 'bad' omen.

It is easy to imagine that Plácida Linero would keep a diary. After all, she has little contact with others from whom she could receive support and in her preferred solitary existence one imagines that she had a good deal of time and opportunity to reflect inwardly on her feelings. This approach offers an opportunity to explore the feelings of a mother who has lost her son in unjust, inhumane circumstances and who is still carrying the pain of his death twenty-seven years later when the narrator returns to speak with her.

Here are some points that you might have noted about the Statement of Intent:

- It reveals the student's sound knowledge of the text.
- It sets the imaginative piece in context.
- It explains the idea of the diary and the opportunity that this approach offers to explore the feelings of the mother.
- It does spend perhaps too much time summarizing the story.
- It relies on a theme of 'fate' rather than suggesting that the author is addressing the social acceptability of 'revenge' killings.
- It lacks a deeper analytical comment on the purpose and effect of the diary piece itself.

Activity   The student went on to write the diary outlined in the Statement of Intent. Here is the opening of the assignment. Read it through and discuss its effectiveness with a partner.

Assignment 2b: A diary entry based on *Chronicle of a Death Foretold* by Gabriel Garcia Marquez

Still the visitors come even though you have been gone more than five months. Intruders. Taking over my thoughts, offering help but giving me their tears. I know they don't come to see me, come to see how I am coping alone, they come to purge their souls and lessen their guilt. They knew. They all knew. I don't want to see them. I just want to be alone.

Today it was the turn of Clotilde Armenta. I was surprised. I thought she might have come sooner. I realized why when, through tears, she confessed to knowing that you, my precious son, were going to be murdered and that she had served drinks to your murderers minutes before they butchered you at the door of my house. I wanted to answer her pathetic attempts to justify why she had not come to tell me by shouting 'why didn't you warn me'. But, instead, I stopped listening. I watched her mouth moving, slowly, forming soundless words which I chose not to hear. Her eyebrows angled to express her condolences. Numb, I looked hard at the pathetic form in front of me - but on her face I could read thoughts of my own. Why didn't I warn you Santiago? How could I have mistaken the warning which came so clearly through your dreams and which you told me on the very day you left me?

I became conscious again of Clotilde's face and looked upon it with heartfelt pity. I have to forgive her if I am ever to forgive myself. She brought a plate out of her bag which was covered with a white linen cloth and although I was still not conscious of her words, I read from her expression that it was a gift. I took it from her and tried to give her the thanks of a smile, but, seeing the white linen cloth, feeling it brush against my hand, I thought about the last time I saw you and rewarded her with tears.

2c Detailed Study

If you take up this option, after choosing the text you are going to use for the assignment, you will need to decide how you are going to approach your study.

You have three approaches to choose from: a formal essay; an analysis of a key passage or two; or a commentary on an extract. Here are some points to bear in mind about each of these.

A formal essay

If you choose this option it is important that you think carefully about the wording of your question. Your essay question should be closely focused, rather than general and broad.

Key passage(s)

In selecting a key passage it is important to choose a passage that is central to your understanding of the work. You should ask yourself the question 'Why is this a key passage in the work?' If you cannot answer this question, you have not selected your passage well. Do not select a passage about which there is little to say or which deals with only minor aspects of the work.

In your analysis you need to explain why the passage chosen is central to our understanding of the work. In order to do this you need show the relationship of the passage to the development of the plot and to examine what it shows about such elements as theme, style, and characters.

Activity

> The following passage is from *Metamorphosis* by Franz Kafka. It presents a key point in the action of the story as Gregor's father drives his son, who has turned into an insect, back into his room for the first time. This passage represents the beginning of the family's rejection of Gregor. Read the passage carefully and write an analysis of the ways in which Kafka presents this incident, and any ideas that you think the passage contains.

Metamorphosis

'Mother, Mother,' said Gregor in a low voice and looked up at her. The chief clerk, for the moment, had quite slipped from his mind; instead, he could not resist snapping his jaws together at the sight of the creaming coffee. That made his mother scream again, she fled from the table and fell into the arms of his father, who hastened to catch her. But Gregor had now no time to spare for his parents; the chief clerk was already on the stairs; with his chin on the banisters he was taking one last backward look. Gregor made a spring, to be as sure as possible of overtaking him; the chief clerk must have divined his intention, for he leapt down several steps and vanished; he was still yelling 'Ugh!' and it echoed through the whole staircase. Unfortunately, the flight of the chief clerk seemed completely to upset Gregor's father, who had remained relatively calm until now, for instead of running after the man himself, or at least not hindering Gregor in his pursuit, he seized in his right hand the walking-stick which the chief clerk had left behind on a chair, together with a hat and great-coat, snatched in his left hand a large newspaper from the table and began stamping his feet and flourishing the stick and the newspaper to drive Gregor back into his room. No entreaty of Gregor's availed, indeed no entreaty was even understood, however humbly he bent his head his father only stamped on the floor the more loudly. Behind his father his mother had torn open a window, despite the cold weather, and was leaning far out of it with her face in her hands. A strong draught set in from the street to the staircase, the window curtains blew in, the newspapers on the table fluttered, stray pages whisked over the floor. Pitilessly Gregor's father drove him back, hissing and crying 'Shoo!' like a savage. But Gregor was quite unpractised in walking backwards, it really was a slow business. If he only had a chance to turn round he could get back to his room at once, but he was afraid of exasperating his father by the slowness of such a rotation and at any moment the stick in his father's hand might hit him a fatal blow on the back or on the head. In the end, however, nothing else was left for him to do since to his horror he observed that in moving backwards he could not even control the direction he took; and so, keeping an anxious eye on his father all the time over his shoulder, he began to turn round as quickly as he could, which was in reality very slowly. Perhaps his father noted his good intentions, for he did not interfere except every now and then to help him in the manoeuvre from a distance with the point of the stick. If only he would have stopped making that unbearable hissing noise! It made Gregor quite lose his head. He had turned almost completely round when the hissing noise so distracted him that he even turned a little the wrong way again. But when at last his head was fortunately right in front of the doorway, it appeared that his body was too broad simply to get through the opening. His father, of course, in his present mood was far from thinking of such a thing as opening the other half of the door, to let Gregor have enough space. He had merely the fixed idea of driving Gregor back into his room as quickly as possible. He would never have suffered Gregor to make the circumstantial preparations for standing up on end and perhaps slipping his way through the door. Maybe he was now making more noise than ever to urge Gregor forward, as if no obstacle impeded him; to Gregor, anyhow, the noise in his rear sounded no longer like the voice of one single father; this was really no joke, and Gregor thrust himself – come what might – into the doorway. One side of his body rose up, he was tilted at an angle in the doorway, his flank was quite bruised, horrid blotches stained the white door, soon he was stuck fast and, left to himself, could not have moved at all, his legs on one side fluttered trembling in the air, those on the other were crushed painfully to the floor – when from behind his father gave him a strong push which was literally a deliverance and he flew far into the room, bleeding freely. The door was slammed behind him with the stick, and then at last there was silence.

Franz Kafka

Commentary

The main difference between the analysis of a key passage and a commentary lies in the focus that you adopt. In the analysis of a key passage you looked at the importance of the passage in relation to the whole work. In the commentary, though, you need to explain why the particular extract has been selected for analysis and the focus is much more closely on the extract itself. You should closely analyse such elements as language, structure, and tone and show how they work together to create meaning and effects.

The passage that follows is from *Waiting for Godot* by Samuel Beckett. This passage marks an important moment in the play leading up to Pozzo's observations on the nature of existence.

Activity

Read the following extract and answer these questions:
1 What do you notice about the ways in which Beckett uses language in this extract?
2 How do the characters seem to interact with each other?
3 What images do you find striking here?
4 What ideas do you think are contained in the extract?

Waiting for Godot

Vladimir: (*Looking round*) It's indescribable. It's like nothing. There's nothing. There's a tree.

Pozzo: Then it's not the Board.

Estragon: (*Sagging*) Some diversion!

Pozzo: Where is my menial?

Vladimir: He's about somewhere.

Pozzo: Why doesn't he answer when I call?

Vladimir: I don't know. He seems to be sleeping. Perhaps he's dead.

Pozzo: What happened exactly?

Estragon: Exactly!

Vladimir: The two of you slipped. (*Pause*) And fell.

Pozzo: Go and see is he hurt.

Vladimir: We can't leave you.

Pozzo: You needn't both go.

Vladimir: (*To Estragon*) You go.

Estragon: After what he did to me? Never!

Pozzo: Yes yes, let your friend go, he stinks so. (*Silence*) What is he waiting for?

Vladimir: What are you waiting for?

Estragon: I'm waiting for Godot.
    (*Silence*)

Vladimir: What exactly should he do?

Pozzo: Well to begin with he should pull on the rope, as hard as he likes so long as he
    doesn't strangle him. He usually responds to that. If not he should give him a
    taste of his boot, in the face and the privates as far as possible.

Vladimir: (*To Estragon*) You see, you've nothing to be afraid of. It's even an opportunity to
    revenge yourself.

Estragon: And if he defends himself?

Pozzo: No no, he never defends himself.

Vladimir: I'll come flying to the rescue.

Estragon: Don't take your eyes off me.(*He goes towards Lucky*)

Vladimir: Make sure he's alive before you start. No point in exerting yourself if he's dead.

Estragon: (*Bending over Lucky*). He's breathing.

Vladimir: Then let him have it.(*With sudden fury Estragon starts kicking Lucky, hurling
    abuse at him as he does so. But he hurts his foot and moves away limping and
    groaning. Lucky stirs.*)

Estragon: Oh the brute! (*He sits down on the mound and tries to take off his boot. But he
    soon desists and disposes himself for sleep, his arms on his knees and his head
    on his arms.*)

Pozzo: What's gone wrong now?

Vladimir: My friend has hurt himself.

Pozzo: And Lucky?

Vladimir: So it is he?

Pozzo: What?

Vladimir: It is Lucky?

Pozzo: I don't understand.

Vladimir: And you are Pozzo?

Pozzo: Certainly I am Pozzo.

Vladimir: The same as yesterday?

Pozzo: Yesterday?

Vladimir: We met yesterday. (*Silence*) Do you not remember?

Pozzo: I don't remember having met anyone yesterday. But tomorrow I won't remember having met anyone today. So don't count on me to enlighten you.

Vladimir: But –

Pozzo: Enough. Up pig!

Vladimir: You were bringing him to the fair to sell him. You spoke to us. He danced. He thought. You had your sight.

Pozzo: As you please. Let me go! (*Vladimir moves away*) Up!

(*Lucky gets up, gathers up his burdens*)

Vladimir: Where do you go from here?

Pozzo: On. (*Lucky, laden down, takes his place before Pozzo.*) Whip! (*Lucky puts everything down, looks for whip, finds it, puts it into Pozzo's hand, takes up everything again*) Rope!

Vladimir: What is there in the bag?

Pozzo: Sand. (*He jerks the rope*) On!

Vladimir: Don't go yet!

Pozzo: I'm going.

Vladimir: What do you do when you fall far from help?

Pozzo: We wait till we can get up. Then we go on. On!

Vladimir: Before you go tell him to sing!

Pozzo: Who?

Vladimir: Lucky.

Pozzo: To sing?

Vladimir: Yes. Or to think. Or to recite.

Pozzo: But he's dumb.

Vladimir: Dumb!

Pozzo: Dumb. He can't even groan.

Vladimir: Dumb! Since when?

Pozzo: (*Suddenly furious.*) Have you not done tormenting me with your accursed time! It's abominable! When! When! One day, is that not enough for you, one day like any other day, one day he went dumb, one day I went blind, one day we'll go deaf, one day we were born, one day we shall die, the same day, the same second, is that not enough for you? (*Calmer*) They give birth astride of a grave, the light gleams an instant, then it's night once more.

(*He jerks the rope*) On!

(*Exeunt Pozzo and Lucky. Vladimir follows them to the edge of the stage, looks after them. The noise of falling, reinforced by mimic of Vladimir, announces that they are down again. Silence.*

Vladimir goes towards Estragon, contemplates him a moment, then shakes him awake.)

Estragon: (*Wild gestures, incoherent words. Finally*) Why will you never let me sleep?

Samuel Beckett

In the following extract from *Chronicle of a Death Foretold* by Gabriel Garcia Marquez, the Vicario twins decide to kill Santiago Nasar, who they believe has dishonoured their sister.

Activity

Write an analysis of this extract focusing closely on the following aspects:
- the narrative style
- the language and effects created
- the tone of the piece
- the presentation of character.

Chronicle of a Death Foretold

There had never been a death more foretold. After their sister revealed the name to them, the Vicario twins went to the bin in the pigsty where they kept their sacrificial tools and picked out the two best knives; one for quartering, ten inches long by two and a half inches wide, and the other for trimming, seven inches long by one and a half inches wide. They wrapped them in a rag and went to sharpen them at the meat market, where only a few stalls had begun to open. There weren't very many customers that early, but twenty-two people declared they had heard everything said, and they all coincided in the impression that the only reason they had said it was for someone to hear them. Faustino Santos, a butcher friend, saw them come in at three-twenty, when he had just opened up his innards table, and he couldn't understand why they were coming on a Monday and so early, and still in their dark wedding suits. He was accustomed to seeing them come on Fridays, but a little later, and wearing the leather aprons they put on for slaughtering. 'I thought they were so drunk,' Faustino Santos told me, 'that not only had they forgotten what time it was but what day it was too.' He reminded them that it was Monday.

'Everybody knows that, you dope,' Pablo Vicario answered him good-naturedly. 'We just came to sharpen our knives.'

They sharpened them on the grindstone, and the way they always did: Pedro holding the knives and turning them over on the stone, and Pablo working the crank. At the same time, they talked about the splendor of the wedding with the other butchers. Some of them complained about not having gotten their share of cake, in spite of their being working companions, and they promised them to have some sent over later. Finally, they made the knives sing on the stone, and Pablo laid his beside the lamp so that the steel sparkled.

'We're going to kill Santiago Nasar,' he said.

Their reputation as good people was so well founded that no one paid any attention to them. 'We thought it was drunkards' baloney,' several butchers declared, the same as Victoria Guzmán and so many others who saw them later. I was to ask the butchers sometime later whether or not the trade of slaughterer didn't reveal a soul predisposed to killing a human being. They protested: 'When you sacrifice a steer you don't dare look into its eyes.' One of them told me that he couldn't eat the flesh of an animal he had butchered. Another told me that he wouldn't be capable of sacrificing a cow if he'd known it before, much less if he'd drunk its milk. I reminded them that the Vicario brothers sacrificed the same hogs they raised, and that they were so familiar to them that they called them by their names. 'That's true,' one of them replied, 'but remember that they didn't give them people's names but the names of flowers.' Faustino Santos was the only one who perceived a glimmer of truth in Pablo Vicario's threat, and he asked him jokingly why they had to kill Santiago Nasar since there were so many other rich people who deserved dying first.

'Santiago Nasar knows why,' Pedro Vicario answered him.

Faustino Santos told me that he'd been doubtful still, and that he reported it to a policeman who came by a little later to buy a pound of liver for the mayor's breakfast. The policeman, according to the brief, was named Leandro Pornoy, and he died the following year, gored in the jugular vein by a bull during the national holidays. So I was never able to talk to him, but Clotilde Armenta confirmed for me that he was the first person in her store when the Vicario twins were already sitting and waiting.

Gabriel Garcia Marquez

Activity

Now think about the assignment that you are going to work on for your World Literature assessment. Make a note of all the texts that you might consider basing the assignment on, and think about which approach you are going to adopt.

The topic

When you have decided on the text you are going to use in your assignment you need to think of a suitable topic. You can discuss your ideas with your teacher and he or she can help to make sure that your topic is appropriate and well-focused, but your teacher is not allowed to set the topic for you. You must have some ideas of your own.

The title

When you have chosen your topic you will need to think of a suitable assignment title.

The outline

When you have decided on your title you then need to prepare an outline of your assignment in which you plan how you will approach it and structure your ideas. Again you should discuss your ideas with your teacher before you begin to write your first draft.

The first draft

You are now ready to write the first draft of your assignment. When you have completed this you can give it to your teacher who can read it and make general comments on it. Your teacher is not allowed to mark it or write any comments on it, however.

Further drafts

After you have completed your first draft and have had some general feedback from your teacher on it, you can go on to write further drafts or, if you feel ready, to complete a final draft of it. After the first draft stage your teacher cannot give any further feedback to you. You now need to work on the assignment on your own.

Summary   Here is a summary of the stages you need to go through in producing your assignment:

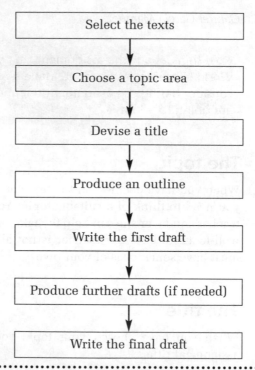

Assessment of your work

Your work will be assessed under four separate criteria. These are:

- Selection of the aspect and its treatment
- Knowledge and understanding of works

- Presentation
- Language.

In order to achieve a good mark you will need to:

- choose an aspect appropriate to the assignment
- ensure that your chosen aspect has a relevant focus
- make sure that your ideas show independence of thought and your treatment is relevant to the aspect chosen
- show detailed knowledge of, and good insight into, the aspects of the works most relevant to the assignment
- show clear and meaningful linking of works
- show good appreciation of the cultural setting relevant to the assignment, where appropriate
- show a clear and logical structure to the assignment
- show precise and pertinent references to the works
- remain within the prescribed word limit
- use an effective register appropriate for the assignment selected
- follow closely the conventions of written work
- write fluently and clearly.

Part 4
Talking about Literature

9 The Individual Oral Commentary

Objectives

- To analyse the requirements of the Individual Oral Commentary
- To prepare for the Individual Oral Commentary by practising responding to extracts

All students studying for English A1 must complete two compulsory oral components, which are internally assessed. The first of these assessments is the Individual Oral Commentary, and we will look at the requirements and methods of approaching this component in this unit. The second component is the Individual Oral Presentation, and we will look at this element in the next unit.

The objectives of the internally assessed oral component are to:

- ensure assessment of all parts of the syllabus
- ensure an overall, balanced assessment of your proficiency in the subject by taking into account performance in teacher-assessed work during the course, as well as in the externally assessed components

- include methods which may not be practicable in the context of external assessment but which are appropriate in the classroom context
- assess your oral skills in a variety of contexts.

The Individual Oral Commentary is based on an extract, selected by your teacher, from one of the works studied in Part 2 of the syllabus. The extract that you are given will be accompanied by guiding questions set by your teacher. You are **not** allowed to choose your own extract.

Any of the works you have studied in Part 2 may be used in the Individual Oral Commentary and you will not be told in advance from which work the extract for the Individual Oral Commentary will be taken.

The choice of extract

Your teacher will choose an extract which plays an important part in the text as a whole and highlights a significant aspect of it. The length of the extract you are given will depend on how complex it is, but normally it will not be longer than 40 lines. With poetry, it is likely that a single poem will be used, unless you have studied a long poem, in which case an extract may be chosen from it.

Guiding questions

Your teacher will set **one** or **two** questions for each extract or poem. The purpose of these guiding questions is to give you a starting point for organizing your commentary. These guiding questions will relate to some of the most significant aspects of the extract and help you to focus on interpreting them. The questions should help you to look at aspects such as:

- the presentation and role of character(s)
- the presentation of relationships
- theme(s)
- the use of language
- the significance of the extract to the development of the plot or text as a whole
- the effects created by the structure, style, and techniques employed by the writer.

You should note, however, that the guiding questions will not:

- refer to specific details or to any particular interpretation of the extract
- restrict your ability to explore independently the significant features or aspects of the extract.

In the activities that follow, you will find examples of the kinds of guiding questions that you may encounter on your Individual Oral Commentary.

The focus and structure of the commentary

The focus and emphasis of your commentary depends on the particular extract chosen. However, in all cases you should aim to identify and explore all the significant features and aspects of the extract. These include:

- placing the extract in context as precisely as you can within the work as a whole
- commenting on the effectiveness of the writer's techniques, including, if you are studying at Higher Level, the writer's use of stylistic techniques and the effects that these create for the reader.

It is important to note, however, that you must **not** be tempted to discuss everything you know about the whole text. Your commentary must **focus** on the specific extract that you are given for discussion. You should relate it to the whole work only where relevant – for example, to establish the context, or discuss its importance to the work as a whole.

Your commentary should be well-structured and your ideas should be presented in an integrated and fluent way – not as a series of separate points. You must also take care to avoid a narrative approach in which you 're-tell the story' of the text or give a line-by-line paraphrase.

Preparation and delivery

Before you give your commentary, you will be allowed 20 minutes supervised preparation time. You will be expected to use this time to:

- read the extract and the accompanying questions carefully
- identify the significant features of the extract and analyse them closely
- make notes in preparation for your commentary
- organize and structure your commentary.

Delivery of your commentary

After you have prepared your commentary you will be given 15 minutes in which to deliver it. You will be able to give your commentary without interruption or distraction, and your teacher should not normally intervene while you are giving your commentary.

After completing the commentary

After listening to your commentary your teacher will discuss it and the extract with you. This discussion may involve other members of your class or group if appropriate. The purpose of this discussion is to allow you to show further understanding and appreciation of the text, and to expand or develop some of the statements made. Your teacher will want to be sure that you have understood specific words, phrases, references, and allusions, and that you have recognized their importance within the extract. Your teacher will also want to be sure that you have understood the significance of the extract within the whole work, or, in the case of a complete poem, the relationship between the poem and others you have studied. Higher Level students in particular must show that they are able to comment on the techniques that the writer uses.

Assessment of your commentary

Your commentary will be assessed against a number of criteria. These are:

A Knowledge and understanding of the text
B Interpretation and personal response
C Presentation
D Use of language.

In order to achieve a good result you will need to show:

- good knowledge and understanding of the content of the extract or work(s)
- thorough knowledge of the appropriate context of the extract or work(s)
- a valid and detailed interpretation of the thought and feeling expressed in the extract or work(s), including a considered critical response
- a good awareness and detailed analysis of the effects of the literary features of the extract or work(s)
- a response supported by relevant references to the extract or work(s)
- a clear and logical structure to the response
- a focused response presented in a clear, coherent, effective, and convincing manner
- integrated supporting references
- a clear, varied, and precise use of language using an appropriate register and style, and relevant literary terms.

The Individual Oral Commentary in practice

We will now look at some examples of Individual Oral Commentary extracts. If you have not studied these texts you will obviously not be able to relate the extracts to the whole text, but the focus of these activities is to give you practise in looking at and thinking about the extracts themselves.

Activity

Look at this poem by Philip Larkin. Think about what you would say about it if you were asked to speak about it to the rest of your class or group. Make a note of the points you would make about the poem, the ways in which Larkin uses language, and the effects that he achieves through his use of language.

Naturally the Foundation Will Pay Your Expenses

Hurrying to catch my Comet
    One dark November day,
Which soon would snatch me from it
    To the sunshine of Bombay,
I pondered pages Berkeley
    Not three weeks since had heard,
Perceiving Chatto darkly
    Through the mirror of the Third.

Crowds, colourless and careworn,
    Had made my taxi late,
Yet not till I was airborne
    Did I recall the date –
That day when Queen and Minister
    And Band of Guards and all
Still act their solemn-sinister
    Wreath-rubbish in Whitehall.

It used to make me throw up,
    These mawkish nursery games:
O when will England grow up?
    – But I outsoar the Thames,
And dwindle off down Auster
    To greet Professor Lal
(He once met Morgan Forster),
    My contact and my pal.

Philip Larkin

Here are some points you might have made:

- It is written in the first person and so the 'voice' could be that of the poet himself speaking, but it might also be that of a persona he has created.
- The 'speaker' of the poem is a narrator figure – the views that he expresses are not necessarily those of Larkin himself. In fact, the 'speaker' here seems to be an English academic who jets around the world giving his paper to major universities.
- Larkin is present here too, but his attitudes and ideas lie behind the words spoken by his character.
- He satirizes his character in order to cast a critical light on the persona he has created, and the views that are expressed through him.
- He uses a range of poetic techniques to achieve his effects (imagery, alliteration, etc.).
- The poem has a clear structure.

Activity

1 Read the following poem, *Churning Day* by Seamus Heaney, and make a note of the initial features that strike you about the way Heaney writes his poem.

2 Now look at the first stanza. How does Heaney begin the poem and how does he use imagery here to create his effects?

3 The next stanza describes the stage where the milk is poured from the crocks into the churn. Make a note of any descriptions or images that strike you here.

4 Now look carefully at the third stanza. What effect is created here by the use of the verb 'dance' (line 19) to describe the butter forming, the metaphor 'coagulated sunlight' (line 24) and the simile 'like gilded gravel' (line 26)?

5 In the final stanza the poet describes the after-effects of churning day. The stanza opens with a shock to the senses. In what way?

6 What is the effect of the final four lines of the poem?

7 Using all the ideas you have noted, write out what you would say if you were giving an Individual Oral Commentary on this poem.

Churning Day

A thick-crust, coarse-grained as limestone rough-cast,
hardened gradually on top of the four crocks
that stood, large pottery bombs, in the small pantry.
After the hot brewery of gland, cud and udder
cool porous earthenware fermented the buttermilk
for churning day, when the hooped churn was scoured
with plumping kettles and the busy scrubber
echoed daintily on the seasoned wood.
It stood then, purified, on the flagged kitchen floor.

Out came the four crocks, spilled their heavy lip
of cream, their white insides, into the sterile churn.
The staff, like a great whisky muddler fashioned
in deal wood, was plunged in, the lid fitted.
My mother took first turn, set up rhythms
that slugged and thumped for hours. Arms ached.
Hands blistered. Cheeks and clothes were spattered
with flabby milk.

      Where finally gold flecks
began to dance. They poured hot water then,
sterilized a birchwood-bowl
and little corrugated butter-spades.
Their short stroke quickened, suddenly
a yellow curd was weighting the churned up white,
heavy and rich, coagulated sunlight
that they fished, dripping, in a wide tin strainer,
heaped up like gilded gravel in a bowl.

The house would stink long after churning day,
acrid as a sulphur mine. The empty crocks
were ranged along the wall again, the butter
in soft printed slabs was piled on pantry shelves.
And in the house we moved with gravid ease,
our brains turned crystals full of clean deal churns,
the plash and gurgle of the sour-breathed milk,
the pat and slap of small spades on wet lumps.

Seamus Heaney

1 Here are some ideas that you might have noted when working through the
poem:

- Heaney uses detail to convey the sights, sounds, smells, and feelings
  associated with the memory he is describing.
- He uses similes and metaphors, adjectives and adverbs to make his
  descriptions more vivid and immediate in our minds.
- The subject – churning cream from milk to make butter – is a simple
  country experience.

2 The poem begins with a detailed description of the four crocks in which the
buttermilk is standing, fermenting, ready for the churning process to begin.
In the simile used to describe the thick crust that has formed on the milk,
he likens it to 'limestone rough-cast'. Heaney uses a metaphor to describe
the crocks as 'large pottery bombs', which perhaps reflects the shape of
these vessels but also gives a sense of the readiness of the milk to be
churned – like a bomb ready to go off. He uses another metaphor – 'the hot
brewery' – to describe how the milk has formed within the cow, creating
milk from grass, the 'cud', in the same way as a brewery takes natural
ingredients to produce beer through a fermentation process. A contrast is
created by the 'hot' brewery and the 'cool' earthenware crocks. The poet
describes all the activity that has taken place to prepare the churn for the
churning. The use of the adjective 'plumping' is unusual and almost has an
onomatopoeic effect, imitating the sound of the kettle boiling. Finally the
churn is cleaned – the word 'purified' gives an almost religious sense to the
rituals that have been carried out to prepare for the transforming of the milk
into butter, perhaps a kind of miracle in itself.

3 • The poet personifies the crocks – the milk coming from their 'white
  insides' as if it is part of them.
- The churn is set up with the staff placed through the wooden lid – a
  simile compares this to a 'whisky muddler', which is a large paddle-
  shaped object used to help whisky ferment.
- The mother takes over and the hard, physical nature of the work is
  expressed in the phrase 'slugged and thumped for hours. Arms ached./
  Hands blistered'.
- Others take their turns and soon they are 'spattered' with 'flabby' milk
  as it begins to coagulate.

4   • The verb 'dance' to describe the gold flecks of butter as they begin to form is suggestive of a kind of celebration, and it also suggests a quickening of pace as they prepare to form the butter into pats.
    • The metaphor 'coagulated sunlight' describes the coagulation of the milk into butter and brings to mind its colour and warmth and glow.
    • The final simile in the stanza repeats this image of a golden colour, with the use of the word 'gilded' emphasizing its richness.

5   The use of the word 'stink' at the beginning of the final stanza is unexpected, but describes the lingering smell of the curd. This is emphasized further by the simile 'acrid as a sulphur mine', graphically giving a sense of the permeating nature of the smell in the house.

6   The ending of the poem creates a sense of a job well done and of satisfaction. Their minds are like 'crystals', the churns are clean and the onomatopoeic effect of 'plash' and 'gurgle', 'pat' and 'slap' gives a satisfying sense of the butter being slapped by the butter spades and turned into slabs.

Activity

The following extract is taken from Shakespeare's play *Hamlet*. Here Hamlet is grieving for his father, the king, who has recently died. Hamlet's mother has married his uncle, who has become king himself.

1 Read the extract carefully, and the guiding questions that follow it.
2 Spend 20 minutes preparing your ideas for an oral commentary on this extract.
3 Write notes on the extract as if you were preparing to give an oral commentary on it.
4 Write down what you would say if you were giving an Individual Oral Commentary on this extract.

Hamlet: O that this too too solid flesh would melt,
            Thaw and resolve itself into a dew,
            Or that the Everlasting had not fixed
            His canon 'gainst self-slaughter. O God, God,
            How weary, stale, flat and unprofitable
            Seem to me all the uses of this world!
            Fie on 't, ah fie, 'tis an unweeded garden
            That grows to seed: things rank and gross in nature
            Possess it merely. That it should come to this –
            But two months dead, nay not so much, not two –
            So excellent a king, that was to this
            Hyperion to a satyr, so loving to my mother
            That he might not beteem the winds of heaven
            Visit her face too roughly. Heaven and earth,
            Must I remember? Why she would hang on him
            As if increase of appetite had grown
            By what it fed on, and yet within a month –

Let me not think on't – frailty, thy name is woman.
A little month or e'er those shoes were old
With which she followed my poor father's body,
Like Niobe all tears, why she, even she –
O God, a beast that wants discourse of reason
Would have mourned longer – married with my uncle,
My father's brother, but no more like my father
Than I to Hercules; within a month –
Ere yet the salt of most unrighteous tears
Had left the flushing in her galled eyes,
She married. O most wicked speed, to post
With such dexterity to incestuous sheets.
It is not, nor it cannot come to good:
But break, my heart, for I must hold my tongue.

Guiding question 1:   (Higher Level and Standard Level)
Discuss Hamlet's state of mind as seen in this extract.

Guiding question 2:   (Higher Level)
How does Shakespeare's use of language in this
extract reflect Hamlet's emotional state?
(Standard Level)
Why does the character feel this way?

This extract is also taken from Shakespeare's play *Hamlet*. The extract shows
Hamlet – who is faced with the prospect of taking revenge for the death of his
father, murdered by Hamlet's uncle, Claudius, now king – debating with
himself the nature of death.

Activity

1 Read the following extract carefully, and the guiding questions that
follow it.
2 Spend 20 minutes preparing your ideas for an oral commentary on this
extract.
3 Write notes on the extract as if you were preparing to give an oral
commentary on it.
4 Write down what you would say if you were giving an Individual Oral
Commentary on this extract.

(*Enter* **Hamlet**)

Hamlet: To be, or not to be, that is the question:
Whether 'tis nobler in the mind to suffer
The slings and arrows of outrageous fortune,
Or to take arms against a sea of troubles,
And by opposing end them? To die, to sleep -
No more; and by a sleep to say we end
The heart-ache, and the thousand natural shocks
That flesh is heir to; 'tis a consummation

Devoutly to be wished. To die, to sleep -
To sleep, perchance to dream, ay there's the rub,
For in that sleep of death what dreams may come
When we have shuffled off this mortal coil,
Must give us pause; there's the respect
That makes calamity of so long life.
For who would bear the whips and scorns of time,
Th' oppressor's wrong, the proud man's contumely,
The pangs of despised love, the law's delay,
The insolence of office, and the spurns
That patient merit of th' unworthy takes
When he himself might be quietus make
With a bare bodkin? Who would fardels bear,
To grunt and sweat under a weary life,
But that the dread of something after death,
The undiscovered country from whose bourn
No traveller returns, puzzles the will,
And makes us rather bear those ills we have,
Than fly to others that we know not of?
Thus conscience does make cowards of us all,
And thus the native hue of resolution
Is sicklied o'er with the pale cast of thought,
And enterprises of great pitch and moment
With this regard their currents turn awry,
And lose the name of action. Soft you now,
The fair Ophelia. – Nymph, in thy orisons
Be all my sins remembered.

Guiding question 1:   (Higher Level and Standard Level)
What does this extract show about Hamlet's character
and his state of mind at this point in the play?

Guiding question 2:   (Higher Level)
Identify the poetic techniques used in this extract.
What effects do they achieve?
(Standard Level)
What do you think are the important themes in this
extract?

This extract taken from a little later in *Hamlet* is from the point in the play
where Hamlet's uncle Claudius, thinking he is alone, tries to repent of his
crime of killing his brother. Hamlet sees him and is aware that this presents
him with a prime opportunity to kill Claudius.

Activity   1 Read the following extract carefully, and the guiding questions that
follow it.
2 Spend 20 minutes preparing your ideas for an oral commentary on this
extract.

3 Write notes on the extract as if you were preparing to give an oral commentary on it.

4 Write down what you would say if you were giving an Individual Oral Commentary on this extract.

King: O my offence is rank, it smells to heaven;
It hath the primal eldest curse upon't,
A brother's murder. Pray can I not,
Though inclination be as sharp as will.
My stronger guilt defeats my strong intent,
And like a man to double business bound,
I stand in pause when I shall first begin,
And both neglect. What if this cursed hand
Were thicker than itself with brother's blood,
Is there not rain enough in the sweet heavens
To wash it white as snow? Whereto serves mercy
But to confront the visage of offence?
And what's in prayer but this two-fold force,
To be forestalled ere we come to fall,
Or pardoned being down? Then I'll look up;
My fault is past. But O what form of prayer
Can serve my turn? 'Forgive me my foul murder'?
That cannot be since I am still possessed
Of those effects for which I did the murder,
My crown, mine own ambition, and my Queen.
May one be pardoned and retain th' offence?
In the corrupted currents of this world
Offence's gilded hand may shove by justice,
And oft 'tis seen the wicked prize itself
Buys out the law. But 'tis not so above;
There is no shuffling, there the action lies
In his true nature, and we ourselves compelled,
Even to the teeth and forehead of our faults
To give in evidence. What then? What rests?
Try what repentance can – what can it not?
Yet what can it, when one can not repent?
O wretched state, O bosom black as death,
O limed soul, that struggling to be free,
Art more engaged! Help, angels, make assay.
Bow stubborn knees, and heart with strings of steel,
Be soft as sinews of the new-born babe.
All may be well.   *(Kneels)*

(*Enter* **Hamlet**)

Hamlet: Now might I do it pat, now he is praying;
And now I'll do 't – and so he goes to heaven;

And so am I revenged. That would be scanned:
A villain kills my father, and for that,
I his sole son do this same villain send
To heaven.
Why, this is hire and salary, not revenge.
'A took my father grossly full of bread,
With all his crimes broad blown, as flush as May,
And how his audit stands who knows save heaven?
But in our circumstance and course of thought,
'Tis heavy with him; and am I then revenged,
To take him in the purging of his soul,
When he is fit and seasoned for his passage?
No.
Up sword, and know thou a more horrid hent,
When he is drunk asleep, or in his rage,
Or in th' incestuous pleasure of his bed,
At game, a-swearing, or about some act
That has no relish of salvation in't -
Then trip him that his heels may kick at heaven,
And that his soul may be as damned and black
As hell whereto it goes. My mother stays.
This physic but prolongs thy sickly days.

King: *(Rising)* My words fly up, my thoughts remain below.
Words without thoughts never to heaven go.

Guiding question 1:   (Higher Level and Standard Level)
What do you think this extract reveals about the two characters?

Guiding question 2:   (Higher Level)
Given the chance, how might you direct this scene to reveal the mental state of each of the characters?
(Standard Level)
Why do you think this scene is dramatically important in the play?

The unusual thing about the following extract, which is taken from Emily Brontë's novel *Wuthering Heights*, is that although the story is told in the third person there are, in fact, two narrators here. Mr Lockwood begins the narrative but then this is taken over by Nellie Dean. If you are studying this novel you will know that there are also other narrators at different points. In this extract it is clear that Lockwood has had a bad experience at Wuthering Heights and knows nothing of the history of the family. Nellie, on the other hand, is an old family servant who has a wealth of knowledge about Wuthering Heights that she is only too willing to share with him. The majority of this information is conveyed to us through the dialogue between the two of them.

Activity

Wuthering Heights

'I see the house at Wuthering Heights has "Earnshaw" carved over the front door. Are they an old family?'

'Very old, sir; and Hareton is the last of them, as our Miss Cathy is of us – I mean, of the Lintons. Have you been to Wuthering Heights? I beg pardon for asking; but I should like to hear how she is.'

'Mrs Heathcliff? she looked very well, and very handsome; yet, I think, not very happy.'

'Oh dear, I don't wonder! And how did you like the master?'

'A rough fellow, rather, Mrs Dean. Is not that his character?'

'Rough as a saw-edge, and hard as whinstone! The less you meddle with him the better.'

'He must have had some ups and downs in life to make him such a churl. Do you know anything of his history?'

'It's a cuckoo's, sir – I know all about it; except where he was born, and who were his parents, and how he got his money, at first. And Hareton has been cast out like an unfledged dunnock! The unfortunate lad is the only one in all this parish that does not guess how he has been cheated.'

'Well, Mrs Dean, it will be a charitable deed to tell me something of my neighbours: I feel I shall not rest, if I go to bed; so be good enough to sit and chat an hour.'

'Oh, certainly, sir! I'll just fetch a little sewing, and then I'll sit as long as you please. But you've caught cold; I saw you shivering, and you must have some gruel to drive it out.'

The worthy woman bustled off, and I crouched nearer the fire; my head felt hot, and the rest of me chill: moreover I was excited, almost to a pitch of foolishness, through my nerves and brain. This caused me to feel, not uncomfortable, but rather fearful (as I am still) of serious effects from the incidents of to-day and yesterday.

She returned presently, bringing a smoking basin and a basket of work; and, having placed the former on the hob, drew in her seat, evidently pleased to find me so companionable.

Before I came to live here, she commenced – waiting no further invitation to her story – I was almost always at Wuthering Heights; because my mother had nursed Mr Hindley Earnshaw, that was Hareton's father, and I got used to playing with the children: I ran errands too, and helped to make hay, and hung about the farm ready for anything that anybody would set me to.

One fine summer morning – it was the beginning of harvest, I remember – Mr Earnshaw, the old master, came downstairs, dressed for a journey; and after he had told Joseph what was to be done during the day, he turned to Hindley, and Cathy, and me – for I sat eating my porridge with them – and he said, speaking to his son, 'Now, my bonny man, I'm going to Liverpool to-day, what shall I bring you? You may choose what you like; only let it be little, for I shall walk there and back: sixty miles each way, that is a long spell!' Hindley named a fiddle, and then he asked Miss Cathy; she was hardly six years old, but she could ride any horse in the stable, and she chose a whip.

He did not forget me: for he had a kind heart though he was rather severe sometimes. He promised to bring me a pocketful of apples and pears, and then he kissed his children good-bye and set off.

Emily Brontë

Guiding question 1:   (Higher Level and Standard Level)
What do you learn about the narrators from this extract?

Guiding question 2:   (Higher Level)
Identify the narrative techniques that Brontë uses here and the effects she creates through them.
(Standard Level)
How is information conveyed to you in this extract?

This extract is from *Tess of the D'Ubervilles* by Thomas Hardy. Here the narrator describes the scene as Tess rises very early in the morning to take the beehives to market at the town of Casterbridge.

Activity

1 Read the extract carefully, and the guiding questions that follow it.
2 Spend 20 minutes preparing your ideas for an oral commentary on this extract.
3 Write notes on the extract as if you were preparing to give an oral commentary on it.
4 Write down what you would say if you were giving an Individual Oral Commentary on this extract.

Tess of the D'Urbervilles

It was eleven o'clock before the family were all in bed, and two o'clock next morning was the latest hour for starting with the beehives if they were to be delivered to the retailers in Casterbridge before the Saturday market began, the way thither lying by bad roads over a distance of between twenty and thirty miles, and the horse and waggon being of the slowest. At half-past one Mrs Durbeyfield came into the large bedroom where Tess and all her little brothers and sisters slept.

'The poor man can't go,' she said to her eldest daughter, whose great eyes had opened the moment her mother's hand touched the door.

Tess sat up in bed, lost in a vague interspace between a dream and this information.

'But somebody must go,' she replied. 'It is late for the hives already. Swarming will soon be over for the year; and if we put off taking 'em till next week's market the call for 'em will be past, and they'll be thrown on our hands.'

Mrs Durbeyfield looked unequal to the emergency. 'Some young feller, perhaps, would go? One of them who were so much after dancing with 'ee yesterday,' she presently suggested.

'O no – I wouldn't have it for the world!' declared Tess proudly. 'And letting everybody know the reason – such a thing to be ashamed of! I think *I* could go if Abraham could go with me to kip me company.'

Her mother at length agreed to this arrangement. Little Abraham was aroused from his deep sleep in a corner of the same apartment, and made to put on his clothes while still mentally in the other world. Meanwhile Tess had hastily dressed herself; and the twain, lighting a lantern, went out to the stable. The rickety little waggon was already laden, and the girl led out the horse Prince, only a degree less rickety than the vehicle.

The poor creature looked wonderingly round at the night, at the lantern, at their two figures, as if he could not believe that at that hour, when every living thing was intended to be in shelter and at rest, he was called upon to go out and labour. They put a stock of candle-ends into the lantern, hung the latter to the off-side of the load, and directed the horse onward, walking at his shoulder at first during the uphill parts of the way, in order not to overload an animal of so little vigour. To cheer themselves as well as they could, they made an artificial morning with the lantern, some bread and butter, and their own conversation, the real morning being far from come. Abraham, as he more fully awoke (for he had moved in a sort of trance so far), began to talk of the strange shapes assumed by the various dark objects against the sky; of this tree that looked like a raging tiger springing from a lair; of that which resembled a giant's head.

Thomas Hardy

Guiding question 1:   (Higher Level and Standard Level)
What do you learn about Tess from Hardy's presentation of her in this extract?

Guiding question 2:   (Higher Level)
Identify the narrative techniques that Hardy uses here and the effects he creates through them.
(Standard Level)
How is information conveyed to you in this extract?

In Hardy's *The Return of the Native*, the story is set against the imposing background of the wild Egdon Heath. The presence of this wild and untamed heath exerts a powerful influence in terms of the mood and atmosphere of the novel as a whole. Hardy gives a good deal of attention to creating a sense of the heath's wildness, as in the following description with which the novel opens.

Activity

1 Read the following extract carefully, and the guiding questions that follow it.
2 Spend 20 minutes preparing your ideas for an oral commentary on this extract.
3 Write notes on the extract as if you were preparing to give an oral commentary on it.
4 Write down what you would say if you were giving an Individual Oral Commentary on this extract.

The Return of the Native

A Saturday afternoon in November was approaching the time of twilight, and the vast tract of unenclosed wild known as Egdon Heath embrowned itself moment by moment. Overhead the hollow stretch of whitish cloud shutting out the sky was as a tent which had the whole heath for its floor.

The heaven being spread with this pallid screen and the earth with the darkest vegetation, their meeting-line at the horizon was clearly marked. In such contrast the heath wore the appearance of an instalment of night which had taken up its place before its astronomical hour was come: darkness had to a great extent arrived hereon, while day stood distinct in the sky. Looking upwards, a furze-cutter would have been inclined to continue work; looking down, he would have decided to finish his faggot and go home. The distant rims of the world and of the firmament seemed to be a division in time no less than a division in matter. The face of the heath by its mere complexion added half an hour to evening; it could in like manner retard the dawn, sadden noon, anticipate the frowning of storms scarcely generated, and intensify the opacity of a moonless midnight to a cause of shaking and dread.

In fact, precisely at this transitional point of its nightly roll into darkness the great and particular glory of the Egdon waste began, and nobody could be said to understand the heath who had not been there at such a time. It could best be felt when it could not clearly be seen, its complete effect and explanation lying in this and the succeeding hours before the next dawn: then, and only then, did it tell its true tale. The spot was, indeed, a near relation of night, and when night showed itself an apparent tendency to gravitate together could be perceived in its shades and the scene. The sombre stretch of rounds and hollows seemed to rise and meet the evening gloom in pure sympathy, the heath exhaling darkness as rapidly as the heavens precipitated it. And so the obscurity in the air and the obscurity in the land closed together in a black fraternization towards which each advanced half-way.

Thomas Hardy

Guiding question 1:   (Higher Level and Standard Level)
What is your overall impression of the heath?

Guiding question 2:   (Higher Level)
How does Hardy use language to describe the heath?
What effects does this create?
(Standard Level)
How does Hardy create a sense of mood and
atmosphere?

Keats's poem *To Autumn* was written about 19 September 1819, and is one of his best-known and best-loved poems. It is addressed throughout to a personified 'Autumn' and in many ways is a valedictory poem which presents the fruitfulness of autumn and signals the approaching winter. It presents a vision of humanity working in close harmony with the natural processes of nature.

Activity

1 Read the poem carefully, and the guiding questions that follow it.
2 Spend 20 minutes preparing your ideas for an oral commentary on this poem.
3 Write notes on the poem as if you were preparing to give an oral commentary on it.
4 Write down what you would say if you were giving an Individual Oral Commentary on this poem.

To Autumn

Season of mists and mellow fruitfulness,
Close bosom-friend of the maturing sun;
Conspiring with him how to load and bless
With fruit the vines that round the thatch-eaves run;
To bend with apples the moss'd cottage-trees,
And fill all fruit with ripeness to the core;
To swell the gourd, and plump the hazel shells
With a sweet kernel; to set budding more,
And still more, later flowers for the bees,
Until they think warm day will never cease,
For Summer has o'erbrimm'd their clammy cells.

Who hath not seen thee oft amid thy store?
Sometimes whoever seeks abroad may find
Thee sitting careless on a granary floor,
Thy hair soft-lifted by the winnowing wind;
Or on a half-reap'd furrow sound asleep,
Drows'd with the fume of poppies, while thy hook
Spares the next swath and all its twinèd flowers;
And sometimes like a gleaner thou dost keep
Steady thy laden head across a brook;
Or by a cider-press, with patient look,
Thou watchest the last oozings, hours by hours.

Where are the songs of Spring? Aye, where are they?
Think not of them, – thou hast thy music too,
While barrèd clouds bloom the soft-dying day,
And touch the stubble-plains with rosy hue;
Then in a wailful choir the small gnats mourn
Among the river sallows, borne aloft
Or sinking as the light wind lives or dies;
And full-grown lambs loud bleat from hilly bourn;
Hedge-crickets sing, and now with treble soft;
The redbreast whistles from a garden-croft
And gathering swallows twitter in the skies.

John Keats

Guiding question 1:   (Higher Level and Standard Level)
What is your response to the opening stanza of the
poem?

Guiding question 2:   (Higher Level)
How does Keats use imagery in the poem? What
effects does this create?
(Standard Level)
What is the overall effect of the poem as reflected in
the final stanza?

Activity   Now read this transcript from a student's oral commentary on *To Autumn* and compare the ideas with your own.

I feel that the first line of the poem immediately captures a sense of the essence of autumn combining the characteristics of 'mists' and 'mellow fruitfulness'. The second line links the season to the sun – a 'maturing' sun in the sense that the natural cycle of the year has reached its maturity. It also introduces the idea of the sun being an essential component of the natural process in bringing the fruits of autumn to ripeness and fruition. In this first stanza autumn is characterized by a strong reproductive force which is traditionally represented as female (in mythology, Ceres, the goddess of corn and the harvest). Just as the earth is generically female (hence phrases like 'Mother Earth'), the sun is traditionally characterized as male (as in the god Apollo) and the two together produce the rich fruits of autumn. Keats describes this union as 'conspiring' (line 3) which gives the impression of the two secretly and mysteriously working together to produce, almost as if by magic, the bounties of autumn. The poem is rich in imagery and here Keats uses it to create a sense of the bounty produced by this union, as in lines 5-11.

The first image in stanza 2 personifies autumn as being 'amid thy store' cleaning the grain of chaff – one of the routine tasks following the harvest called 'winnowing' – hence Keats's reference to the 'winnowing wind' (line 15). I feel that this again has feminine connotations, created by the reference to 'Thy hair soft-lifted' (line 15). He follows this with a second image, this time of the field worker asleep on a 'half-reap'd furrow'. The reference to 'Drows'd with the fume of poppies' suggests not only sleep but a sleep that is drug-induced and therefore a state of heightened subconscious awareness. The worker's scythe is suspended, sparing the 'next swath and all its twinèd flowers' (line 18).

A third image Keats uses here creates a picture of a gleaner carrying a head of corn across a brook. The 'laden head' (line 20) creates the sense of plenty.

A final image in this stanza gives me a picture of a worker at the cider-press crushing the juice from the apples to make cider. This image reminds me of the richness of the apple harvest, which was created in stanza 1.

These images together present a series of mental pictures which capture some of the activities that typify autumn and the harvest. As well as reinforcing the impression of abundance, they also suggest a sense of progression – the reaper cuts the crop, the gleaner gathers it after the reaper, the winnower winnows it. The crushing of the apples marks a stage of progression from apple to cider. Each of these activities, then, brings us closer to the end of nature's annual cycle of life and prepares us for the final stanza.

In the final stanza Keats unites his images and the experiences of the first two stanzas. It presents an acceptance of autumn's passing, with its suggestion of death and the impending winter. However, the opening question with its reference to spring has a consoling effect in that it reminds us not only that the 'songs of Spring' (line 23) have passed and winter is approaching, but that spring will come again too. The poet consoles himself also with the idea that although autumn signals the approaching end of the natural cycle, it too has its own beauty. The compensation for the loss of the 'songs of Spring' lies in the beauty of natural maturity and it is this that the poem celebrates. There are compensations in that although autumn has no 'songs' it has its own 'music'. There is a melancholy in this music, though: 'in a wailful choir the small gnats mourn' (line 27) and the 'full-grown lambs loud bleat from hilly bourn' (line 30). On the other hand the 'Hedge-crickets sing' (line 31) and the 'redbreast whistles' (line 32) while the swallows 'twitter in the skies' as they prepare to migrate for the winter; like autumn, their stay is nearing its end. The ending of the poem, however, does not strike me as depressing but rather has a sense of optimism. I think that Keats is pointing here to the natural cycle, and although autumn is at an end and winter is drawing close, that too in its turn will be followed by another spring and another summer. In that sense I think that this poem not only celebrates the end of the natural year but also looks forward to celebrating the start of a new one.

10 The Individual Oral Presentation

Objectives
- To analyse the requirements of the Individual Oral Presentation
- To prepare for the Individual Oral Presentation by practising topic work

The Individual Oral Presentation is the second compulsory oral activity that all Language A1 students must complete and is based on a work or works studied in Part 4 of the syllabus. This presentation is based on a topic that you have chosen in consultation with your teacher.

Choice of topic

When thinking about what topic you are going to choose as the subject for your Oral Presentation, you should be aware that you may choose a topic which reflects your personal interests. Obviously if you choose a topic that you have some interest in you are likely to produce a more effective and interesting presentation than if you choose a topic you find boring. You have quite a wide choice as it can be based on any work or works you have studied in Part 4 of the syllabus. Your topic may be based on any aspect or aspects of the work(s) studied, including:

- cultural setting of the work(s) and related issues
- thematic focus
- characterization

- techniques and style
- author's attitude to particular elements of the works such as character(s), subject matter
- interpretation of particular elements from different perspectives.

Possible activities

The range of activities that you could choose for your Individual Oral Presentation is very wide and the suggestions that follow are simply examples of the kinds of things you could do. You should discuss your own ideas with your teacher and select an activity that is appropriate to the topic you have chosen.

Structured discussions

These could be:
- Class discussions where you have been given special responsibilities, such as doing advance preparation, giving a short report, adopting a provocative position, etc. The whole class may participate in this kind of activity, although only the presenter will be assessed.
- The presentation of material that promotes class discussion, such as presenting opposing readings of a work. This would probably involve the presenter answering questions from the class.
- An interview conducted by the teacher on an agreed topic or work(s).

Oral exposés

These could be:
- An introduction to a writer, a work, or a particular text.
- An explanation of a particular aspect of an author's work.
- The setting of a particular writer's work against another body of material, such as details on social background or political views.
- A commentary on the use of a particular image, idea, or symbol in one text or in a writer's work.
- An imitation of a poem that you have studied. This activity should be followed by some explanation of, and discussion on, what you have tried to do and to show.
- A comparison of two passages, two characters, or two works.
- A commentary on an extract from a work you have studied in class which has been prepared at home.
- An account of your developing response to a work.

Role play

This could involve:
- A monologue by a character at an important point in the work.
- Reminiscences by a character from a point in later life.
- An author's reaction to a particular interpretation of his or her work.

If you choose to do a role play for your Oral Presentation, it is important that you provide a rationale explaining what you have done and what you hoped to achieve.

Focus of your Individual Oral Presentation

The main focus of your oral presentation will depend very much on the nature and scope of the topic that you choose. However, in order to do well in your presentation you will be expected to show a good level of literary appreciation. Naturally it is expected that this will be more sophisticated at Higher Level that at Standard Level. Whatever the topic you choose you will be expected to show:

- Knowledge and understanding of the work(s).
- Thorough appreciation of the aspect discussed.
- Knowledge and use of the linguistic register appropriate for the type of presentation, which means being sensitive to your use of such elements as vocabulary, tone, sentence structure, and modes of expression, and ensuring that they are appropriate to the task.
- At Higher Level, where appropriate, you should consider the effects created by the ways in which the writer(s) have explored the material you are presenting.

Structure of your Individual Oral Presentation

Again the precise structure of your oral presentation depends, to a large extent, on the type of activity you have chosen and your topic. Some activities, such as a discussion and an oral exposé, may be suited to a more formally structured discussion approach which follows a logical sequence from one point to another. Others, such as a role play, may not be so effectively presented through a formal, structured approach. The main thing is that you should decide on the type of presentation most likely to achieve the objectives you have for your topic. Whatever you choose, however, you should bear in mind that all presentations must have some kind of coherent structure.

Preparation of your Individual Oral Presentation

You will be expected to do the preparation work for your Individual Oral Presentation outside class time. When you have chosen your topic it is your responsibility to:

- select appropriate material for your presentation
- organize the material into a coherent structure
- choose and rehearse the appropriate register for your presentation.

Presentation and discussion

Your presentation should last between 10 and 15 minutes. Once you have started to give your presentation you will not be interrupted and you will not be allowed any assistance.

When you have completed your presentation your teacher will discuss the material with you further to explore your knowledge and understanding of the work(s) or topic you have presented. Your teacher will want to make sure that you can justify your selection of:

- the material used in your presentation
- the activity you have chosen to present the topic
- the linguistic register you have used for the presentation of your topic.

The whole class may take part in the discussions following your presentation.

Assessment of your presentation

Your presentation will be assessed against a number of criteria. These are:

A Knowledge and understanding of the text
B Interpretation and personal response
C Presentation
D Use of language.

In order to achieve a good result you will need to show:

- good knowledge and understanding of the content of the extract or work(s)
- thorough knowledge of the appropriate context of the extract or work(s)
- a valid and detailed interpretation of the thought and feeling expressed in the extract or work(s), including a considered critical response
- a good awareness and detailed analysis of the effects of the literary features of the extract or work(s)
- a response supported by relevant references to the extract or work(s)
- a clear and logical structure to the response
- a focused response presented in a clear, coherent, effective, and convincing manner
- integrated supporting references
- a clear, varied, and precise use of language using an appropriate register and style, and relevant literary terms.

The Individual Oral Presentation in practice

When you are preparing your presentation it is important that you approach the task in a structured and coherent way, in order to produce a structured and coherent presentation.

Activity   The following notes were made by a student in preparation for a presentation on John Steinbeck's use of language, structure, and style in his novel *Of Mice and Men*. These notes represent the first stage in the student preparing ideas that will ultimately be included in the final presentation.

Read them carefully and think about the following points:
- the range of ideas they contain
- the way they are structured
- how effectively they convey their ideas.

Language, structure, and style in John Steinbeck's novel *Of Mice and Men*

One of the striking features of Steinbeck's story is the realistic way in which it is presented. His writing shows an interest in the lives of the poor and of the socially deprived. There are certain aspects of the way that he uses language that the reader becomes aware of when reading his novel. For example:

- The story is written in the third person. In other words, the writer seems 'invisible' but readers can see everything that goes on and even what is inside people's minds. The writer of a third-person account can describe characters' thoughts, speech, and actions to the reader. In this story, however, Steinbeck does not use the technique of looking into people's minds very much. In fact, only once do we see directly into people's thoughts.
- Steinbeck uses simple language and straightforward vocabulary, which means that his story is told in a direct, plain, and uncomplicated fashion.
- The dialogue is written as it would have been spoken, and Steinbeck makes use of dialect forms.
- He uses a different kind of speech for different characters. For example, Lennie's sentences are very childlike in character. Curley's language tends to be full of pent-up aggression and anger. Slang, or colloquial language, is used in the novel, again to reflect the way that real people speak.

Style

Here are some important features of the style in which *Of Mice and Men* is written:

- The story is a blend of description and drama.
- When Steinbeck uses description, which is most notable in the first and last scenes, he creates a vivid picture of nature and the natural world. Although not vital to the development of the story, these descriptions form a background against which the story is set and also contain a symbolic importance. The events at the ranch, on the other hand, are written very economically with very little description. Everything there is designed to develop or reveal a theme or a character trait, most of which indicate the fate which is to befall Lennie and George.
- The dramatic style that Steinbeck intended from the outset consists mainly of dialogue and of short exchanges, and the story is developed through these

exchanges. Originally, Steinbeck intended the story to be easily adapted for the stage, and so the writing is very similar to the way in which a play would be written.

Imagery

Imagery is the use of words to create pictures or images in the reader's mind and is used by a writer to make his or her words more effective and powerful. Although *Of Mice and Men* is written in simple and straightforward language, Steinbeck uses several images as symbols. A symbol is something which is used to represent or indicate something else. For example, he begins with the description of the river and the path and the campsite. Wildlife is referred to only in the opening and closing scenes, which are set by the river. Perhaps here Steinbeck is drawing a contrast between the ongoing cycle of nature and a human being's temporary appearance in this scene, which typifies the transient lifestyle of the itinerant workers. Although animals feature prominently in the plot, the images of them often emphasize the harshness of the workers' lives. They also feature in the descriptions of people, particularly Lennie. He is compared to a bear and a horse, and later in the first scene Steinbeck likens him to a terrier when he shows reluctance to give up his pet mouse to George. Imagery to do with hands is also used in the novel. For example, Lennie's hands are referred to several times as 'paws', and the gloved fist of Curley plays an important part in the story.

The use of light

Steinbeck often refers to light and dark, or sunshine and shadow, and frequently these are used to create atmosphere.

The structure of the story

When we talk of the structure of the story we really mean the way that the story is put together. This is quite a short story but it nonetheless has a very tight and clearly defined structure and within the structure everything comes full circle. For example, the action ends in the same place as it began.

Six central scenes comprise the story

- Scene One: sets the scene and introduces the main characters
- Scene Two: we meet Curley and there is the shooting of Candy's dog
- Scene Three: the damage to Curley's hand
- Scene Four: the confrontation with Curley's wife
- Scene Five: her death
- Scene Six: Lennie's death.

Activity   The following represents the transcript of an oral presentation that a student prepared on the topic of the sonnets of John Keats. The student selected for herself a range of sonnets and prepared her presentation on them.

Read the transcript through carefully and make a note of the impression that you get of the presentation. Ask yourself the following questions:

1 How well does the student seem to know and understand the sonnets she presents?
2 How effectively has she analysed the effects of literary features such as diction, imagery, tone, structure, style, and technique?
3 How structured is the student's response?
4 How effective and convincing is her presentation?
5 How appropriately does she integrate supporting references to illustrate her ideas?
6 How accurate, clear, and precise is her use of language?
7 How appropriate is her choice of register and style for the presentation?
8 How do you think the presentation could be improved?

The sonnets of John Keats

In this presentation I will look at a selection of sonnets written by the English Romantic poet, John Keats. The sonnets I have chosen reveal the progression in style that Keats's writing underwent as his style developed.

On first looking into Chapman's Homer
Before studying this sonnet it may help you to know that Keats wrote it in October 1816 after reading for the first time a translation by George Chapman of Homer's *Iliad* and *Odyssey*. It is often regarded as Keats's first poem of any real significance. Keats himself could not read Greek and so his knowledge of the works of Homer was limited to the refined translation of the eighteenth-century writer Alexander Pope. However, one night his friend and teacher, Charles Cowden Clarke, introduced him to Elizabethan translator Chapman's version, which he found much more exciting and powerful than the previous versions he had read.

Probably the most immediately striking thing about the opening lines is the richness of the language. Words like 'realms', 'gold', 'goodly', 'kingdoms' give an immediate impression of one whose experience has brought him into contact with a wealth of riches. Notice too the reference to 'bards' (poets) who express their 'fealty' (loyalty) to their lord, Apollo (the Greek god of poetry and music).

Keats continues the metaphor of him as a traveller journeying in rich and mystical lands in the next few lines and speaks of how he had been told of a 'wide expanse' that Homer, the Greek poet and writer of the *Iliad* and *Odyssey*, ruled as his kingdom. However, he says that he had never breathed the clear air ('pure serene') of Homer until he heard 'Chapman speak out loud and bold'. In other words, although he had heard of Homer before he had never really fully experienced his work until he read Chapman's translation.

In the closing six lines of the poem, or the sestet as it is called, Keats uses two similes. In the first he compares his excitement on reading Chapman's version with that felt by an astronomer who discovers a new planet. He then compares his feelings to those experienced by Cortez when he discovered the Pacific Ocean and looked upon it from a hill in Darien (an isthmus in Central America).

Both these similes stress the magnitude of the effect that Chapman's Homer had on Keats. It is perhaps worth noting here that many critics and writers have observed that, in fact, Balboa and not Cortez was the first European to discover the Pacific. It is known that Keats had read Robertson's *History of America* which contains descriptions of Balboa's discovery of the Pacific and Cortez's discovery of Mexico City. Some feel that Keats deliberately wrote 'Cortez' because he preferred the sound of that name to that of 'Balboa'. However, in poetic terms the point is an insignificant one as the poetic intention here is not to present a historically accurate account but to convey a sense of Keats's experience. It could be argued that the name of 'Cortez' has a more musical quality to it as well as carrying connotations of excitement and discovery that 'Balboa' lacks.

In these last six lines there are a number of words or phrases that add power to the sense of the excitement of a new discovery that Keats creates. For example, 'stout Cortez' and 'eagle eyes' give an impression of the intrepid, observant, and sharp-eyed explorer constantly looking for new discoveries. The description of his men looking at each other 'with a wild surmise' reinforces the impression of hardly being able to believe the discovery. 'Silent' again reinforces this idea as Cortez's men are speechless as the enormity of their discovery sinks in.

Keats also uses the structure of the poem to develop his ideas. The poem is written in the sonnet form and in the first eight lines or octave Keats describes his experiences of reading a wealth of rich literature in the past. In the final two lines of the octave, though, Keats prepares us for the final lines of the sonnet by telling us that despite such reading he had never truly experienced its beauty and wonder until he read Chapman. The final six lines of the sonnet (the sestet) go on to describe how he felt at this exciting discovery, through the imagery of an astronomer discovering a new star or an explorer discovering a new ocean. The poem is unified through the central metaphor of the traveller and the voyage of discovery.

It is worth remembering that many critics regard this poem as being Keats's first poem of any real significance and it records, as many of his later poems do in different ways, the thrill of an aesthetic experience and the power of art to influence the human mind.

To My Brothers

This sonnet was written in November 1816 on the 19th birthday of Keats's youngest brother, Thomas. At that time Keats was living with his brothers George and Thomas in London.

In the octave of the sonnet the poet observes the flames playing over the coals in the fire and contemplates the quietness of the house in which he and his brothers reside, and the 'household gods that keep/A gentle empire o'er fraternal souls'. He thinks of how, as he searches for poetic inspiration, his younger brother's eyes 'are fix'd, as in a poetic sleep' on his learning, and how the fall of night offers comfort to their cares.

In the sestet he develops these ideas further. In these lines Keats focuses on the fact that it is his brother Tom's birthday and he expresses gladness that it has passed in such a tranquil mood. He also expresses the wish that they may pass many such quiet evenings together and to experience life's true joys before they die.

The mood of this poem is very meditative, as the poet weighs in his mind 'What are the world's true joys'. Overall, the tone is conversational, although there are some more elevated poetic images such as 'A gentle empire o'er fraternal souls' and 'I search around the poles'. These help to suggest a more universal message in the poem, beyond that of the domestic scene he celebrates.

Addressed to [Haydon]

Another poem written in the sonnet form, *Addressed to [Haydon]*, was also written in November 1816. The poem is addressed to Benjamin Robert Haydon, a painter whom Keats had met earlier that year.

In the octave he speaks of 'Great spirits', who are staying or travelling on earth. The first of these 'Great spirits', 'He of the cloud, the cataract, the lake' refers to the poet William Wordsworth (Haydon's painting, *Wordsworth Musing Upon Helvellyn*, is in the National Portrait Gallery – Helvellyn is a mountain in the Lake District). Keats says that the inspiration of Wordsworth's poetry came from the wing of an angel of the highest order.

'He of the rose, the violet, the spring' refers to Leigh Hunt, who was imprisoned 'for Freedom's sake' and who, while in prison, turned his cell into a bower of flowers using wallpaper. The third reference is to Raphael (both the name of an archangel and the famous Renaissance painter) and is a tribute to the painter, Haydon.

In the final lines of the poem the poet ponders on the fact that other great spirits will appear from ages yet to come and these spirits too will have an important and shaping influence upon the world: 'these will give the world another heart,/And other pulses.' His emphasis here is upon the shaping of humanity and imagination. He asks the reader 'Hear ye not the hum/Of mighty workings?' These are the workings of the imagination within the human spirit, and he urges all to be silent and listen to the imagination.

The structure of this sonnet is in the conventional form except for the unconventional thirteenth line, which is, in fact, half a line. Originally Keats completed this line with the words 'in a distant Mart'. He then decided to leave out the second part of the line. By omitting the second part of this line the poet allows the silence to take its place in a real sense in response to his question. 'Hear ye not the hum/Of might workings?'

Unlike *To My Brothers*, the tone of this sonnet is elevated, in keeping with the sense of admiration Keats wants to create for Wordsworth, Leigh Hunt, and Haydon, and it is specific in its reference to the poets and the painter.

On the Sea

This sonnet was written on 16 or 17 April 1817, when Keats was staying at Carisbrooke on the Isle of Wight.

In the octave his imagery brings out the eternal nature of the sea and the use of personification adds power to this. There is little elevated language here (despite the reference to Hecate – a goddess who had power over the heavens, earth, and the sea). Notice the description here – the 'desolate shores', 'its mighty swell' – and the finely observed detail – 'the very smallest shell' – which create a contrast between the sea's mightiest and minutest effects.

The sestet opens with an invocation to those 'who have your eye-balls vexed and tired' to look upon the sea; and to those whose 'ears are dinned with uproar rude' to sit near the mouth of a sea-cave and listen to the sounds of the sea. Keats captures the noise of the sea through a succession of onomatopoeic consonants 'dinned with uproar rude', for example.

The poem then reveals Keats's admiration, not only for the sea's eternal nature and awesome power, but also for its restorative effects on the human heart and mind.

On Sitting Down to Read King Lear Once Again

This sonnet was also written in January 1818 and contains Keats's thoughts as he sits down to read *King Lear* again.

In the opening lines here he dismisses the idea of 'Romance', which he personifies as 'golden-tongued Romance, with serene lute!' He is referring here to a kind of self-indulgent writing which has lured him in the past – note the use of 'Syren', in mythology a bewitching figure. He bids farewell to this kind of writing, for he must 'burn through' the 'fierce dispute/Betwixt damnation and impassioned clay'. The latter refers directly to the theme of the play *King Lear*, while 'burn through' presents the reading of the play as a kind of ordeal by fire – an image which is picked up again in the final couplet of the sonnet. Note also the image of the play as a 'bitter-sweet . . . fruit'.

In the final lines he speaks of 'Albion' – the ancient name for Britain, and the setting of *King Lear* and therefore the 'Begetters of our deep eternal theme'. The 'old oak forest' into which Keats speaks of going points to the endurance or suffering that the poet must face but his plan is that when he is consumed by fire he can be re-born with the poetic self-discipline and determination that he desires. It is worth noting that this sonnet concludes in the style of a Shakespearean sonnet with a rhyming couplet, and in that it differs from the early sonnets that we have looked at. This rhyming couplet adds a sense of finality to the ideas expressed. It is also worth noting that uncharacteristically the last line contains an extra foot, which breaks the pattern of pentameters that is established in the rest of the sonnet. It is unclear whether this was an oversight on Keats's part or a deliberate feature. An interesting effect is achieved through this lengthened final line.

When I have fears that I may cease to be

Written between 22 and 31 January 1818, this sonnet shows even more clearly than the previous one the influence of Shakespeare on Keats's writing. The 36 sonnets Keats wrote up to the beginning of 1818 are all Petrarchan in form – the pattern used by Milton and Wordsworth. This is a form which strictly follows the pattern of an octave rhyming *abbaabba* followed by a sestet of two tercets (three lines) rhyming either *cdcdcd* or *cde cde*. He moved away slightly from this form in *On Sitting Down to Read* King Lear *Once Again*, which is basically Petrarchan in form but with a concluding rhyming couplet. However, *When I have fears that I may cease to be*, written a day or two later, is fully Shakespearean in form.

The rhyme scheme is *abab/cdcd/efef/gg*. This form of three quatrains concluding with a rhyming couplet is one that Shakespeare commonly uses in his sonnets. Its lines are end-stopped and the three quatrains, although separate, are logically linked and develop one from the other. The concluding couplet links back to the whole of the rest of the poem, to give both a sense of unity and conclusion. However, the influence extends beyond the rhyme scheme: Keats's subject matter also has features that are reminiscent of Shakespeare's (and Keats's) concerns, i.e. 'death', 'love' and 'poetic destiny'.

The poet expresses the fear that death will come to him before he has been able to write all that is in his mind. He thinks of all the beauty that exists and regrets that he 'may never live to trace/Their shadows with the magic hand of chance'. He thinks of the 'fair creature of an hour!' (often regarded as a reference to a young woman he met briefly in a chance encounter, but transformed into a metaphor for man in quest of a rare, nameless, and unattainable beauty) and the fact that he will 'never look upon thee more'. At the end of the poem he is left empty and alone to face death, in the face of which 'love and fame to nothingness do sink'.

He uses a number of images in the poem which create a particular effect. For example, the first part of the poem is rich in harvest and cosmic imagery: 'gleaned my teeming brain', ' like rich garners the full-ripened grain', 'the night's starred face', 'Huge cloudy symbols'. These images blend together the richness and fruitfulness of the poetic imagination and ambition within the context of the universe.

The imagery of the second part of the poem elevates the ephemeral experience to an importance greater than that of ambition, but this is a level that he will never attain – 'Never have relish in the faery power/Of unreflecting love!'

Images of death run throughout the poem – 'fears that I may cease to be', 'I may never live', 'I shall never look upon thee more', 'I stand alone'.

Although it is perfectly possible to read this poem as an expression of a universal experience without reference to biographical overtones, the poem does possess these overtones.

The main factor here relates to the tuberculosis that ran through Keats's family. As a young man he had nursed his mother through the last stages of the disease and by January 1818 he was already becoming concerned about the state of his brother Tom's health. It is understandable, therefore, particularly bearing in mind his medical training, that he might have thought too about the prospects for his own health. He had, in fact, already begun to think that he did not have long to live himself, even though no signs of the disease had yet shown themselves. As it turned out, his own misgivings turned out to be remarkably accurate, as his death came only three years later.

Here are some points you might have noted about how the presentation could be improved.

- The student tends to deal with the sonnets individually. The presentation would be improved if links were drawn between them.
- More developed comments could be made on Keats's style.
- There could be more detailed analysis and evaluation.

In the next section we will look at how a student worked through a specific theme to prepare a presentation based on the literature of war. In this instance the student took as his theme: 'The First World War in Literature'.

He began by setting the literature in a historical context.

Activity Read the historical context which follows. How well do you think this sets the context for the presentation?

The historical context

The 'Great War' of 1914–1918, one of the greatest catastrophes of modern times, cast a long shadow over twentieth-century Europe. This so-called 'war to end wars' did nothing of the kind, but it did bring about profound changes in society, culture, and ways of thinking. It is said to have marked the true beginning of the 'modern age'.

You may have some knowledge of the events of the First World War, which often feature in television documentaries or history programmes. Here is a helpful summary from Paul Fussell's introduction to *The Bloody Game*, a huge, fascinating anthology of the literature of modern war.

'It had all begun in June 1914, when Archduke Francis Ferdinand, heir to the throne of Austria-Hungary, was assassinated in Sarajevo, Bosnia-Herzegovina, by a Serbian patriot fed up with Austrian domination of his country. Austria-Hungary used the occasion to pick a long-desired quarrel with Serbia and to issue an ultimatum that could only produce war. At this point the system of European alliances, negotiated over many decades, had to be honored: Russia came to the aid of Serbia, whereupon Germany jumped in on the side of Austria-Hungary. France then honored her treaty with Russia, Britain hers with France. By October 1914, Turkey had joined the side of Germany and Austria-Hungary (the 'Central Powers'). By the end of the year the notorious trench system was emplaced in Belgium and France, running 400 miles from its northern anchor at the North Sea to its southern end at the Swiss border, while in the east, another front developed along the Russian border with Austria-Hungary. Italy came in on the side of the Allies in 1915, opening a front against Austria. And in April 1917, the United States, exasperated by German sinking of its ships, joined the Allies, although it took many months for an American army to be assembled, supplied, trained, shipped to Europe and installed in the line. The Americans arrived so late in the war that although they fought impressively and were generally credited with supplying the needed weight to win the war, they suffered only about one-tenth the casualties of the British, and more American soldiers died from influenza than from gas and bullets and shells.'

The student went on to identify certain features which were peculiar to the First World War.

Certain features of the First World War made it different from anything that had gone before.

- The sheer number of casualties: Over 37 million people died or were wounded.
- War was a mass activity: All eligible (male) civilians were called up or conscripted to fight, where previously wars had been fought by professional armies at a distance from civilian life. The first ever air raids – from Zeppelin airships – also brought war much closer to home.
- Technology such as machine guns, tanks, barbed wire, and poison gas were used for the first time. These new weapons killed indiscriminately, regardless of whether soldiers were 'brave' or not. Enemies did not have to see each other and the personal element of face-to-face combat was removed. It became easier, literally and psychologically, to kill.
- Trench warfare: Much of the war was fought in a system of deep, muddy ditches in which soldiers lived, in appalling conditions, for months on end, facing the 'enemy' across fifty yards of 'no man's land'.
- Gender issues: Women did not participate directly in the fighting – although some did experience the war at close quarters through serving as army nurses – but the war had a drastic effect on their lives. The loss of so many men left gaps in the workforce and caused an imbalance between the genders. Some women took on roles that had never been open to them before, while many more, who had lost husbands or lovers, had no choice but to remain single.

The student then went on to set a literary context for the material he was going to discuss.

Writing the war: the literary context

The war occurred at a time when literature flourished and was highly respected, and it prompted a great outpouring of writing of all sorts. Its peculiar horrors have continued to inspire and fascinate authors to the present day.

To understand the literature of the war, you need some understanding of how people typically thought and felt about these events, both at the time and afterwards. There are recurring themes, ideas and 'motifs' in First World War literature. Here are some.

- The features of First World War combat, mentioned above, are reflected in an increasing sense of depersonalization. Soldiers became mere numbers, not individuals. Literary accounts of the dehumanizing experience of the trenches became more graphic as the war went on, while contemporary authors like Pat Barker and Sebastian Faulks continue the trend. Their language and imagery reflect this.
- First World War literature is full of starkly contrasted images. The war generated a tendency to see things in 'black and white', in terms of two-sided 'splits' or contrasts, between for example:
  - 'us' and 'them' (the 'enemy')

- people who fought and people who stayed at home
- soldiers at the front and high-ranking officials who gave their orders from safe places
- men and women – men could not communicate the full horror of their experiences to women who had stayed at home, which caused misunderstanding and resentment
- the horror of war and the comfort of home; the smart restaurants and theatres of London were sometimes no more than seventy miles from the trenches
- the ugliness of the war-torn landscape and the beauty of nature.

- In 1914, people were filled with a patriotic fervour and idealism which, with hindsight, appears painfully naive. Young men, susceptible to propaganda, saw the war as a 'big picnic', and dying for their country was regarded as an honour, or a religious duty. By the time the war ended, those who were left felt resigned or cynical. Religion no longer offered consolation, and soldiers had little to rely on except the comradeship they shared. British poetry before and early in the war tended to be lyrical and pastoral, or 'Georgian', extolling nature and idealizing English country life. It is easy to see the contrast between the high-flown rhetoric and religious language used early in the war and the bitter realism, which doesn't mince words, of later writing.

- Away from the front, governments and the press – which was heavily censored – continued to present the war to the public in old-fashioned, idealized language. Soldiers were still 'gallant warriors' and horses were 'steeds'. Writers like Siegfried Sassoon and Wilfred Owen wanted to expose this dishonesty, and poetry was a 'safe' way of expressing protest. When Sassoon protested openly in a public statement, he was sent to a mental institution.

- Trench warfare generated a language of its own. As well as vocabulary associated with the trenches themselves ('dugouts', 'funk-holes') and the technology of war ('whizz-bangs', 'five-nines'), soldiers had their own codes and euphemisms to describe their activities. Some who were stationed in France also developed a kind of 'pidgin' French.

Writers of the First World War

This is just a selection of those who have written significantly about the war.

Writers who experienced the war

Rupert Brooke: Poetry; also letters
Robert Graves: Memoir *Goodbye to All That*
R.C. Sherriff: Drama *Journey's End*
Wilfred Owen: Poetry; letters
David Jones: Memoir *In Parenthesis*
Siegfried Sassoon: Poetry; memoirs, especially the semi-fictional *Memoirs of an Infantry Officer* and *Sherston's Progress*; diaries
Ivor Gurney: Poetry; letters
Erich Maria Remarque: Memoir *All Quiet on the Western Front*
Charles Hamilton Sorley: Poetry
Julian Grenfell: Poetry
Vera Brittain: Memoir *Testament of Youth*; poetry; letters.

Later writings

Virginia Woolf: Her novel *Mrs Dalloway* includes a portrait of a shell-shocked soldier attempting to come to terms with his experience and the lack of understanding of the people around him

Sebastian Faulks: Novel *Birdsong*

Pat Barker: Novels *Regeneration, The Eye in the Door, The Ghost Road;* also *Another World.*

Many other authors have written on the war, and their work is included in anthologies, which are a very useful way of seeing the variety of writing produced.

Activity

Consider what you have read so far. Do you think it provides a sound introduction to the theme 'The First World War in Literature', or would you add any other details? Do you think some could be left out?

The student went on to look at some specific texts. The texts and extracts that the student chose were selected to demonstrate a range of different genres, styles, and points of view. These pieces could be approached in various ways.

One of the poems selected for the presentation was Laurence Binyon's poem *For the Fallen* which was written very early in the war and is characteristic of the mood of religious, idealized, patriotic fervour.

For the Fallen

(September 1914)

With proud thanksgiving, a mother for her children,
England mourns for her dead across the sea.
Flesh of her flesh they were, spirit of her spirit.
Fallen in the cause of the free.

Solemn the drums thrill: Death august and royal
Sings sorrow up into immortal spheres.
There is music in the midst of desolation
And a glory that shines upon our tears.

They went with songs to the battle, they were young,
Straight of limb, true of eye, steady and aglow.
They were staunch to the end against odds uncounted,
They fell with their faces to the foe.

They shall grow not old, as we that are left grow old:
Age shall not weary them, nor the years condemn.
At the going down of the sun and in the morning
We will remember them.

They mingle not with their laughing comrades again;
They sit no more at familiar tables of home;
They have no lot in our labour of the day-time;
They sleep beyond England's foam.

But where our desires are and our hopes profound,
Felt as a well-spring that is hidden from sight,
To the innermost heart of their own land they are known
As the stars are known to the night.

As the stars that shall be bright when we are dust,
Moving in marches upon the heavenly plain,
As the stars that are starry in the time of our darkness,
To the end, to the end, they remain.

Laurence Binyon

Activity

1 Working on your own or with a partner, read the poem carefully and make notes. In particular, think about:
  • how England and death are presented in the poem
  • how the soldiers are described in stanza 3
  • the effect of the form and rhythm of the poem
  • the imagery of stars in stanzas 6 and 7
  • how imagery, vocabulary, rhyme, rhythm, and sound are used to create the atmosphere or tone of the poem, and to reinforce the message Binyon wishes to convey
  • Binyon's use of 'we' for the voice of the poem
  • whether the ideas in the poem are 'concrete' (real, down to earth) or 'abstract'.
2 Use your notes to write a detailed account of the poem, suitable for use in an Individual Oral Presentation. Include your own response to Binyon's view of what it means to die for your country.

Also selected for the presentation on the First World War were these two letters, in which young officer poets relate some of their experiences to loved ones at home. They illustrate the change in attitude that occurred between the excitement of the early months of the war and the disillusionment of the later years, as well as the different personalities of the writers. The first is from Rupert Brooke to his friend Katharine Cox, and was written from a transport ship in the Aegean Sea, between Greece and North Africa. At this stage, he can still describe the experience of war as 'romantic'. In the second letter, Wilfred Owen writes to his mother of the realities of 'Flanders'. Both letters show evidence of the censorship that prevented soldiers from giving away too much about their activities. Neither of these young men survived the war: Rupert Brooke died at sea and was buried on a small Greek island, and Owen was killed only days before the Armistice in 1918.

To KATHARINE COX　　　　　　　　　*19–24 March [1915]*

　　　　　　　　　　　　　　　　　Somewhere
　　　　　　　　　　　　　　　　　(some way from the front)

Dear Ka,

Your letter of the 3rd of March has just reached me. Fairly quick. There are said to be 80 bags of mail still (parcels, if anything, I suspect) at headquarters (here). But your letter is the only letter I've had since we sailed. It is fun getting letters. Tell people – Dudley and such – to write occasionally. I can't write much. There's very little I *could*, of interest. And that, as a rule, I *mayn't*. This letter is to be censored by the Brigade Chaplain. . . . Here three quarters of the day is dullish – routine – and the society is unnatural – over a long period – all men. Anyway, it's nice to hear.

. . . Yes: this is romantic. (But I won't admit that Flanders isn't.) But I'm afraid I can't tell you most of the romantic things, at present.

My own lot have seen no fighting yet, and very likely won't for months. The only thing that seems almost certain is that one doesn't know from day to day what's to happen. The other day we – some of us – were told that we sailed next day to make a landing. A few thousand of us. Off we stole that night through the phosphorescent Aegean, scribbling farewell letters, and snatching periods of dream-broken, excited sleep. At four we rose, buckled on our panoply[1], hung ourselves with glasses compasses periscopes revolvers food and the rest, and had a stealthy large breakfast. *That* was a mistake. It is ruinous to load up one's belly four or five hours before it expects it: it throws the machinery out of gear for a week. I felt extremely ill the rest of that day.

We paraded in silence, under paling stars, along the sides of the ship. The darkness on the sea was full of scattered flashing lights, hinting at our fellow-transports and the rest. Slowly the day became wan and green and the sea opal. Everyone's face looked drawn and ghastly. *If* we landed, my company was to be the first to land . . . We made out that we were only a mile or two from a dim shore. I was seized with an agony of remorse that I hadn't taught my platoon a thousand things more energetically and competently. The light grew. The shore looked to be crammed with Fate, and most ominously silent. One man thought he saw a camel through his glasses . . .

There were some hours of silence.

About seven someone said 'We're going home.' We dismissed the stokers, who said, quietly, 'When's the next battle?'; and disempanoplied, and had another breakfast. If we were a 'feint', or if it was too rough to land, or, in general, what little part we blindly played, we never knew, and shall not. Still, we did our bit; not ignobly, I trust. We did not see the enemy. We did not fire at them; nor they at us. It seemed improbable they saw us. One of B Company – she was rolling very slightly – was sick on parade. Otherwise no casualties. A notable battle.

All is well. Good-bye.

　　　　　　　　　　　　Rupert

1 *Panoply*: full suit of armour (old-fashioned word; suggests what knights would wear)

To Susan Owen

Friday, 19 January 1917   *2nd Manchester Regiment,*
                                                  British Expeditionary Force.

We are now a long way back in a ruined village, all huddled together in a farm. We all sleep in the same room where we eat and try to live. My bed is a hammock of rabbit-wire stuck up beside a great shell hole in the wall. Snow is deep about, and melts through the gaping roof, on to my blanket. We are wretched beyond my previous imagination – but safe.

Last night indeed I had to 'go up' with a party. We got lost in the snow. I went on ahead to scout – foolishly – alone – and when half a mile away from the party, got overtaken by

    GAS

It was only tear-gas from a shell, and I got safely back (to the party) in my helmet, with nothing worse than a severe fright! And a few tears, some natural, some unnatural.

Here is an Addition to my List of Wants:
Safety Razor (in my drawer) & Blades
Socks (2 pairs)
6 handkerchiefs
Celluloid Soap Box (Boots)
Cigarette Holder (Bone, 3d. or 6d.)
Paraffin for Hair.
(I can't wash hair and have taken to washing my face with snow.)

Coal, water, candles, accommodation, everything is scarce. We have not always air! When I took my helmet off last night – O Air it was a heavenly thing!

Please thank uncle for his letter, and send the Compass. I scattered abroad some 50 Field Post Cards from the Base, which should bring forth a good harvest of letters. But nothing but a daily one from you will keep me up.

I think Colin might try a weekly letter. And Father?

We have a Gramophone, and so musical does it seem now that I shall never more disparage one. Indeed I can never disparage anything in Blighty again for a long time except certain parvenus living in a street of the same name as you take to go to the Abbey [*i.e. Westminster*].

They want to call No Man's Land 'England' because we keep supremacy there.

It is like the eternal place of gnashing of teeth; the Slough of Despond could be contained in one of its crater-holes; the fires of Sodom and Gomorrah could not light a candle to it – to find the way to Babylon the Fallen.

It is pock-marked like a body of foulest disease and its odour is the breath of cancer.

I have not seen any dead. I have done worse. In the dank air I have *perceived* it, and in the darkness, *felt*. Those 'Somme Pictures' are the laughing stock of the army – like the trenches on exhibition in Kensington.

No Man's Land under snow is like the face of the moon, chaotic, crater-ridden, uninhabitable, awful, the abode of madness.

To call it 'England'!

. . . Now I have let myself tell you more facts than I should, in the exuberance of having already done *'a Bit'. It is done*, and we are all going still farther back for a long time. A long time. The people of England needn't hope. They must agitate. But they are not yet agitated even. Let them imagine 50 strong men trembling as with ague for 50 hours!

Dearer & stronger love than ever. W.E.O.

Activity

1 Read the letters carefully, thinking about the following questions:
   • What are the main topics and concerns of each writer?
   • In what ways are the letters alike? How do they differ?
   • What is each writer's attitude to his experience of war?
   • What are their attitudes to people at home – public figures and/or their family and friends?
   • How is each letter influenced by the time at which it was written?
   • How does each writer reveal that his words are subject to censorship?
   • What evidence can you detect, from the ways they use language, that these two young soldiers are also poets?
2 Write as fully as you can about these two letters, in a form that you could use for an Individual Oral Presentation. Examine the similarities and differences between the ways in which these young men portray their experience of war.

Now look at two poems in which the same writers reveal contrasting attitudes to death in battle. Brooke's five patriotic *Sonnets 1914* won huge popularity early in the war. For Owen, however, exposing the horror and the pity of war is the main concern.

The Dead

Blow out, you bugles, over the rich Dead!
    There's none of these so lonely and poor of old
    But, dying, has made us rarer gifts than gold.
These laid the world away; poured out the red
Sweet wine of youth; gave up the years to be
    Of work and joy, and that unhoped serene,
    That men call age; and those who would have been,
Their sons, they gave, their immortality.

Blow, Bugles, Blow! They brought us, for our dearth,
    Holiness, lacked so long, and Love, and Pain.
Honour has come back, as a king, to earth,
    And paid his subjects with a royal wage;
And Nobleness walks in our ways again;
    And we have come into our heritage.

Rupert Brooke

Futility

Move him into the sun –
Gently its touch awoke him once,
At home, whispering of fields unsown.
Always it woke him, even in France,
Until this morning and this snow.
If anything might rouse him now
The kind old sun will know.

Think how it wakes the seeds, –
Woke, once, the clays of cold star.
Are limbs, so dear-achieved, are sides,
Full-nerved – still warm – too hard to stir?
Was it for this the clay grew tall?
– O what made fatuous sunbeams toil
To break earth's sleep at all?

Wilfred Owen

Activity   Looking closely at the language and imagery of each poet, write a comparison of their attitudes to death and war.

These examples represent just a small range of the approaches that you can adopt for your Individual Oral Presentation. The key things to remember are:

• Choose a topic or work that you are interested in.
• Discuss your ideas with your teacher.
• Prepare carefully and thoroughly.
• Make sure that your presentation focuses on aspects on which you will be assessed.

Part 5
Writing About Literature

11 Writing Exam Essays

Objectives
- To think about appropriate ways of approaching exam essays, essay planning, and working under timed conditions
- To plan the revision of your set texts
- To understand how examiners will mark your work

Range of question topics

As part of your Language A1 Diploma programme you will need to sit two examinations. The first is the Commentary, which we looked at in units 1-3. The second exam is the Essay paper, in which you will have 1 hour 30 minutes (Standard Level) or 2 hours (Higher Level) to answer **one** question based on at least **two** of the Part 3 works you have studied. You may include in your answer a discussion of a Part 2 work of the same genre if relevant. You will have a choice of answering on drama, poetry, prose: the novel and short story, or prose: other than the novel and short story.

The questions on this paper will focus on various aspects of the texts that you have studied and these require different approaches and different kinds of responses, depending on the specific question you are answering. But ultimately their objective is the same – to allow you to show to the best of your ability your knowledge, understanding, and informed critical response to the particular texts.

One way you can prepare yourself for the exam is to be fully aware of the various kinds of question topics you can be asked to respond to. Here are some of the topics that you might be asked to write about in the exam:

Drama

- how dramatists present characters and communicate to the audience their thoughts and motivations
- the structure of the plays
- the importance of conflicts in drama
- dramatic techniques and staging
- how dramatists present their ideas and thematic strands
- the use of language in plays.

Poetry

- features of different poets' writing
- the use of imagery
- use and effects of various poetic techniques
- the use of poetic voice
- the effects created through the use of structure, rhyme, rhythm
- the presentation of ideas.

Prose: the novel and short story

- how writers create, present, and develop characters
- techniques writers use to open novels and short stories
- techniques writers use to bring their narrative to conclusions
- how writers present themes and ideas
- how writers use language to create different effects.

Prose (other than the novel or short story)

- how effective you have found the writing in various works
- what the writing has to say about the writers
- ideas, themes, and descriptions you have found effective
- ways in which ideas, views, and descriptions are presented.

A very useful way to begin to understand the kinds of things you might be asked in the exam is to spend time looking at past or specimen papers to become completely familiar with the format and phrasing that are commonly used in the questions. Your teacher may be able to provide you with specimen and past-paper questions, or you can obtain these from the IB.

Approaching questions

When you are presented with any question it is vital that you read it carefully to make sure you are perfectly clear about what it is asking of you. One useful tactic is to identify the key words and the focus of the question. Circle or underline the key words or phrases, and then jot down in a few words of your own what the question is asking you to focus on.

Activity

Practise this technique for yourself. Look at a selection of essay questions on the texts you have studied. You could take these from past papers, or use ones supplied by your teacher. Go through them identifying clearly the key words and the focus of each. It can be useful to work in pairs on this and to discuss your ideas with a partner.

Becoming familiar with the phraseology and formats frequently used in such questions will help you to handle different types in the exam.

Activity

1 Choose two texts from one genre that you have studied as part of your course, and create a question based on those texts.

Your question should:
 • refer to a specific topic or idea
 • ask something quite specific which will involve looking in detail at the texts.

2 Exchange questions with a partner and plan an answer to each other's questions. Discuss the plans you make.

The use of quotation

Students often feel unsure about how much direct quotation to include in an answer. In any kind of literature exam, lengthy quotation is definitely not advisable. The two key points about any quotation are that it should be short and it should be relevant. Include a quotation only to illustrate a comment or to act as a discussion point. Do not be tempted to over-quote to illustrate your points. Remember: time is too short to waste on simply writing out quotations.

Examiners also say that the same few quotations crop up in essay after essay from a particular centre, as if students are parroting information from a common set of notes. Obviously, certain quotations will be particularly relevant to a question, but it is not likely that there will be only the same three or four! Think for yourself and use the material that best suits the points you want to make. Then you will be articulating informed, independent opinions and judgements.

It is important not only to choose your quotations carefully, but to weave them into the fabric of your writing so they become an essential part of what you have to say. Very short quotations of three or four words are best worked into the structure of your own sentences. For example:

In this soliloquy Hamlet appears deeply depressed as he considers whether it is better 'To be, or not to be . . .', and his mind dwells on what death might hold.

Longer quotations need to be set out on a separate line, but they should still be worked into the fabric of your argument. Avoid using a quotation that seems to be just inserted into the text of your essay and detached from the structure of your own writing, as in this example:

Hamlet thinks that people carry on even though life is painful for them because they are afraid of the unknown and what death might hold.
'But that the dread of something after death,
The undiscovered country, from whose bourn
No traveller returns, puzzles the will,
And makes us rather bear those ills we have,
Than fly to others that we know not of?'

This quotation would be more effective if it were integrated into the student's writing in a shortened form. As it is, it appears as a 'chunk' of text lacking any sense of continuity with the student's own words. A more effective use of the same material would be:

Hamlet thinks that people carry on even though life is painful for them because they have a
'. . . dread of something after death,
The undiscovered country, from whose bourn
No traveller returns . . .'
It is this fear that '. . . makes us rather bear those ills we have' than willingly go to others that are unknown.

It is not always necessary to use direct quotation to support your ideas. 'With reference to the text' means just that – it is perfectly possible to refer to the text without quoting verbatim from it. You can explain the significance of a certain comment or draw examples from the text without using direct quotation at all. It is textual reference in support of your argument that matters, not quotation for its own sake. For example, this student makes the same point but without using direct quotation at all:

Hamlet thinks that people carry on even though life is painful for them because of the fear of what might come after death. It is this fear that drives people to continue with life no matter how hard or painful, rather than go into the unknown, which might be even worse.

Remember that the whole point of using quotation or textual support is to reinforce a particular point or to support close analysis: in short, to add to the overall meaning or relevance of your essay.

Revising set texts

The texts you have studied obviously play a key role in your final assessment for your Diploma course, and it is essential that you revise them very carefully in readiness for the exam. Exactly how many texts you have studied will depend on your particular course, designed by your teacher. Your grade will depend on the quality and effectiveness of your preparation, and so it is well worth planning how you intend to revise your set texts in good time. This is not a matter that you should put off until the last minute; hasty, inadequate revision could well damage your chances of getting the grade that you want. Students who do well will show an independence of mind which reveals the ability to think for themselves and to think under the pressure of exam conditions. Revision is key to these skills.

Now let us have a look at some of the things you can do to help revise your set texts and prepare yourself for the exam.

Reading and re-reading

By this stage you will, no doubt, have read your texts a number of times. This reading and re-reading of the texts is essential to the development of your understanding and appreciation of them.

However, different kinds of reading are appropriate depending on why you are doing the reading. You may read a text quickly before you start to study it in detail. The next time you read it you will probably read it quite slowly and thoroughly so as to follow the plot carefully, to examine the ways in which the characters emerge, and to get used to the style and language used. Subsequent readings will be different again. You may skim through the text to quickly refresh your memory of the whole thing, or you may scan the text looking for particular references to images or ideas. These various readings are extremely important for a number of reasons:

- They help you to become very familiar with the text, not just in terms of the plot (although some books do need to be read several times just to sort out what is happening) but also in terms of picking up on the details of the text. Often when you re-read them you notice something new, something that you had not picked up the first, second, or even third time round.
- You tend to come to an understanding of a text over a period of time. You do not just read it, understand it, and that is that. The kinds of texts that you will have encountered need thinking about. You need to allow yourself this thinking time in order to reflect on what you have read, to absorb the material, and then return to it again.

Obviously this kind of reading is part of a developmental process which enhances your knowledge and understanding of your set texts and, therefore, it needs to be planned for over a period of time.

Time management

Time is a crucial factor in your revision programme. Building time into your programme for sufficient practice on a variety of tasks is vital. To make sure that you do this, it is advisable to draw up a revision programme to cover the build-up to the final exams. This can be quite loose in the initial stages but the closer you get to the exams, the tighter it needs to be. Make sure that you cover every aspect of assessment that you need to. Here are some basic principles to think about when drawing up your revision programme.

- Be realistic – do not overestimate how much you can get through in a given time. It is far better to start your revision programme earlier than to try to cram everything in at the last minute.
- Make sure that your programme gives the necessary attention to every text. Don't ever think 'I know that one well enough so I needn't revise it'. Often, when you come to revise a text that you studied months before, you remember things about it that you had forgotten or that had become hazy.
- Create a balance between revision activities which are based on reading and those which involve writing tasks. For example, as well as the various reading activities there are those involving written responses, such as practice on past papers, timed essays, and essay planning.
- Build into your programme some time off to relax. You will not work at your best if you spend all your time studying. Revision is best done with a fresh mind and in relatively short sessions with breaks. You can only take in so much at one sitting. One to two hours at a stretch is enough.

Activity   Try planning out a short revision programme for yourself lasting a week. If you are approaching examinations you could make the programme a little longer and use it to give some structure to your revision.

Past-paper and specimen paper questions

As part of your revision programme, try to look at as many questions from past papers as you can. The value of this lies in giving you the flavour of the question types that examiners set. Certainly, looking at past-paper questions on your texts will show you a range of topics that questions have focused on in the past, and sometimes similar questions do appear again. However, do not learn 'model' answers and hope to be able to use these in the exam. If you come across specimen or model answers, regard them critically and as one possible way of answering, but do not take them to be the definitive answer. Remember, in the exam you will be expected to respond using your own ideas and thoughts, and examiners can spot immediately if you are parroting a 'model' answer you have learned.

Activity   Gather as many questions as you can on the texts that you have studied. Draft out a rough essay plan for each of these questions. (Do not spend more than two or three minutes on each plan.)

As well as giving you ideas of the types of things that have been asked about before, looking at past-paper questions will also give you a clear idea of how questions can be worded and the style in which they are presented. The more you know in this respect, the less likely you are to be thrown by question phrasing or terminology. Looking at past papers can also show up gaps in your knowledge of a set text and allow you to remedy them.

Timed essays

One of the main worries that students have in terms of answering on their set texts is how they are going to get all their ideas down in the time available. It is important that you get a good deal of practice in writing under timed conditions. You will, no doubt, do some timed pieces in class but there is no reason why you should not practise them at home as well. All you need are some suitable questions, a quiet place, and some time. In one sense it does not even matter if the work is not marked (although obviously you will get even more benefit from it if it is) – what really matters with this is building up your experience of writing against the clock. One thing is certain – the more you practise, the quicker you will get. It really will help you to speed up and it will also show you how much information you can deal with in a specified time and how well you can plan your work under time pressures.

Essay planning

Practice in essay planning should form another key part of your revision process. The best essays are those where students have thought about what they want to say before they start to write. By planning essays you can ensure that your argument is coherent and that you are using your knowledge and evidence to best effect. Essays that are not planned can easily drift away from the main point of the question or become rambling and jumbled.

In the exam itself you will have little time to spend on planning; you will feel an in-built pressure to start writing as soon as possible. However, what you do in that first two or three minutes after reading the question can be vital to the success of your answer. Practice in the build-up to the exam will help you to develop the skills to plan quickly and effectively. There are a number of things you can do to help:

- Read the question very carefully and make sure that you understand all parts of it.
- Identify which aspect or aspects of the text the question is about – use the key words approach already discussed
- Analyse the question and note down the key topic areas it deals with.
- Briefly plan how you intend to deal with these areas – this may mean only three or four points each, summed up in a few words. The main thing is that you will have a checklist of the points you are going to cover before you begin writing your essay.

Immediately after reading the question it is likely that ideas will whiz through your mind very quickly. If you do not get these down on paper in the form of a rough plan, there is a chance you might miss out an important point in the finished essay.

As well as doing your timed essays it will also be useful preparation if you can make essay plans for as many questions as you can. This will help to get you into the routine of planning, but it will also give you the opportunity to think about a wide variety of issues related to your texts.

Writing your essay

Here are some things to bear in mind when writing your answers.

Summary

- Always begin your essay by addressing the question directly. It can be a very useful technique to use some of the words of the question in your introduction. Your introduction should give a general indication of your response to the question or summarize the approach you intend to take, perhaps stating your viewpoint. The introduction might consist of your basic essay plan, expanded a little. However, keep the introduction brief and never include biographical information or plot summary.
- An alternative way to begin your essay, and one that can be very effective, is to respond to the question by starting with a strong, perhaps contentious idea that captures the reader's attention immediately. This will launch you straight into points that will support your argument.
- Develop your points clearly, using evidence and references to the text to support your ideas.
- Assume that the examiner has read the text you are writing about and knows it extremely well, so there is no need to explain the plot or who the characters are.
- Make sure that your essay deals with all parts of the question.
- If your answer is similar to an essay you have written before, make sure that you are being relevant at all times and are not simply regurgitating a 'set' answer that is in your mind. Also, avoid rehashing your notes as an answer to a question.
- Use quotations that are short and relevant.
- Make sure that your essay has a conclusion in which you sum up your arguments and analysis. It is often through the conclusion that the relevance of certain points you have made is brought into focus and the essay is given a sense of unity and completeness.

Throughout your revision period, bear in mind what you will be expected to show in the exam. Some factual knowledge will be required, but not much. That you know the 'facts' about a text, the story-line, who the characters are, etc., will be taken for granted. The emphasis will be much more on showing judgement, analysis, sensitivity, and perception in your responses.

What the examiner looks for

An important person in the process of your assessment is the examiner who will mark your work. 'Examiners' are not some special breed of people who spend their lives marking examination scripts. For the most part, they are practising teachers who work with students like yourself and help them to prepare for exams. However, they can mark only the work that you present to them, and the mark that is awarded depends solely on the quality of the work. It is a fallacy that one examiner might be more generous with you than another. Careful procedures are followed to ensure that the mark you receive from one examiner is just the same as the mark you would receive if another assessed your work. Indeed, it is not simply a case of one examiner looking at your work and giving a mark. Exam scripts go through a number of processes which involve responses being looked at by several people before a final mark is awarded. How well you do is up to you, not the examiner.

It is also worth dispelling another misconception that some students have concerning the role of the examiner. They picture him or her as some kind of merciless inquisitor who takes delight in catching them out. Examiners, so the thinking goes, look only for negative aspects in responses, and they ruthlessly dismantle every essay they come across. Questions are their tools, designed to catch students out.

In fact, nothing could be further from the truth. Questions are designed to let you show your knowledge to the best of your ability. Obviously examiners will not reward qualities which are not present in your responses, but they will look for the positive features in your work. Examiners take far more pleasure and satisfaction in reading good quality material that they can reward than they do in poor work that achieves poor marks. Think of the examiner as an interested and positive audience for your writing, who will award marks fairly and look positively on responses wherever there are positive qualities to be found.

The questions

Questions are rarely prescriptive. They are 'open' so as to invite you to debate the issues and encourage you to develop informed judgements on the texts and the issues they raise. It is these judgements that the examiner is interested in seeing.

Where the question contains some kind of proposition, you are never expected to simply accept it. Acceptance or rejection needs to be supported with evidence and justification. One criticism frequently made by examiners is that some students simply agree with or reject the proposition, and then go on to write about something else entirely. This still happens with worrying regularity.

The key thing is to read the question and do what it says.

Technical accuracy

Clearly the ideas that you express in your answers are of primary importance. However, these ideas will be not presented most effectively if your writing suffers from various technical inaccuracies. It is, therefore, crucial that your answers are as free from technical errors as you can make them.

There are several points that examiners draw attention to in this respect.

- **Punctuation** Ensure that you use full stops, commas, quotation marks, etc. where appropriate. It is easy for these things to be forgotten in the heat of the exam, but poor punctuation can mean that your ideas are communicated to the reader less effectively, and this may affect your mark.
- **Sentences** Make sure that you write in sentences and that you avoid long, convoluted ones.
- **Paragraphing** Few candidates fail to use paragraphs at all, but examiners often point to the inappropriate use of paragraphs. For example, one-sentence paragraphs should be avoided and so should excessively long paragraphs.
- **Vocabulary** Try to vary your vocabulary without becoming verbose simply to make your essay sound more 'impressive'.
- **Spelling** Obviously you should try to make your work free of spelling errors. However, in the heat of writing under exam conditions some errors may well creep in. You should do your best to check each answer as you complete it, to keep these to a minimum. If nothing else, make sure that you are spelling the titles of the texts, the names of the characters, and the names of the authors correctly. It does not give a good impression if, after two years' study, you are still writing about 'Shakespear's play' or 'Jayne Austin's novel'.
- **Cliché, flattery, and slang** Avoid the use of well-worn phrases such as 'Jane Eyre is a victim of male domination' or 'Lear acts like a man possessed'. Flattery towards authors, such as 'Shakespeare's portrayal of a man in emotional turmoil is second to none' or 'It is clear that Keats is one of the giants of English poetry' are equally to be avoided; so are slang expressions, such as 'Laertes goes ballistic when he hears about his father's death'.
- **Quotation** If you are using quotation, make sure it is accurate. If you are relying on memory, it is very easy to misquote. Perhaps all that needs to be said is that it is better not to use a quotation than to misquote or worse still 'invent' a quote based on a rough idea of how it goes.

Model and prepared answers

There is nothing wrong with reading model answers as long as you use them wisely. They can be useful in presenting you with new ideas, but be aware that they represent just one way of answering a question. The examiner is interested in what *you* have to say on a particular topic or question, not what the writer of a prepared answer has to say.

Remember that the best responses are those in which your own voice can be heard. The whole point of the course that you are studying is to develop your ability to write confidently, relevantly, and thoughtfully about your ideas on the texts you have studied. Do not be afraid to use the pronoun 'I' occasionally in your essays, and do not be afraid to respond genuinely to a question. Attempts to memorize prepared answers never work.

How the examiner will mark your work

Above all, examiners marking scripts are trained to be positive and flexible. The examiners will look for the good qualities in your work. They will not approach your response with a preconceived idea of an 'ideal answer', but will have an open mind. They will evaluate your efforts to provide an informed, personal response to the question.

Answering the question

Examiners are always aware of students who do not read the questions carefully enough. You should make absolutely sure that you are well trained in studying carefully the exact wording of the question. Remember that the question should be the whole basis and framework of your answer.

Length

Examiners do not award marks on the basis of the length of your essay but they will look for what you have achieved in your writing. An essay may appear brief but on closer inspection it may be a succinct and well-argued response, and therefore worthy of a high mark. It is true to say, though, that essays that are very short often lack sufficient depth in the development of ideas. On the other hand, over-long essays can become repetitive, rambling and lacking in a coherent structure. Do your best to create a balanced answer.

Assessment of your work

Your answer will be assessed against the following categories:

- Knowledge and understanding of the works
- Response to the question
- Appreciation of literary features
- Presentation
- Formal use of language.

In order to achieve a good mark you need to show:

- a good understanding of the Part 3 (and Part 2) works used to answer the question
- detailed and appropriate references to the works
- that your ideas are relevant and include a personal response, where appropriate

- a detailed analysis of ideas illustrated by relevant examples
- analysis of the effects of the literary features of the works in relation to the question
- analysis that is appropriately illustrated by relevant examples
- a clear and logical structure to the essay
- supporting examples that are integrated into the body of the essay
- clear, varied, and precise use of language
- no significant lapses in grammar, spelling, and sentence construction
- effective and appropriately varied use of vocabulary, idiom, and style
- suitable choice of register.

In reading these descriptions you will see the key features that can bring you success in the exam, and to achieve them there are some basic things you can do. In fact if you are to achieve success there are certain things that you *must* do. You must make sure that:

- you have read your texts carefully several times
- you know your texts thoroughly
- you are fully aware of the issues, ideas, themes, etc. they contain
- you are aware of the stylistic features of the texts you have studied
- you can support your ideas and comments effectively.

Remember: The secret of success is to be well prepared. Know your material and know what you think about it. If you can show through your responses that you possess independent opinions and you can use these to express your 'knowledge' and 'understanding' of the works, then you will have every chance of achieving the success that you seek in your studies.

12 The Extended Essay

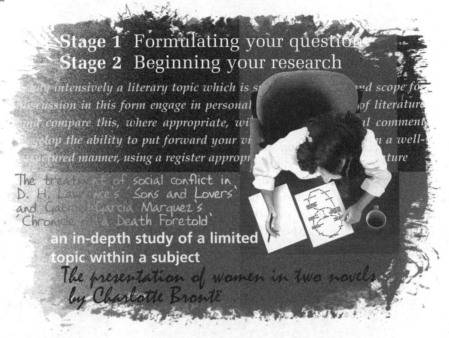

Stage 1 Formulating your question
Stage 2 Beginning your research

*study intensively a literary topic which is s... ...d scope fo...
...scussion in this form engage in personal... ...of literature*
...d compare this, where appropriate, wi... ...al comment
...velop the ability to put forward your vi... ...n a well-
...uctured manner, using a register appropr... ...ature

The treatment of social conflict in
D. H. Lawrence's 'Sons and Lovers'
and Gabriel Garcia Marquez's
'Chronicle of a Death Foretold'

**an in-depth study of a limited
topic within a subject**

The presentation of women in two novels
by Charlotte Brontë

Objectives • To identify the key features of the Extended Essay
• To identify ways in which you can approach your planning of the
  Extended Essay
• To prepare for researching and writing the essay

In addition to the literature you will study as part of your Diploma course,
you will also be required to complete an Extended Essay of 4000 words. In
this essay you will have the opportunity to investigate a topic of special
interest to you and to undertake the kind of independent research and writing
that is expected at university. This unit will look at the central features of this
element of the Diploma and give guidance on ways in which you can
approach an Extended Essay for English A1.

The nature of the Extended Essay

The IBO guidelines define the Extended Essay as '*an in-depth study of a
limited topic within a subject*'. The purpose of the essay is '*to provide
candidates with an opportunity to engage in independent research*'. This
personal research is at the centre of the Extended Essay and your task is to
research your topic and to communicate your ideas and information in a
logical and coherent way. Your work needs to be structured and presented in
the form of a piece of formal research and conform to certain criteria.

In order to undertake your extended essay you will first need to find a teacher who is prepared to act as your supervisor. Your supervisor will provide help and guidance with:

- defining a suitable topic
- formulating your research question
- accessing appropriate resources
- how to gather and analyse evidence and data
- how to acknowledge your sources
- how to write your abstract.

The Extended Essay provides the opportunity to:

- study intensively a literary topic which is suitable in nature and scope for discussion in this form
- engage in personal critical judgement of literature and to compare this, where appropriate, with established critical comment
- develop the ability to put forward your views persuasively and in a well-structured manner, using a register appropriate to the study of literature.

It can help in planning and approaching your Extended Essay if you use the following stages to prepare for it:

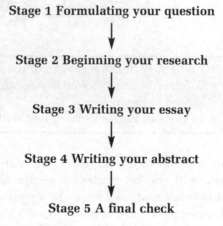

Stage 1 Formulating your question

↓

Stage 2 Beginning your research

↓

Stage 3 Writing your essay

↓

Stage 4 Writing your abstract

↓

Stage 5 A final check

Stage 1 Formulating your question

Choosing your subject

Careful selection of the subject of your Extended Essay is essential and it is advisable to decide on the overall subject area before you decide on the specific topic and research question that you will work on. Here are some points you should bear in mind when deciding on your subject:

- Your subject must be literary in nature.
- Choose a subject that you have a personal interest in. You are likely to produce a much more effective Extended Essay if the subject you are researching is one that you are interested in.

- Make sure that you have sufficient knowledge of the subject area on which you have chosen to pursue an in-depth study.

Your first task may well be to find a supervisor for your work. Approach a teacher of the subject first, and when you have been accepted by a supervisor, you can choose your topic.

Activity

Make a list of subject areas that you might be interested in researching for your Extended Essay. Think about each one and make a note of the advantages of each. From your list select the subject on which you think you would be able to produce the best essay. Make sure you have a supervisor willing to take you on.

Choosing your topic

Having decided on the general subject area of your study, you then need to think about the topic that you want to research within your chosen subject, and to discuss it with your supervisor. This needs very careful thought and you should consult the specific subject guidelines published by the IBO before making your final decision. When choosing your topic you should aim to:

- choose a topic which is of interest to you
- choose a topic which you will find challenging
- make sure that your topic is limited enough in scope and sufficiently narrow to allow you to examine it in depth
- choose a topic which will allow you opportunities to collect and research information that you can analyse and evaluate
- make sure that your topic is based on the study of literature.

You should note, though, that your research is not expected to add to the body of knowledge that already exists on a chosen subject.

If your topic is too broad and you try to cover too much ground you will not be able to focus in sufficient depth. You should also avoid the kind of topic which does not require any research on your part and which could lead to a narrative or descriptive approach. On the other hand, although secondary sources will probably be important to your research, you should avoid the kind of topic that might be dealt with by simply summarizing these sources.

Your topic should be based on one of the two following categories stated by the IBO:

Category 1
The essay should be based on literature originally written in English.

Here are some examples of topics in this category:

- The presentation of women in two novels by Charlotte Brontë.
- The importance of natural imagery in the poetry of Seamus Heaney.
- The nature and role of marriage in Restoration comedy.

Category 2

Essays in this category should be a comparison of at least one literary work originally written in English with a literary work or works originally written in a different language and probably studied in translation.

Here are some examples of topics in this category:

- The presentation of women in Alice Walker's *The Colour Purple* and Ken Saro-Wiwa's *Lemona's Tale*.
- The treatment of social conflict in D. H. Lawrence's *Sons and Lovers* and Gabriel Garcia Marquez's *Chronicle of a Death Foretold*.

The topic you choose must be a literary one and could be a particular aspect, or comparative study of works or authors.

Whichever category you choose for your Extended Essay, here are some ideas to think about in terms of the treatment of your topic:

- Although literary works often deal with social, philosophical, psychological, or political issues, the main focus of your essay should be on the literary aspects of the texts chosen for study.
- The essay should not be used as a vehicle for your own thoughts but you should offer careful analysis of the writer's ideas and the ways in which the writer has treated the subject.
- Your essay should use your own personal ideas to test the ideas of critics, not just to confirm them. Concentration on the views of the established literary critics alone will not result in a successful Extended Essay.
- Any narrative or descriptive material included should be directly relevant to your critical analysis of the material. Simply summarizing your reading will not result in an acceptable piece of work. Your essay must be analytical, not descriptive.

Activity Think carefully about which category of essay will suit you best in terms of giving you scope to explore a topic of interest to you. Decide on the topic area you want to write about. If you have more than one topic in mind it can help to make notes on how you would approach each one and decide which one you could write about most effectively.

The research question

Once you have decided on an appropriate topic for research you now need to decide on a specific research question that you are going to investigate. This research question should narrow the focus of your investigation and it is important that you think carefully about how you phrase it. Very often students phrase it as a straightforward question, but it could also be presented as a hypothesis or idea which forms the springboard of the investigation. You might find it useful to write it out in both forms. You should make sure that your question or thesis statement:

- is challenging

- can be explored within the constraints of the length of the essay and the time and resources available
- is clearly and precisely stated and sharply focused.

Here is a summary of Stage 1:

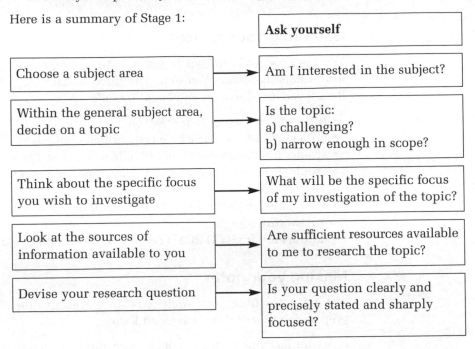

	Ask yourself
Choose a subject area	Am I interested in the subject?
Within the general subject area, decide on a topic	Is the topic: a) challenging? b) narrow enough in scope?
Think about the specific focus you wish to investigate	What will be the specific focus of my investigation of the topic?
Look at the sources of information available to you	Are sufficient resources available to me to research the topic?
Devise your research question	Is your question clearly and precisely stated and sharply focused?

Stage 2 Beginning your research

Having selected your subject, decided on your topic and produced your research question you are now ready to begin Stage 2, starting to research your topic.

Preparatory reading

The first thing you need to do is to (re-)read the books you will be writing about. Then you can begin your research with some preparatory reading around your research question. This will enable you to focus closely on the requirements of your question as well as giving you a preliminary overview of the ideas relating to it.

Outline planning

Having done some preparatory reading you will now be in a position to create an outline plan for your essay. This outline plan should cover the key points of:

- the introduction
- the main body
- the conclusion in which you will state your findings.

Activity   Make an outline plan for your essay and show the plan to your supervisor. You can always make amendments to this at a later stage, but is important to get something down on paper.

Gathering your sources

You are now ready to start to gather together the source materials that will form the basis of your research. The information you gather may be drawn from a variety of sources and could include:

- texts you are basing your essay on
- critical works – either whole texts or parts of texts
- articles from magazines and periodicals such as *The Use of English*
- articles from newspapers and publications such as *The Times Literary Supplement*
- information gathered from the Internet (but make sure it comes from a trustworthy source)
- information from CD ROMs related to the literature you are studying.

Making your notes

Making notes from your sources is an extremely important part of your preparation to write your Extended Essay.

Everyone has their own ways of learning and this is often true of note-making too – everyone has their own, preferred method and there is no 'right' way of doing this. However, students often waste a good deal of time making 'notes' which are not really notes at all but consist of copying out chunks of the text that is the source material. Here are some points you might like to bear in mind:

- Read the material through carefully before making notes – you cannot decide which points you need to make a note of until you know what the material is saying.
- Focus on the key points of the material – and be aware of their relevance to your research title.
- Use your own words for the bulk of your notes rather than copying out the text – you are much more likely to understand it, and using your own words also avoids accusations of plagiarism.
- Note page references for important points so that you can go back to the source material and find the sections you need easily.
- Make a note of all the relevant details of the source of the notes, e.g. title of book; author; publisher; date; page references, etc. You will need all these details for your bibliography, and there is nothing more annoying than having notes or references that you want to use but you cannot find where they came from.

How you keep your notes is also very important. Students keep notes in all kinds of ways but there are advantages in keeping them in some form that allows you to insert paper and add to them as new materials are found. A ring file allows you to do this. Some students also find a card indexing system for their notes very useful.

When you feel that you have gathered together all the notes and materials you need you are ready to make a start on writing your Extended Essay.

Here is a summary of Stage 2:

Beginning your research

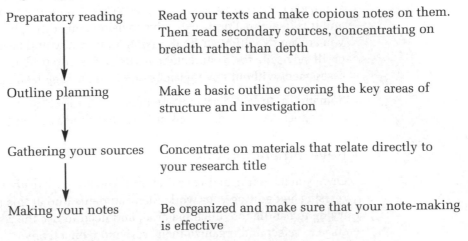

Preparatory reading — Read your texts and make copious notes on them. Then read secondary sources, concentrating on breadth rather than depth

Outline planning — Make a basic outline covering the key areas of structure and investigation

Gathering your sources — Concentrate on materials that relate directly to your research title

Making your notes — Be organized and make sure that your note-making is effective

Stage 3 Writing your essay

Structuring your material

Having gathered your research material together you are now in a position to begin the process of writing your Extended Essay. To begin with you should look carefully at the outline plan that you made and review it in the light of your research and create from it a firm plan for your essay. This plan will provide the basic structure that you will work to in producing your essay and it is useful to bear in mind several points:

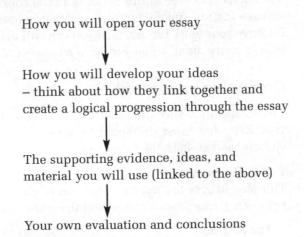

How you will open your essay

How you will develop your ideas
– think about how they link together and
create a logical progression through the essay

The supporting evidence, ideas, and
material you will use (linked to the above)

Your own evaluation and conclusions

Once you have the structure of your essay firmly planned, you are ready to start writing your first draft.

The first draft

Very often, students find actually starting to write the essay quite difficult and sometimes they have great difficulty in deciding on the exact form of words or the exact starting point. The main thing here, though, is to get something down on paper that you can then begin to develop. It is worth taking this approach to the essay as a whole, too. This is only the first draft of the essay and it is likely that quite extensive revision and editing will take place before you are happy with your final version. In fact, it would be extremely unusual, or ill advised, for a student to write a first draft that was submitted for assessment without any revisions or editing having taken place.

Sometimes students write several drafts before arriving at the finished version. Your supervisors needs to look at all drafts of the essay, but especially the first.

Revising and editing

Once you have finished your first draft you are now ready to begin the task of revising and editing your work. Many students find at this point that they are trying to handle too much material, and need to use the revising and editing stage to select and organize their work more effectively.

Different students have different ways of approaching revision and editing but it can be useful to read through your work marking any alterations, deletions, amendments, etc. with a different coloured pen. Sections that require more extensive re-writing or alterations can be asterisked and numbered and new sections written and inserted. When your revisions are complete you are ready to begin your final draft.

The final draft

Working from your revisions you now need to write your final draft. However, it is worth remembering when you are writing the draft that you can still make alterations to it even at this stage. If, in the course of your writing, you come across a section you are not happy with or a new idea strikes you that would improve your work further, then you can still make changes. Your 'final' draft is only really 'final' when you have handed it to your tutor.

Organizing your essay

The IB specifies very precisely just how you should organize the work for your Extended Essay. It should be word-processed (preferably with double spacing) and contain the following.

1 The title page

This should give the research question in clear and precise terms, as well as your name, candidate number, and the word count.

2 The abstract

The abstract gives a brief synopsis or summary of your research question, the scope of your investigation, and your conclusion. You are advised to write your abstract after you have finished your essay, as it is a synopsis of the whole essay (see Stage 4 below).

3 Contents

Your table of contents should give your main section headings with page numbering.

4 Introduction

Your work should also include an introduction which opens the main body of your essay. It *must* contain the research question in some form. The introduction can be included as a separate section or as the first part of your essay.

5 The main body

The main body of your essay should be logically structured and it can contain sections/chapters if appropriate.

6 Conclusion

Your conclusion must be clearly linked to your research question and should draw out the important aspects that you have found through your research and, if appropriate, indicate new questions or issues that have emerged through your work, or questions that have remained unresolved. The conclusion should be clearly stated and substantiated by the evidence presented.

7 Illustrations

These may not be required for an Extended Essay in English A1. However, if they are necessary to your essay they should be included. Do not include illustrations that are not necessary or appropriate, simply for visual effect. It is far better to spend your time revising your text, rather than illustrating it.

8 Appendix (or appendices)

This an optional section. If you have information or any other material that supplements the text of the main body of your essay then it can be included in an appendix. For example, if you have made reference to a particularly important letter in your essay, you might include a copy of this in an appendix. However, you should make sure that any essential information is included in the main body of the text as examiners are not required to read appendices.

9 References

If you refer either directly or indirectly to the words of someone else, whether written, oral, or electronic in form, you must acknowledge the source of your reference. Using material from sources without acknowledgement is known as plagiarism. Plagiarism is a serious matter and is a form of malpractice which can have serious consequences, so it is vital that you acknowledge all your sources. If plagiarism is discovered, the candidate concerned will not be awarded a Diploma, regardless of how well he or she has done in the examination as a whole.

There are three basic methods you can use to acknowledge your references:

Method 1: Number each reference as they crop up in your work (1, 2, 3, 4, etc.). At the end of your essay make a list of each reference linked to the corresponding number in the text. Each reference should give: the name or editor of the work; the publication date; title of book or periodical; the page references; publisher.

Method 2: Number the references as in method 1 but place the details of each source at the bottom of the page on which the reference occurs.

Method 3: Place the details of the reference source in brackets in the body of the text, immediately after the reference. If you use this method, remember not to include the references in your word count.

Whichever method you choose, be consistent and employ the same method throughout your essay.

10 Bibliography

Your bibliography should list the works, such as books, journals, Internet material, etc. that you have used in the writing of your essay. Every work that you have consulted should be listed in the bibliography, even those you have already cited as references. In your bibliography you should give the following details for each text: author(s)/editor; title; date; place of publication; publisher.

Your list should be organized in alphabetical order of the writers' surnames.

Here is a summary of Stage 3:

Writing your essay

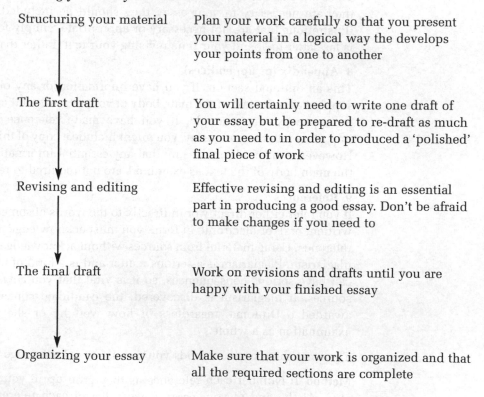

Structuring your material	Plan your work carefully so that you present your material in a logical way the develops your points from one to another
The first draft	You will certainly need to write one draft of your essay but be prepared to re-draft as much as you need to in order to produced a 'polished' final piece of work
Revising and editing	Effective revising and editing is an essential part in producing a good essay. Don't be afraid to make changes if you need to
The final draft	Work on revisions and drafts until you are happy with your finished essay
Organizing your essay	Make sure that your work is organized and that all the required sections are complete

Stage 4 Writing your abstract

This is a short piece of writing which gives a brief synopsis or summary of your research question, the scope of your investigation, and your conclusion. You should note that your abstract should not exceed 300 words.

Many students find it difficult to write an effective abstract, but it is important to make the effort to produce a clear and useful one, as this gives an examiner a much better impression and understanding of your work.

Stage 5 A final check

Proof-reading

When your final draft is completed you need to proof-read your work very carefully. Proof-reading is different from revising and editing because at this stage you are not looking to make changes to the text – you are simply checking that the punctuation, spelling, sentence structure, etc. are in order.

The final check

Before you hand in your Extended Essay it is a good idea if you go through a final checklist to make sure that you have done everything you should have done and all the necessary elements are completed. Here is a suggested checklist you could use:

Make sure the essay has:

- title page ✓
- abstract ✓
- contents list ✓
- introduction ✓
- main body ✓
- conclusion ✓
- illustrations (if required) ✓
- appendix (if required) ✓
- references acknowledged ✓
- bibliography ✓

Also make sure that:

- the essay is within 4000 words excluding the bibliography and references, and the abstract is within 300 words ✓
- presentation is excellent ✓
- spelling has been checked ✓
- all pages are numbered ✓

Here is a summary of Stage 5:

Proof-reading Make sure that you proof-read your essay very carefully. An essay which contains technical errors or is poorly written will not gain higher marks

Final check Use the checklists above to make sure that you have completed all the necessary sections and have checked your work carefully before handing it in.

How your work will be assessed

Your Extended Essay will be assessed by an external examiner using a range or criteria. These criteria are divided between general and subject assessment criteria.

General assessment criteria

You are awarded marks for each of the following:

- how effectively you have stated the research question
- how appropriate your approach is in addressing the research question
- how effectively you consider relevant materials, sources, data, and evidence and how effectively you carry out your analysis and interpretation
- how effectively you develop your argument in response to the research question and how well you organize and express your ideas
- the quality of your conclusion in terms of being clearly stated, relevant, and consistent with the argument expressed in your essay
- the effectiveness of your formal abstract in presenting a clear synopsis of the essay within the word limit of 300 words
- the formal presentation of your essay in terms of neatness, completion of all required sections, pages numbered, and not exceeding the word limit of 4000 words
- holistic judgement giving an overall assessment of qualities such as personal engagement, initiative, depth of understanding, insight, inventiveness, and flair.

Subject assessment criteria

You are awarded marks for the following:

- how effectively you show your knowledge and understanding of the literature studied, and where appropriate your reference to secondary sources
- the quality of your personal response, and how well it is justified by literary judgement and/or analysis
- how effectively you use the language appropriate to a literary essay.

Glossary

Allegory:	an allegory is a story or narrative, often told at some length, which has a deeper meaning below the surface. *The Pilgrim's Progress* by John Bunyan is a well-known allegory. A more modern example is George Orwell's *Animal Farm*, which on a surface level is about a group of animals who take over their farm but on a deeper level is an allegory of the Russian Revolution and the shortcomings of Communism.
Alliteration:	the repetition of the same consonant sound, especially at the beginning of words. For example, 'Five miles meandering with a mazy motion' (*Kubla Khan* by S. T. Coleridge).
Allusion:	a reference to another event, person, place, or work of literature – the allusion is usually implied rather than explicit and often provides another layer of meaning to what is being said.
Ambiguity:	use of language where the meaning is unclear or has two or more possible interpretations or meanings. It could be created through a weakness in the way the writer has expressed himself or herself, but often it is used by writers quite deliberately to create layers of meaning in the mind of the reader.
Ambivalence:	this indicates more than one possible attitude is being displayed by the writer towards a character, theme, or idea, etc.
Anachronism:	something that is historically inaccurate, for example the reference to a clock chiming in Shakespeare's *Julius Caesar*.
Anthropomorphism:	the endowment of something that is not human with human characteristics.
Antithesis:	contrasting ideas or words that are balanced against each other.
Apostrophe:	an interruption in a poem or narrative so that the speaker or writer can address a dead or absent person or particular audience directly.
Archaic:	language that is old-fashioned – not completely obsolete but no longer in current use.
Assonance:	the repetition of similar vowel sounds. For example: 'There must be Gods thrown down and trumpets blown' (*Hyperion* by John Keats). This shows the paired assonance of 'must', 'trum', 'thrown', 'blown'.
Atmosphere:	the prevailing mood created by a piece of writing.
Ballad:	a narrative poem that tells a story (traditional ballads were songs) usually in a straightforward way. The theme is often tragic or contains a whimsical, supernatural, or fantastical element.
Bathos:	an anti-climax or sudden descent from the serious to the ridiculous – sometimes deliberate, sometimes unintentional on the part of the writer.
Blank verse:	unrhymed poetry that adheres to a strict pattern in that each line is an iambic pentameter (a ten-syllable line with five stresses). It is close to the natural rhythm of English speech or prose, and is used a great deal by many writers including Shakespeare and Milton.

Caesura: a conscious break in a line of poetry (see Unit 5, page 122).

Caricature: a character described through the exaggeration of a small number of features that he or she possesses.

Catharsis: a purging of the emotions which takes place at the end of a tragedy.

Cliché: a phrase, idea, or image that has been used so much that it has lost much of its original meaning, impact, and freshness.

Colloquial: ordinary, everyday speech and language.

Comedy: originally simply a play or other work which ended happily. Now we use this term to describe something that is funny and which makes us laugh. In literature the comedy is not a necessarily a lightweight form. A play like Shakespeare's *Measure for Measure*, for example, is, for the most part a serious and dark play but as it ends happily, it is often described as a comedy.

Conceit: an elaborate, extended, and sometimes surprising comparison between things that, at first sight, do not have much in common.

Connotation: an implication or association attached to a word or phrase. A connotation is suggested or felt rather than being explicit.

Consonance: the repetition of the same consonant sounds in two or more words in which the vowel sounds are different. For example: 'And by his smile, I knew that sullen hall, By his dead smile I knew we stood in Hell' (*Strange Meeting* by Wilfred Owen). Where consonance replaces the rhyme, as here, it is called half-rhyme.

Couplet: two consecutive lines of verse that rhyme.

Dénouement: the ending of a play, novel, or drama where 'all is revealed' and the plot is unravelled.

Diction: the choice of words that a writer makes. Another term for 'vocabulary'.

Didactic: a work that is intended to preach or teach, often containing a particular moral or political point.

Dramatic monologue: a poem or prose piece in which a character addresses an audience. Often the monologue is complete in itself, as in Alan Bennett's *Talking Heads*.

Elegy: a meditative poem, usually sad and reflective in nature. Sometimes, though not always, it is concerned with the theme of death.

Empathy: a feeling on the part of the reader of sharing the particular experience being described by the character or writer.

End stopping: a verse line with a pause or a stop at the end of it.

Enjambment: a line of verse that flows on into the next line without a pause.

Epic: a long narrative poem, written in an elevated style and usually dealing with a heroic theme or story. Homer's *The Iliad* and Milton's *Paradise Lost* are examples of this.

Euphemism: expressing an unpleasant or unsavoury idea in a less blunt and more pleasant way.

Euphony: use of pleasant or melodious sounds.

Exemplum: a story that contains or illustrates a moral point put forward as an 'example'.

Fable: a short story that presents a clear moral lesson.

Fabliau: a short comic tale with a bawdy element, akin to the 'dirty story'. Chaucer's *The Miller's Tale* contains strong elements of the fabliau.

Farce: a play that aims to entertain the audience through absurd and ridiculous characters and action.

Feminine ending: an extra unstressed syllable at the end of a line of poetry. (Contrast with a stressed syllable, a masculine ending.)

Figurative language: language that is symbolic or metaphorical and not meant to be taken literally.

Foot: a group of syllables forming a unit of verse – the basic unit of 'metre'. (See Unit 5, pages 124–5.)

Free verse: verse written without any fixed structure (either in metre or rhyme).

Genre: a particular type of writing, e.g. prose, poetry, drama.

Heptameter: a verse line containing seven feet.

Hexameter: a verse line containing six feet.

Hyperbole: deliberate and extravagant exaggeration.

Iamb: the most common metrical foot in English poetry, consisting of an unstressed syllable followed by a stressed syllable.

Idyll: a story, often written in verse, usually concerning innocent and rustic characters in rural, idealized surroundings. This form can also deal with more heroic subjects, as in Tennyson's *Idylls of the King*. (See **Pastoral**.)

Imagery: the use of words to create a picture or 'image' in the mind of the reader. Images can relate to any of the senses, not just sight, but also hearing, taste, touch, and smell. 'Imagery' is often used to refer to the use of descriptive language, particularly to the use of metaphors and similes.

Internal rhyme: rhyming words within a line rather than at the end of lines.

Inter-textual: having clear links with other texts through the themes, ideas, or issues which are explored.

Irony: at its simplest level, irony means saying one thing while meaning another. It occurs where a word or phrase has one surface meaning but another contradictory, possibly opposite meaning is implied. Irony is frequently confused with sarcasm. Sarcasm is spoken, often relying on tone of voice, and is much more blunt than irony.

Lament: a poem expressing intense grief.

Lyric: originally a song performed to the accompaniment of a lyre (an early harp-like instrument) but now it can mean a song-like poem or a short poem expressing personal feeling.

Metaphor: a comparison of one thing to another in order to make description more vivid. The metaphor actually states that one thing *is* the other. For example, a simile would be: 'The huge knight stood like an impregnable tower in the ranks of the enemy', whereas the corresponding metaphor would be: 'The huge knight was an impregnable tower in the ranks of the enemy'. (See **Simile** and **Personification**.)

Metre: the regular use of stressed and unstressed syllables in poetry. (See **Foot** and Unit 5, pages 124–5.)

Mock heroic: a poem that treats trivial subject matter in the grand and elevated style of epic poetry. The effect produced is often satirical, as in Pope's *The Rape of the Lock*.

Monometer: a verse line consisting of only one metrical foot.

Motif: a dominant theme, subject or idea which runs through a piece of literature. Often a 'motif' can assume a symbolic importance.

Narrative: a piece of writing that tells a story.

Octameter: a verse line consisting of eight feet.

Octave: the first eight lines of a sonnet.

Ode: a verse form similar to a lyric but often more lengthy and containing more serious and elevated thoughts.

Onomatopoeia: the use of words whose sound copies the sound of the thing or process that they describe. On a simple level, words like 'bang', 'hiss', and 'splash' are onomatopoeic, but it also has more subtle uses.

Oxymoron: a figure of speech which joins together words of opposite meanings, e.g. 'the living dead', 'bitter sweet', etc.

Paradox: a statement that appears contradictory, but when considered more closely is seen to contain a good deal of truth.

Parody: a work that is written in imitation of another work, very often with the intention of making fun of the original.

Pastoral: generally, literature concerning rural life with idealized settings and rustic characters. Often pastorals are concerned with the lives of shepherds and shepherdesses presented in idyllic and unrealistic ways. (See **Idyll**.)

Pathos: the effect in literature which makes the reader feel sadness or pity.

Pentameter: a line of verse containing five feet.

Periphrasis: a round-about or long-winded way of expressing something.

Personification: the attribution of human feelings, emotions, or sensations to an inanimate object. Personification is a kind of metaphor where human qualities are given to things or abstract ideas, and they are described as if they were a person.

Plot: the sequence of events in a poem, play, novel, or short story that make up the main storyline.

Prose: any kind of writing which is not verse – usually divided into fiction and non-fiction.

Protagonist: the main character or speaker in a poem, monologue, play, or story.

Pun: a play on words that have similar sounds but quite different meanings.

Quatrain: a stanza of four lines which can have various rhyme schemes.

Refrain: repetition throughout a poem of a phrase, line, or series of lines, as in the 'chorus' of a song.

Rhetoric: originally, the art of speaking and writing in such a way as to persuade an audience to a particular point of view. Now this term is often used to imply grand words that have no substance to them. There are a variety of rhetorical devices, such as the rhetorical question – a question which does not require an answer as the answer is either obvious or implied in the question itself. (See **Apostrophe**, **Exemplum**.)

Rhyme: corresponding sounds in words, usually at the end of each line but not always. (See **Internal rhyme**.)

Rhyme scheme: the pattern of the rhymes in a poem.

Rhythm: the 'movement' of the poem as created through the metre and the way that language is stressed within the poem.

Satire:	the highlighting or exposing of human failings or foolishness within a society through ridiculing them. Satire can range from being gentle and light to being extremely biting and bitter in tone, e.g. Swift's *Gulliver's Travels* or *A Modest Proposal*, and George Orwell's *Animal Farm*.
Scansion:	the analysis of metrical patterns in poetry. (See Unit 5, pages 124–5.)
Septet:	a seven-line stanza.
Sestet:	the last six lines of a sonnet.
Simile:	a comparison of one thing to another in order to make description more vivid. Similes use the words 'like' or 'as' in this comparison. (See **Metaphor**.)
Soliloquy:	a speech in which a character, alone on stage, expresses his or her thoughts and feelings aloud for the benefit of the audience, often in a revealing way.
Sonnet:	a fourteen-line poem, usually with ten syllables in each line. There are several ways in which the lines can be organized, but often they consist of an octave and a sestet.
Stanza:	the blocks of lines into which a poem is divided. (Sometimes these are, less precisely, referred to as verses, which can lead to confusion as poetry is sometimes called 'verse'.)
Stream of consciousness:	a technique in which the writer records thoughts and emotions in a 'stream' as they come to mind, without giving order or structure.
Structure:	the way that a poem or play or other piece of writing has been put together. This can include the metre pattern, stanza arrangement, and the way the ideas are developed, etc.
Style:	the individual way in which a writer has used language to express his or her ideas.
Sub-plot:	a secondary storyline in a story or play. Often, as in some Shakespeare plays, the sub-plot can provide some comic relief from the main action, but sub-plots can also relate in quite complex ways to the main plot of a text.
Sub-text:	ideas, themes, or issues that are not dealt with overtly by a text but which exist below the surface meaning of it.
Symbol:	like images, symbols represent something else. In very simple terms a red rose is often used to symbolize love; distant thunder is often symbolic of approaching trouble. Symbols can be very subtle and multi-layered in their significance.
Syntax:	the way in which sentences are structured. Sentences can be structured in different ways to achieve different effects.
Tetrameter:	a verse line of four feet.
Theme:	the central idea or ideas that the writer explores through a text.
Tone:	the tone of a text is created through the combined effects of a number of features, such as diction, syntax, rhythm, etc. The tone is a major factor in establishing the overall impression of the piece of writing.
Trimeter:	a verse line consisting of three feet.
Zeugma:	a device that joins together two apparently incongruous things by applying a verb or adjective to both which only really applies to one of them, e.g. 'Kill the boys and the luggage' (Shakespeare's *Henry V*).

Index